TITLES IN THIS SERIES

ACT OF POSSESSION

ACT OF POSSESSION

BY
ANNE MATHER

MILLS & BOON LIMITED
Eton House, 18–24 Paradise Road
Richmond, Surrey TW9 1SR

*First published in Great Britain 1985
by Mills & Boon Limited*

© Anne Mather 1985

Australian copyright 1985
Philippine copyright 1985
Reprinted 1985
This edition 1989

ISBN 0 263 76400 1

Set in Monophoto Times 10 on 10pt.
19-8904 – 58945

Made and printed in Great Britain

CHAPTER ONE

'Do come! It's just going to be an informal affair,' invited Celia warmly, her friendly smile brightening the rather gloomy hallway of the apartment building. 'I'm sure it's not much fun, living next door to someone who's constantly giving parties!' She grimaced. 'That's Liz's fault really; but this time I'm to blame. It's just a little celebration, you see, for a few friends. A kind of delayed birthday-cum-engagement party combined!'

Antonia's eyes widened. 'You're engaged!' she exclaimed, looking swiftly at Celia's bare finger, and the other girl laughed.

'I shall be after tomorrow evening,' she confessed, with a contented sigh. 'I'm going to marry Reed Gallagher. You may have seen his car outside. He drives a super black Lamborghini!'

'Oh, yes.' Antonia smiled. 'I think I know the one you mean.'

'How could you miss it?' exclaimed Celia dramatically. 'Well? Will you come? I wish you would.'

Antonia hesitated. Since moving into the ground floor apartment of the converted Victorian mansion six weeks ago, she had had little opportunity to get to know her neighbours. Her work at the institute kept her pretty much occupied, and besides, she had not come to London to enjoy a social life.

Nevertheless, she had not been able to ignore the occupants of the apartment above her own. They were the kind of people she had hitherto only read about in glossy magazines, their lifestyle totally different from her own. According to Mrs Francis—who was the caretaker's wife and inclined to gossip—Celia Lytton-Smythe was the only daughter of the Conservative member of parliament for one of the south London constituencies, while her flatmate Liz, *Elizabeth* Ashford actually, was very well-connected.

Whatever the truth of it, and Antonia had no reason to doubt what Mrs Francis had said, they seemed nice girls. In fact, Antonia had only spoken to Celia, but she was not opposed to being friendly with both of them. Even so, she had no wish to get involved in a situation where she was obliged to return their hospitality. The salary she was getting at the institute was useful, but she did not fool herself that things were going to be easy. The rent for the apartment, for example, was still quite considerable, even if Uncle Harry had reduced the burden, and she wanted to be able to send some money home to her mother for Susie. Giving extravagant parties was simply beyond her means. Perhaps it would be more honest to admit that right away.

'It's very kind of you, Celia,' she murmured now, shifting the carrier bag containing her week's shopping from one hand to the other, 'but I really don't think——'

'Oh, don't say no!' Celia tilted her head disarmingly, the inverted bell of her hair swinging confidingly against her cheek. 'I'm sure it can't be much fun, sitting down here on your own every night.' She dimpled ruefully. 'Forgive me, if that sounds impertinent, but both Liz and I have noticed, you don't get many visitors.'

Antonia coloured. She couldn't help it. Even though she surmised she was at least five years older than the other girl, Celia's remark had still had the power to strike a raw nerve. 'No,' she answered quietly. 'No, I don't. I'm afraid I must seem a very dull creature compared to your friends.'

'Oh, don't be silly!' Celia touched her sleeve in protest, and Antonia guessed she had not intended to sound patronising. 'But as you do go out so seldom, surely you'd enjoy a party, just for once! I mean, you wouldn't have to stay long, if you didn't want to. Just come and have a drink and wish Reed and me well.'

Antonia sighed. 'Oh——'

'You'll come?' Celia took her indecision as a sign that she was weakening. 'Of course, you will.' Her warm smile appeared again. 'Make it about eight-thirty, or thereabouts. There'll be some food of sorts, if you're hungry, and Daddy's promised me at least a dozen bottles of champagne!'

Once inside her apartment, Antonia leaned back against the door with some misgivings. She should have been more decisive, she thought impatiently. She should have refused Celia's invitation outright, instead of allowing the other girl to think she might change her mind. How could she go to their party? She didn't know anyone; except Celia, of course. And besides, they were not her sort of people. Even Uncle Harry did not have Mercedes' and Lamborghinis parked at his door.

Shaking her head, she pushed herself away from the panels and walked resolutely through the small living room and into the kitchen. Unpacking her shopping on to the drainer, she determinedly put all thoughts of the following evening's activities out of her head. Concentrating instead on an examination of what she had bought, she quickly disposed of her groceries into the fitted cupboards, and then plugged in the kettle.

Pausing in the doorway to the living room, she surveyed her surroundings without emotion. When she had first seen the apartment, it had been unfurnished, and the rooms had seemed bigger then. Now, with her mother's comfortable, chintz-covered sofa and arm-chairs taking up most of the space, there was hardly room for the gate-legged table she ate from. But then, her mother's furniture had been bought to furnish a generously proportioned four-bedroomed semi, not a single person's flat.

It was after six o'clock, she saw, with some surprise, the mellow rays of evening sunlight striking the face of the square carriage clock that stood on the mantelpiece. The apartments were centrally heated, but the old-fashioned fireplace still remained in Antonia's living room, modernised now by the addition of a rather ugly electric fire.

However, it was not the incongruity of the heating system that concerned her now. She must have spent longer with Celia than she had thought. Her mother would have been expecting her to ring at six o'clock, as usual, and abandoning any thought of dinner for the moment, Antonia picked up the phone.

These bi-weekly calls to Newcastle were going to prove expensive, Antonia reflected now, as she dialled her mother's number, but they were the only way she could keep in touch with Susie. Letters were not a satisfactory means of expression to an almost six-year-old, particularly one who found it hard to understand why her mother should have to go so far away to work. It simply wasn't enough to say there were no suitable jobs in Newcastle. Susie wanted to know why, if her mother had to live in London, she couldn't do so as well.

Mrs Lord answered the phone after the first couple of rings, and over her: 'Hello, Antonia? Is that you?' the protesting sound of Susie's voice was clearly audible.

'Yes, Mum, it's me,' Antonia answered ruefully, guessing her daughter was being quite a handful. 'I'm sorry I'm late. I was talking to one of the girls who lives upstairs.'

'You were? *Susie, behave yourself!* How nice, dear,' her mother responded disjointedly. 'But otherwise, you're all right, are you? Have you had a good week?'

'A busy one,' conceded Antonia, sinking down onto the arm of the sofa close by. 'Mr Fenwick has been away, and I've had to handle any emergencies myself.'

'Really? *Susie, put Tuppence down, there's a good girl!* They must have confidence in you then.'

'Not necessarily.' Antonia's tone was dry. 'But there is no one else, is there? Except Tom Brandon, of course, and he won't do anything he's not being paid for.' She paused, and then added reluctantly: 'I gather Susie's playing up again.'

'Oh, you know she has these phases,' exclaimed Mrs Lord tolerantly. 'Perhaps I'd better let her speak to you. There'll be no peace for either of us until I do.'

Antonia felt the familiar constriction in her throat when she heard her daughter's voice. She missed Susie terribly. Not just her company, and the mischief she got up to, but also her untidiness—the simple absence of anybody's occupation of the apartment but her own. At home, she had seemed to spend her time clearing up after the child, and she remembered grumbling about doing so. Now, she would have welcomed the activity with open arms.

'Are you being a good girl?' she asked Susie now, after the initial greetings were over. 'I can hear what's going on, you know. While Nanna was talking to me, you were making a nuisance of yourself, weren't you?'

'No.' Susie spoke with the convincing logic of someone who didn't regret her actions.

'But you were tormenting Tuppence, weren't you? You know she doesn't like being picked up.'

'Tuppence is fat!' declared Susie irrelevantly, as if the cat's weight had anything to do with it. Then, her voice taking on a heartbreakingly tearful note, she added: 'When are you coming to see me, Mummy? I don't like staying here with Nanna. Nanna won't play games with me like you do, and I don't like watching television.'

'Oh, Susie!' Antonia pressed her lips together tightly, fighting back a similar kind of emotion. This was the first time she and her daughter had been parted. When Simon walked out, she had worried for a time that he might try and take the child away from her, but her fears had proved groundless. Now, she had done what she had always declared she would never do: leave Susie without either of her parents.

'Couldn't I come and stay with you?' persisted the little girl now, taking her mother's prolonged silence as an encouraging sign, and Antonia hated to have to disappoint her.

'Darling, you have to go to school,' she said, choosing her words with care. 'And you have to take care of Nanna, too. She wouldn't like to live in that big old house on her own.'

Susie sniffed mutinously. 'Nanna wouldn't mind . . .'

'Yes, she would.'

'. . . and I could go to school in London, couldn't I?' she added reasonably.

Antonia shook her head. 'And what would you do when you came home from school and I wasn't here?' she asked gently. 'Susie, you know if there was any way we could be together, we would be so.' She hesitated. 'You know I'll be home for your birthday in two weeks time.'

Susie sniffed again. 'Why can't you come tonight? It's Friday. You don't work on Saturdays and Sundays, do you?'

'Well . . . no . . .'

'There you are then!'

'. . . but it would be too expensive,' explained Antonia, sighing. 'Darling, the train fare to Newcastle costs too much for Mummy to come and see you every weekend.'

There was more of the same, and then when Susie finally dissolved into tears as she usually did, Mrs Lord came back on the line. 'Don't worry, Antonia,' she assured her daughter airily, 'five minutes after I've put down this receiver, Susie will have forgotten all about it. And Howard and Sylvia are coming tomorrow, so she'll have the twins to play with.'

'Yes.' Antonia wished she felt more enthusiastic about that. Her brother's twin boys were seven years old, and in her experience Susie had never looked forward to their advent. Still . . .

'Don't worry, Antonia,' said her mother again, more brusquely now. 'Look, my dear, I've got to go. Susie has to have her bath yet, and I haven't fed Tuppence, and . . . and . . .'

'And it's Friday night,' remarked Antonia, with controlled irony. 'I know.' Her mother usually played bridge on Friday evenings. 'Okay, Mum. I'll ring again on Monday as usual.'

With the receiver replaced on its rest, Antonia found her will to go and make herself something to eat had been sadly diminished. The kettle had switched itself off in her absence, and allowing herself to slide disconsolately off the arm of the sofa, she subsided on to the cushioned seat. She always had this awful sense of emptiness after speaking to her mother and Susie, and it was incredibly difficult not to give way to a totally selfish desire to burst into tears.

But self-pity was not something she allowed herself to indulge in for long, and presently Antonia got up from the couch and went to make a cup of tea. A pizza she had bought in the supermarket on her way home, was soon heated under the grill, and putting her cup and plate on a tray, she carried them back into the living room.

The portable black-and-white television her mother had insisted she brought from home to keep her company held no interest for her, and propping the paperback novel she was presently reading on the cushions beside her, she tried to become involved with its cardboard characters. But it was no use. Susie's face kept intruding, and after eating half the pizza, Antonia put the book aside and turned on the radio.

The music programme she tuned into was soothing, and depositing the tray on the floor, Antonia curled her long legs up beside her. Had she really done the right thing by taking this job? she asked herself, for the umpteenth time, feeling the familiar sense of melancholy stealing over her. Was the fact that she had been looking for suitable employment for over three years a reasonable excuse for accepting a position so far from home? Uncle Harry, her mother's brother, had certainly thought so; but then, he had done the same more than twenty years ago, so he was biased.

'It's not as if you're a slip of a lass,' he had remarked candidly, when he drove up to Newcastle to offer her this flat. He was referring to Antonia's height of five feet eight inches, of course, and to the fact that she was five years past her twenty-first birthday. 'And you have been married,' he added, as if that was some further qualification. 'Your mother won't have to worry that you'll get yourself into trouble, if you see what I mean.'

Antonia did see, and Uncle Harry's words were valid. Her marriage to—and subsequent divorce from—Simon, had certainly taught her to be wary of the opposite sex. But as she had no intention of allowing any emotional relationship to develop, he could have saved his breath. Once bitten, twice shy, she quoted a little bitterly. She was free now, and self-supporting. No man was worth the sacrifice of surrendering those basic liberties.

Saturday was not one of Antonia's favourite days of the week. It was the day she cleaned the flat for a start and, like Sunday, it was inclined to drag. Uncle Harry, who lived in Wimbledon, had suggested she should go to them on Sundays, for lunch, but Antonia did not think it was fair on Aunt Mary. Their own two sons, and their wives and families, often turned up for lunch on Sundays, and although that first lonely weekend in London Antonia had taken them up on their offer, she had felt an intruder. They had tried to make her feel at home, but they had their own lives, their own friends; people they could talk about, but who meant nothing to her. After several awkward interludes, when Antonia had been excluded from their conversation, an awkward silence had fallen, and Antonia had never repeated the experience.

Perhaps she was too sensitive, she thought wearily, as she was vacuuming her bedroom. Perhaps if she had gone every Sunday, she would eventually have fitted in to their lives. The trouble was, they had not known what to say to her, beyond asking about her mother and Susie. The subject of Simon was apparently taboo, and when she would have explained that she had long recovered from the effects of his rejection, Aunt Mary had steered the conversation into other channels.

Later that afternoon, as she sat in an armchair drinking a well-earned cup of tea, she became aware of the sound of furniture being shifted in the room above. Apparently, Celia and her friend were getting ready for the party, Antonia reflected, half-enviously. It was years since she had attended anything but family get-togethers. Her marriage to Simon had cut her off from all her college friends, and when they split up, it simply wasn't possible to pick up the threads of her social life as if nothing had happened. Besides, there had been Susie to consider, and Antonia had tried to keep her life as stable as possible. But, after the divorce, the house she and Simon had bought with their savings had had to be sold, and Antonia had had no choice but to take her mother's advice and go back to living with her.

Realising she was allowing herself to sink into a state of depression, Antonia got up from her chair and carried her cup into the kitchen. Then, flexing her aching shoulders, she walked into the tiny bathroom that adjoined her bedroom. Turning on the bath taps, she squeezed some scented bath gel into the water, and then turned back into the bedroom to find herself some clean underwear.

Ten minutes later she was soaking in the deliciously perfumed water, feeling the tensions she had been experiencing easing out of her. Even the uncertain weather beyond her windows, that sent raindrops pattering against the pane, no longer had the power to depress her, and she relaxed lazily, allowing her thoughts to drift.

Perhaps she should go to the party, she mused reflectively. After all, she had been invited, and she didn't want to offend Celia. She was a nice girl, and she hoped she would be happy. No doubt this young man of hers—what was his name? Reed ... Gallagher? No doubt, he was capable of supporting her in the manner to which she was accustomed. Celia would never be expected to do her own housework, or look after her own children, not unless she wanted to, of course. Antonia already knew that Mrs Francis paid a twice-weekly visit to the apartment upstairs: *Just to give the place the once-over!* as she put it; and whenever there was to be a party, the catering van from a very exclusive establishment was generally to be seen outside.

The water was cooling by the time she got out of the

bath, and after drying herself vigorously to restore her circulation, Antonia slipped on the pink towelling bathrobe her mother had bought for her at Christmas. Her hair needed drying, and collecting the hand-drier from the cupboard, Antonia seated herself in front of the dressing-table mirror. Removing the towel she had wound around her head while she got dry, she surveyed her reflection wryly. At least, she had no problems about what to do with her hair, she thought, tugging a brush through the damp strands. Shoulder-length and straight, it defied any attempt she made to put curl into it; and although once she had gone so far as to try perming, the result had been so awful, she had never tried again.

Dry, the toffee-brown ends tipped silkily against her shoulders. Combed from a centre parting, the two shining swathes framed the oval contours of her face, a feathery fringe brushing eyebrows that were several shades darker. Examining her skin for any unsightly blemish, Antonia had to admit that the polluted air of London had done nothing to mar it. Hazel eyes, which could look green in some lights, looked back at her from between her lashes, their slightly elongated shape giving her face a mildly interesting look. She was not beautiful; she knew that. Although she had good bone structure, her mouth was too wide, the lower lip too full. In the early days of their relationship, Simon used to say she had a sexy face, but she had long since dismissed any claims he made. Simon had wanted to get her into bed, and he had succeeded. The result had been Susie, and the rest was history.

Abandoning this particular train of thought, Antonia got up from the mirror and expelled her breath heavily. What was she going to do? she asked herself. Go to the party; or consign herself to another night of self-recrimination? She was becoming far too morose and introspective, she thought; and dull, painfully dull! Just because she had had one bad experience, she was allowing its aftermath to colour her whole outlook on life. All right, so she didn't want to get involved ever again. She didn't have to. She could still enjoy a party, with no strings attached.

The problem of what she was going to wear if she did go loomed next on her horizon. What did one wear to an informal party of this kind? She could wear jeans, she supposed, or cotton trousers; but as she wasn't absolutely sure how informal *informal* was, she decided it would be safer to stick with a skirt.

The fitted wardrobe easily accommodated her clothes with room to spare. One advantage of not leading a hectic social life was that one had less reason to buy expensive outfits, and Antonia's needs were not extensive. She generally wore a suit or a tailored dress to the office, and casual wear at other times. In consequence, what choice she had was limited, and she doubted there was anything to completely suit her purpose.

A pretty green batiste dress was appealing, but it seemed too summery for an April evening. A cotton two-piece was discarded for similar reasons, and the dark brown corded trouser suit, which always looked good, was dismissed on two counts: it was too warm to wear indoors, and it didn't have a skirt.

Sighing, Antonia eventually pulled out the only item she might regard as wearable. It was a cream shirt-waisted dress, with full sleeves and a narrow skirt, that ended just above her knees. Made of Thai silk, she had bought it in a sale in Newcastle the previous January, and since then, she had simply not had an occasion to wear it. Even in the sale, it had not been cheap, and her mother had thought her quite mad to spend her money on one item when she might have had two. Now, however, Antonia knew it was exactly what she was looking for, and stripping off the bathrobe, she put it on.

She had never realised how flattering the colour was, she thought, lifting her hair out of the neckline and turning this way and that. The low vee in front drew attention to the enticing swell of her breasts, and for once she did not deplore their fullness. Since having

Susie, her breasts had become heavier, and she had seen
no advantages in the contrast they posed to the
narrowness of her waist. Now, however, she saw that
the dusky hollow just visible above the buttons of the
dress was not unappealing, and her lips parted à little
wryly at her unwarranted enthusiasm. What did it
matter what she looked like, after all? She wasn't going
to the party in the hope of attracting some man.
Nevertheless, there was a certain satisfaction to be
found in knowing she was looking her best, and she was
still woman enough not to want Celia to go on feeling
sorry for her.

When she left her flat at eight-thirty to climb the
stairs to the apartment upstairs, she joined several other
young people, evidently with the same destination. But
they were not on their own, as she was. They were in
groups of two or three, all laughing and talking
together, with the easy cameraderie of long practice.
They cast faintly speculative glances in Antonia's
direction—not unfriendly actually, but not specially
kind—and one or two of the young men eyed her with a
more than passing interest. But generally they all
regarded her with some curiosity, and Antonia became
increasingly convinced she should not have come.
Perhaps if she turned round now, she thought, having
reached the first floor landing where the buzz of music
and conversation coming through the open door of the
apartment was quite overpowering. Who would notice?
she asked herself. Who would care? But the realisation
that she would have to run the gauntlet of several more
people climbing the stairs behind her drove her on, and
because she had no alternative, she was obliged to take
the plunge.

At least, what she was wearing was acceptable, she
mused, with some relief. Although it was raining
outside, it was not a cold evening, and she had seen one
or two girls wearing dresses similar to her own. There
were girls in trousers, but not as many as she might
have expected, and the men's clothes reflected their
girlfriends' casual tastes.

It soon became apparent that the apartment Celia and her friend occupied was approximately twice the size of Antonia's. Unlike the floor below, which was divided into two flats—the other being occupied by the caretaker and his wife—the first floor was given over entirely to the apartment leased by the two girls. Halting on the threshold of a warmly lit entrance hall, Antonia was immediately impressed by an atmosphere redolent with the mingled scents of expensive perfumes, Havana tobacco, and fine wines; and she didn't need to see the banks of flowers or feel her feet sinking into the Persian carpet to know that everything Mrs Francis had hinted must be true.

Ahead of her, the young men and girls who had preceded her up the stairs were soon absorbed into the welcoming surge of people swelling through the matching doors that gave access to the living room. The amplified projection of the song that was presently topping the popular music charts made any formal introductions impossible, and the couple behind Antonia were compelling her to move forward. Almost without her own volition, she was propelled through the doors, and was soon engulfed by that noisy jostling throng.

The room was literally full of people, spilling over the arms of brocade-covered sofas and squashy leather armchairs on to stools and bean-filled cushions, and even the floor. The living room was large by anybody's standards, but although Antonia had heard of its silk-hung walls and high moulded ceilings from Mrs Francis, it was difficult to appreciate its elegance tonight. The rhythm emanating from the hi-fi system and its accompanying speakers created a constant vibration, and the smoke from more than a dozen cheroots and cigarettes was sending a hazy cloud drifting irresistibly upwards. Those people who had just arrived, or perhaps those who simply preferred to circulate, made up the relaxed gathering that swelled from the entrance into the middle of the floor; and Antonia found herself a part of that gathering; anxious, and decidedly *not* relaxed. Where was Celia? she wondered, turning on heels that were a little higher than she usually wore. Surely she had to be here somewhere! But where?

'Are you looking for somebody in particular, or will I do?' enquired an attractive male voice close to her ear, and Antonia swung round with incautious haste to face the questioner. Incautious, because her heel caught in the shaggy pile of the carpet, and had her inquisitor not been there to grab at, she might easily have disgraced herself completely and landed at his feet.

Instead, she clutched rather wildly for his arm, her grappling fingers barely registering the subtle softness of his suede-covered sleeve. As she struggled to disentangle her heel from its infuriating cohesion with the carpet, she was scarcely aware of him using his free hand to help her regain her balance until, in doing so, he brought her up against the lean hardness of his body. Then, as her heel came loose, she was able to look up at him, and the humorous gleam in his grey eyes made her quickly put some space between them.

'I'm sorry,' she said, colouring hotly as she apprehended what had happened. 'I caught my heel . . .'

'I know.' The amused grey eyes were regarding her with frank appreciation. 'But I guess I was responsible. I did attract your attention.'

'It was you . . .'

'. . . who spoke to you? Yes, it was.' He smiled, his lips parting to reveal even white teeth. 'You looked— lost. I wanted to help you.'

'Not bring me to my knees?' countered Antonia wryly, the humour of the situation restoring her composure. 'Well—thank you, anyway. I'm all right.'

'I'm pleased to hear it.' But he did not move away as she had expected. Instead, he collected two long-stemmed glasses of a beige, bubbling liquid, from a tray being held by a passing waiter, and handed one to her. 'Be my guest!'

Antonia took the glass reluctantly, but a surreptitious glance about her assured her that their exchange was not attracting any unnecessary attention. On the contrary, the music and the buzz of conversation was going on as before, and it was only in her mind that she and this man who had rescued her from instant ignominy had isolated themselves from the rest.

Licking an errant drop of champagne—for that was what it was, she realised—from her lips, she cast covert eyes in his direction. Disconcertingly, he was watching her, but that didn't prevent her hastily averted gaze from noticing how attractive he was. Straight dark hair, rather longer than was fashionable; a lean, narrow-boned face; skin that still bore the tan of a winter holiday; even without the fact that he could look down at her from the advantage of at least three inches, notwithstanding her high heels, he was a disturbing man. But it was his eyes that really disrupted her carefully composed indifference; grey, as she already knew, they were fringed by thick straight lashes, that gave a wholly sensual appeal to an otherwise ascetically handsome face.

'Do you like it?' he enquired lazily, and Antonia controlled her colour with difficulty.

'Like what?' she asked, rather too sharply for politeness.

'Why—the champagne, of course,' he replied smoothly, and Antonia concentrated on the wine in her glass to avoid his knowing gaze.

'It's—very nice,' she answered, determinedly taking another sip. It was infuriating, but he was making her feel as gauche as a schoolgirl, and she had to remind herself that she was a divorcee with a six-year-old daughter.

'You're different from what I expected,' he remarked suddenly, surprising her into looking at him again. 'Cee said you were shy and rather ordinary. But you're not. Though I suppose another female might not realise it.'

Antonia caught her breath. 'Has she been discussing me with her friends? Is that why she invited me here? To satisfy their curiosity?'

Her voice had risen slightly as she spoke, and the

man beside her expelled his breath a little impatiently. 'I didn't say that,' he told her evenly. 'And if you knew Cee, you wouldn't accuse her of it. She's not like that.'

'She told you, didn't she?' asked Antonia hotly, her eyes sparkling with resentment. His words seemed to confirm all her worst imaginings, and she thought how right she had been to have doubts about coming here. 'If you'll excuse me . . .'

'Where are you going?'

His hand circling her wrist was the final humiliation, and she was on the point of threatening to throw the remainder of her champagne in his face if he didn't release her, when another hand touched her shoulder.

'Darling,' exclaimed Celia, as Antonia was abruptly released. 'You've met my downstairs neighbour already. Antonia,' the other girl circled them to slide a possessive arm over the man's sleeve, 'what do you think of this Irish rogue who's asked me to be his wife?'

CHAPTER TWO

ANTONIA's office adjoined that of Martin Fenwick's. It wasn't much of an office really, just a desk and a chair and a filing cabinet, in a room large enough to accommodate them and her, but at least it offered her some privacy. And her work was interesting.

Seven years ago, when she had had to give up all thoughts of a career to have Susie, she had been in the second year of a sociology degree at Durham university. Working *with* people and *for* the community had always interested her, and her intention had been to try and get a job in some branch of the social services. But Simon's advent into her life had interrupted her plans, and afterwards, when she had found it necessary to look for work, her qualifications were sadly limited. Of course, had she had the money, she could have returned to university as a mature student and taken up her studies again, but that was out of the question with Susie to support. Instead, she had applied for any job that had offered the chance of working in a similar field, and in spite of its disadvantages in terms of distance, she had been delighted to accept her present position.

The institute, where she worked as Assistant to the Director, was an independently operated youth training establishment, offering skills in various manual trades, as well as academic qualifications. Courses in book-keeping and accountancy, shorthand and typewriting, competed with mechanical engineering and carpentry, and the students were encouraged to try more than one course before deciding on the one that suited them best.

Antonia considered herself very fortunate to have been offered the post, and she felt she owed a debt to her past tutor at Durham for giving her his backing and support. Without the reference he had been able to supply, she felt sure she would not have been so lucky, and the doubts she had had about leaving the north of England had been stifled by the faith he had had in her.

To her relief Mr Fenwick, who had been absent the previous week due to an apparently seasonal attack of lumbago, was back at work on Monday morning, and Antonia was able to return to her own duties. Her experience at the job had not yet equipped her to handle all the hundred and one little problems that could occur in the course of a working week, and there were several outstanding difficulties she was going to have to discuss with him when he had the time.

But to begin with, the institute's director had enough to do handling the enormous backlog of mail, which had required his personal attention, and Antonia spent most of Monday morning trying to catch up on her own duties.

Even so, she did not find it easy to apply herself to practical matters. It wasn't that her work was difficult or anything. It was simply that her mind kept drifting away from what she was doing, and several times she found herself staring into space, totally detached from her surroundings.

It was the remembrance of Saturday night that was troubling her, of course. The party, which she had not wanted to attend, and which was now lodged painfully in her memory. Just thinking of that scene in Celia's living room caused Antonia's face to flood with colour, and it still amazed her that she had stayed so long when all she had really wanted to do was escape.

She should have made her apologies as soon as a decent interval had elapsed, she thought, and hurried back to her own apartment. Certainly, Celia's flatmate, the *Honourable* Elizabeth, *Liz*, Ashford, had thought so. It had soon become apparent that the other occupant of the first floor apartment did not share her friend's enthusiasm to mix with their neighbours, and her greeting had been distant, to say the least. The other female guests seemed to take their lead from her, and regarded Antonia with something less than cordiality, and it was left to Celia and the male contingent to try and put her at her ease.

That it hadn't worked was mainly due to Antonia's own behaviour. She had not come to the party to be propositioned, and she was not used to finding herself the centre of attraction. Besides, if she was honest she would admit that the awareness of Reed Gallagher in the background, watching her embarrassed attempts to break free of her admirers, had coloured her attitude towards them, and what might have been an amusing situation turned into a trial of nerves.

Learning that the man she had been so arbitrarily crossing swords with was really Celia's fiancé had been a shock. Not that she had any interest in him personally, she assured herself, but his attitude towards her had not been that of a man desperately in love with his fiancée. At least, not in her experience it hadn't. Perhaps their sort of people behaved differently. Perhaps, even in this day and age, it was to be a marriage engineered for convenience. But then, remembering the way Celia had clung to her fiancé's arm and the adoring looks she had cast in his direction, Antonia felt convinced that for her part, Celia cared madly for her handsome Irishman. And probably he did, too, she reflected cynically, refusing to admit that initially she, too, had been disarmed. Whatever his feelings, she was unlikely to discover them, though she had the distinct suspicion he was not as careless and superficial as he would have had her believe. And when he had taken hold of her wrist . . .

Shaking her head to dislodge the irritating recollection of the cool strength of Reed's fingers against her skin, Antonia endeavoured to apply herself to the application forms in front of her. The institute was always oversubscribed on all their courses, and it was to be part of her duties to consider each application on its merit, and winnow them down to a more manageable thirty-five or forty from which Mr Fenwick could make his final choice. New trainees were admitted in September, and interviews were apparently held in May and June to reduce the eventual intake to approximately twenty in each department. It promised to be an interesting part of her work, particularly as Mr Fenwick had informed her that in his opinion aptitude for a particular occupation was worth more than any number of academic qualifications.

This morning, however, Antonia's brain refused to function, and by eleven o'clock she was still studying the second form. When Martin Fenwick appeared to ask her to come into his office, she abandoned her task with a feeling of relief, following him into his room with an enthusiasm untempered by her usual impatience to get on with her own job.

Blowing his nose before taking his seat, her boss regarded her rather speculatively. 'Are you feeling all right, Mrs Sheldon?' he asked, gesturing her to a chair on the other side of his desk. 'You're looking rather tired. Did you go home at the weekend?'

Not entirely relishing his probably well-meant enquiry, Antonia shook her head. 'If you mean to Newcastle—then, no,' she answered politely, wondering if she had bags under her eyes. 'I . . . er . . . didn't sleep very well last night.'

Martin Fenwick nodded. 'I haven't been sleeping too well myself,' he confessed, sinking down into his chair. 'Lumbago's the devil of a thing. Wakes you up, every time you turn over.'

'I'm sorry.' Antonia summoned a small smile. 'But you're feeling better now.'

'Well—it's bearable,' he essayed heavily, shuffling the papers on his desk. 'I suppose at my age I have to expect something. Be thankful yours is not a chronic condition.'

'Yes.'

Antonia conceded his point, although lying awake in the early hours it had felt very much as though it was. She had blamed the fact that on Sunday she had done nothing but laze around the flat, but that wasn't entirely true either. What she was really doing was coming to terms with the rather unpalatable realisation that in spite of her unfortunate experience with Simon, she was still not immune to sexual attraction.

'So—shall we get down to business?' suggested Mr Fenwick now, smoothing one hand over his bald pate as he read through the report she had prepared for him. 'This is good, very good. Very comprehensive.' His slightly rheumy eyes twinkled as he looked up at her. 'I knew you were the woman for the job, as soon as I set eyes on you.'

Antonia was grateful for his confidence, and she did her best to satisfy all his enquiries, and learn how to deal with problems in his absence in the process. The failure of the hydraulic lift in the motor repair workshop had caused her some difficulties, she confessed, and the trainee joiner who had cut his hand badly on an electric saw deserved a reprimand she had not felt able to give him. Nevertheless, on the whole, there had been no insurmountable set-backs, and she knew by the end of their discussion that Mr Fenwick felt his belief in her abilities had been justified.

The afternoon proved rather less traumatic. After a snack lunch in the dining hall with Heather Jakes, Mr Fenwick's secretary, Antonia returned to her desk to find her concentration was much improved. Determining not to waste any more time weighing the pros and cons of her attendance at the party, she put all thoughts of Celia Lytton-Smythe and her fiancé aside, and applied herself instead to the relative merits of a certificate in woodwork and an ability to type.

It was nearing six o'clock when Antonia reached the stone gate-posts that marked the boundary of Eaton Lodge. She had been grateful to find there was a short drive leading up to the house. Her rooms, being on the ground floor, would have adjoined the street otherwise, and she was still not accustomed to the sound of traffic at all hours of the day and night. Her mother's house, in a suburb of Newcastle, was situated in a quiet cul-de-sac, and it had not been easy for her to make the transition.

Even so, she was glad that she did not have expensive

train fares to add to her living expenses. The flat, in Clifton Gate, was only a bus ride from the institute in the Edgware Road, and on summer days she planned to walk to and from work. The exercise would do her good, and the resultant savings might enable her to pay more frequent visits to Newcastle—and Susie.

As she walked up the short path to the house, the black Lamborghini overtook her, and for the first time she saw Reed Gallagher at the wheel. It was early for him, she thought, aware of an unwelcome tightening of her stomach muscles. She couldn't remember seeing the car in the drive much before seven-thirty or eight o'clock in the past, though she had to admit that until Celia pointed it out, she had paid little attention to their visitors. Now, however, she was all too aware of its occupant, and it took a certain amount of stamina to continue up the drive as if nothing untoward had happened.

By the time she reached the entrance, Reed had parked the powerful sports car, crossed the forecourt, and was waiting for her. In a dark blue three-piece business suit and a white shirt, he looked little different from the less formally dressed individual she had met at the party. With a conservative tie narrowly concealing the buttons of his shirt, and his hands pushed carelessly into the pockets of his jacket, he appeared relaxed and self-assured, confident in his cool male arrogance—and Antonia resented his somehow insolent supposition that she might be pleased to exchange a few words with him.

'Hi,' he said, as she came up the steps, his lean frame successfully blocking her passage. 'How are you?'

Antonia held up her head and without looking at him, made her intentions evident. 'I'm fine, thank you, Mr Gallagher,' she responded stiffly, edging towards the door. 'Do you mind?'

Reed regarded her steadily for a few moments—she could almost *feel* those disturbing grey eyes probing her averted lids—then he politely stepped aside. 'My pleasure,' he assured her, allowing her to precede him into the gloomy entrance hall. 'It's cold out tonight, isn't it? *Very* chilly!'

Pressing her lips together to suppress the immature retort that sprang into her mind, Antonia rummaged in her handbag for her key. If only she'd thought to do this before she came inside, she thought frustratedly. It was difficult to see what she was doing without the benefit of a light.

Aware that Reed had not continued on upstairs as she had expected, her fingers were all thumbs, and when she eventually found the key, it slithered annoyingly out of her grasp. With a little ping, it landed on the floor at Reed's feet, and with a feeling of helplessness, she watched him bend and rescue it for her with a lithe graceful movement.

'Let me,' he said, avoiding her outstretched hand, and she stood stiffly by as he inserted the key in the lock and deftly turned the handle. 'No problem,' he added, dropping the key into her palm, and knowing she was behaving badly, but unable to do anything about it, Antonia gave him a curt nod before scurrying into the flat.

She was still leaning back against the closed door, her heart beating rather faster than was normal, when she heard the brisk tattoo on the panels behind her. Realising it could be no one else but him, she was tempted to pretend she hadn't heard his knock, but she knew that would be childish. There was no likelihood that she might not have heard his summons, and by not answering her door she would look as if she was afraid to do so.

Taking a deep breath, she gathered together the two sides of her camel-hair jacket, which she had just unbuttoned, and turned. With carefully schooled features, she swung open the door again, holding on to the handle, as if there was any chance that he might try to force himself inside.

Reed was leaning against the wall to one side of the door, but when she looked out he straightened, and turned to face her. 'Yes?' she said tersely, unable to keep the hostility out of her voice, and his dark features took on a rueful aspect.

'Can I come in?'

Antonia could not have been more surprised, and it showed. 'I beg your pardon . . .'

'I said, can I come in?' he repeated levelly, glancing over her shoulder into the small apartment. 'I want to talk to you, and I'd prefer not to do so in Mrs Francis's hearing.'

'Mrs Francis?' Antonia's tongue circled her lips, and Reed nodded.

'Any minute now, her door is going to open—just a crack,' he confided drily. 'So?'

Antonia cast a half-glance behind her, suddenly conscious of the enormous contrast between her modest apartment and the luxurious rooms occupied by his fiancée. And she realised she didn't want him to see where she lived. She didn't want him coming into her flat, comparing her shabby furnishings with the designer fabrics upstairs. This was her home, such as it was, and she didn't want his disruptive influence invading its sanctuary.

'I don't think that's a very good idea,' she said now, endeavouring to maintain a politely indifferent tone. 'I can't think of anything we have to say to one another, Mr Gallagher. If Celia's not at home, I'm sorry, but I'm afraid you can't wait here.'

Reed expelled his breath noisily. 'I don't know if Cee's at home or not,' he retorted, his lean face losing its humorous expression. 'Look—I'm not about to ravage you or anything. I simply wanted to apologise if you think I was indiscreet.'

Antonia looked at him unwillingly, her diffident gaze drawn to the clean-cut lines of his face. 'Indiscreet?'

'By telling you what Cee had said,' he inserted flatly. 'And by not telling you who I was.'

Antonia's nostrils flared, ever so slightly. 'It's not important . . .'

'I think it is.'

'Why?' Her fingers tightened on the metal handle. 'We are hardly likely to meet again, are we?'

'Why not?' The long straight lashes narrowed his eyes. 'Cee likes you. She told me.' He paused, and when she made no response, he added: 'Well—I guess that's all I came to say.'

Antonia drew an unsteady breath. 'Is it?' she murmured, her long fingers fidgeting with the collar of her coat. Suddenly, she was disappointed. 'I—is your fiancée at home?'

Reed glanced carelessly up the stairs. 'I doubt it,' he responded, pulling one hand out of his pocket and combing his fingers through the dark vitality of his hair. 'The shop doesn't close until six, and it's barely that now. But don't worry about it,' he finished with some irony. 'I have a key.'

Antonia hesitated. 'I—I was just going to make some tea,' she offered, regretting the words almost as soon as they were uttered. Whatever had possessed her to offer him her hospitality? she asked herself impatiently. Did she want him carrying tales upstairs of the straightened circumstances in which she lived? 'I mean,' she added awkwardly, 'I don't suppose you—drink tea.'

'Well, I don't survive on honeydew and nectar,' he responded, his grey eyes gently teasing. 'Thank you, Miss Sheldon. I'd love a cup of tea.'

She had to step aside then, and treading silently on suede-booted feet, Reed entered the flat. Unlike the apartment occupied by Celia and her friend, there was no entrance hall. One stepped directly into Antonia's living room, and her colour deepened embarrassingly as Reed looked about him with evident interest.

With the door closed behind him, Antonia did not linger to correct his assumption of her status. Shedding her coat on to a chair as she passed, she walked through the living room into the kitchen, leaving him to make what he liked of the flat. She simply wasn't interested, she told herself, filling the kettle at the tap and pushing in the electric plug. The sooner he had his tea and departed, the better. And after all, Celia might not approve of his making a detour, when he was evidently on his way to visit her.

She was examining the contents of the biscuit tin when his shadow fell across her. 'A watched pot never boils, isn't that what they say?' he remarked drily, surveying the pristine neatness of the kitchen. 'Come and sit down. You must be tired.'

'Do I look tired?'

After what Mr Fenwick had said earlier, Antonia's tone was unnecessarily tense, and Reed regarded her with rueful tolerance. 'I guess I always seem to say the wrong thing, don't I?' he averred, running a lazy hand around the back of his neck. 'Now, how can I redeem myself? By telling you I was only being polite, or by assuring you that you look pretty good to me?'

Antonia bent her head. 'Neither. It doesn't matter. I—you go and sit down. I'll join you presently.'

'Okay.'

With a careless shrug he left her, and Antonia took cups out of the cupboard above the drainer, and set them on their saucers. By the time she had put milk into a jug and set it, along with the sugar bowl, on a tray, the kettle had boiled. Filling the teapot, she put it on the tray, too, and then after checking she had everything, she carried it through to the living room.

Reed was lounging on the sofa, flicking through the pages of a self-help magazine she had bought to learn how to do minor repairs. In her absence, he had loosened the top two buttons of his shirt and pulled his tie a couple of inches below his collar, and the slightly dishevelled appearance suited him. But then, anything would, thought Antonia woodenly, refusing to respond to his lazy smile. He was vibrant; magnetic; the kind of man one could not help but be aware of, his unconscious sexuality a challenge in itself.

Conscious of this, she seated herself on the armchair opposite him, and made a play of pouring the tea. 'Milk and sugar?' she enquired, the jug poised just above the cup, but he shook his head, and responded lightly: 'As it is.'

Belatedly, she guessed he was used to taking it with lemon, but in any case, she didn't have any. And besides, her tea was not Lapsang or Orange Pekoe. It was just common-or-garden quick-brew that she bought at the supermarket.

Still, he seemed to enjoy it, resting his ankle across his knee, emptying his cup and accepting a second. She should have known he would feel at ease anywhere, she thought, going to cross her legs and then thinking better of it. Like a chameleon, he adapted to his surroundings, totally indifferent to anyone's feelings but his own. He was making her feel a stranger in her own apartment, and she resented his easy manner almost as much as his sex appeal.

'Why don't you like me, Miss Sheldon?' he asked suddenly, setting his cup back on the tray while Antonia's clattered noisily in its saucer. 'Do I frighten you? Is that it? Are you afraid of men, perhaps? I'd be interested to know what I've done to provoke such a reaction.'

Antonia replaced her cup on the table with rather more care than she had picked it up. 'I think you're imagining things, Mr Gallagher.'

'Am I?' His eyes were shrewdly assessing. 'We may not know one another very well—which I'm sure is your next line of defence—but I can sense hostility when I feel it, Miss Sheldon.'

'It's not—*Miss* Sheldon,' she corrected him abruptly. 'It's *Mrs* I am—I *was*—married.'

'Ah!'

His long-drawn sigh infuriated her, and abandoning any further attempt at politeness, she sprang to her feet. 'It's not what you're thinking, Mr Gallagher,' she declared hotly, her hands clenching and unclenching at her sides. 'I'm not *afraid* of the opposite sex. I don't hate all men, or anything like that. I simply—I simply don't care for . . . for men of your type, that's all!'

'My type?' he prompted softly, and she felt the instinctive thrill of knowing she was getting into deep water without any means of saving herself. 'Men like your ex-husband perhaps?'

Like Simon! Antonia knew an hysterical desire to

laugh. No one less like Simon could she imagine. Oh,
Simon himself might have seen himself as being
attractive to women, as knowing all the answers, but
compared to Reed Gallagher, he had only been an
amateur. And she had probably been at least partly
responsible for the high opinion Simon had had of
himself. Although it had meant giving up her degree at
university, she had been flattered that the local heart-
throb should have chosen her as his girlfriend, and she
had fallen for his good looks without ever questioning
what might lie beneath the surface. Until it was too late.

'You're nothing like my husband!' she retorted now,
suddenly losing enthusiasm for the argument. The
reason she resented Reed Gallagher had nothing to do
with Simon's defection, and she felt ridiculously gauche
for having lost her temper. 'I—I shouldn't have implied
that you were.'

Aware of her discomfort, Reed got resignedly to his
feet and tightened the knot of his tie once again. 'I
think I'd better go,' he remarked, stepping sideways
round the low table on which she had set the tray.
'Thanks for the tea. It was—delicious.'

Antonia was sure it had been nothing of the kind,
and her own behaviour had been unforgivable, but
there was nothing she could say. Short of offering an
apology, which she had no intention of doing, she could
only spare him a tight smile as he walked towards the
door, and with a knowing inclination of his head, he let
himself out of the flat.

Conversely, as soon as he had gone, Antonia wanted
to call him back. Sinking down on to the edge of her
chair, she cupped her chin in her hands and stared
humiliatedly at the spot on the sofa where he had been
sitting. What a fiasco! she thought bitterly. What an
absolute fool she had made of herself. She hadn't
wanted him to leave with that impression of her,
particularly not when she thought how amusing it
would seem when he related the incident to Celia—and
Liz.

The disturbing dampness of a tear sliding down to

touch her fingertips brought Antonia a measure of relief. It *wasn't* that important, she told herself, dashing the tear away and making a concerted effort to pull herself together. Putting the teapot and her cup on to the tray, she picked it up and carried it into the kitchen. It wasn't as if she and Celia were close friends or anything. It would teach her to be more wary of them in future. They were not like her, and she should remember that.

CHAPTER THREE

IT was over a week before Antonia encountered either of her upstairs neighbours again.

It had been an unsettled week for her, not helped by the discovery, when she came home from work on Tuesday evening, of the delicate bouquet of creamy narcissus, hazy blue irises and nodding yellow daffodils residing in her kitchen sink.

'I didn't know where else to put them,' declared Mrs Francis confidentially, knocking at her door only minutes after Antonia had arrived home to explain that she had taken delivery of the flowers. 'It seemed a shame to leave them lying in the hall,' she added, regarding her newest tenant with rather more interest than before. 'They're so beautiful, aren't they? You've evidently got an admirer, Mrs Sheldon.'

Antonia smiled, but her thoughts were not as tranquil as her expression. She had already perceived that there was no card with the flowers, and there was only one person in her estimation who could have sent them. Reed Gallagher.

'I—I'm very grateful, Mrs Francis,' she said now, hoping the garrulous caretaker's wife would not pursue the subject, but she was disappointed.

'I had to put them in the sink,' Mrs Francis, continued, looking beyond Antonia, into the living room. 'I . . . er . . . I didn't like to look for a vase, and as there were *so many* . . .'

'Yes. Well, thank you.' Antonia lifted her shoulders apologetically. 'I'll find something.'

'I could lend you a vase, or maybe two, if you need them,' offered Mrs Francis helpfully, but Antonia was adamant.

'I'm sure I can manage,' she refused politely, feeling distinctly mean for not satisfying the older woman's

curiosity. But how could she tell Mrs Francis that Celia
Lytton-Smythe's fiancé had sent her the flowers? How
dare Reed Gallagher put her in this position?

'Well, if you're sure ...' Reluctantly, Mrs Francis
was having to abandon her enquiries. 'You're a lucky
girl!' she remarked, starting back across the hall. 'They
must have cost someone a pretty penny.'

Antonia smiled again to soften her words. 'I'm sure
they must,' she agreed, and closed the door firmly
before any further comment could be made.

Nevertheless, as she filled every bowl and jug and
milk bottle she possessed with the softly scented
blossoms, Antonia couldn't help inhaling their delicious
fragrance. She had never possessed so many flowers in
her life before, and while her initial instinct had been to
return the bouquet to its sender, the practicalities of
such an action deterred her. For one thing, she had no
idea where Reed Gallagher lived or worked, and even if
she had, could she take the risk of embarrassing Celia
should she be with him at the time? In addition to
which, there was always the possibility—however
slight—that Reed Gallagher might not have sent them.
How ridiculous she would look if she returned the
flowers to him and he knew nothing about them!

One final solution occurred, but it was one she did
not consider for long. The idea of returning the flowers
to the shop that had sent them did not appeal to her at
all. She could not consign such delicate blooms to
instant destruction, and besides, if Reed had sent the
flowers anonymously, as she suspected, he might never
learn of her sacrifice.

Stifling her conscience with this thought, she found
she derived a great deal of pleasure from the colour
they gave to her rather dull living room. Coming into
the flat after a day's work, she found herself
anticipating their vivid presence, and when they
eventually began to fade, she bought herself some
daffodils to mitigate their loss.

She spoke to Susie again on the phone, and promised
her the days to her birthday would soon pass. 'I'll come

on the six o'clock train next Friday evening,' she told her mother, a week before she was due to leave. 'I'm looking forward to it so much. It seems much more than eight weeks since I came to London.'

The weekend was uneventful. She guessed Celia and her friend must have gone away, for there was no sound from the apartment upstairs all Saturday and Sunday. Antonia spent the time giving her kitchen a brightening lick of paint, and determinedly avoiding the inevitable comparisons between this weekend and last.

On Monday evening, however, she came face to face with Celia in the entrance hall. The other girl was on her way out as she arrived home, and the bunch of daffodils in Antonia's hand drew Celia's attention.

'Aren't they lovely!' she exclaimed, bending her head to inhale their fragrance. 'I love spring flowers, don't you?' Then her eyes took on a mischievious glint. 'Of course, you do. Mrs Francis told me someone sent you absolutely loads of them!'

Antonia caught her breath. She should have realised that if Mrs Francis gossiped to her, she would gossip to her other tenants as well. 'Oh—yes,' she managed now. 'I . . . was rather fortunate. A . . . a friend from work. He . . . he sent them.'

Now why had she said that? she asked herself impatiently, as Celia nodded her head. Who at the institute was likely to send her flowers? And how could she be sure Reed hadn't confided his generosity to his fiancée?

'I love receiving flowers,' Celia was saying now, her words justifying Antonia's caution. 'Reed sends me roses all the time. He knows I love them.'

Antonia moistened her lips. 'You're very lucky.'

'Yes, I am.' Celia sighed contentedly, and Antonia felt the biggest bitch of all time. 'Did you see my ring?' She extended her hand. 'Isn't it gorgeous?'

It was. A large square-cut sapphire, surrounded by a cluster of diamonds, it glowed, even in the subdued light of the hall, and Antonia did not have to affect her admiration. 'It's beautiful,' she said, her smile warmly sincere. 'When ... when are you getting married? Or haven't you decided yet?'

'In December, I think,' Celia replied, admiring the ring herself. 'Reed's pretty tied up until then, but I'm hoping we can have a Christmas honeymoon.'

'How nice.'

Antonia's tone was a little forced now, but Celia didn't seem to notice. 'Yes, isn't it?' she responded, lifting her shoulders. 'But now, enough about me, I've not seen you since the party: how did you enjoy it?'

'Oh——' Antonia swallowed. 'It was ... very enjoyable. I'm sorry. I should have rung. But what with one thing and another——'

'Think nothing of it.' Celia shook her head dismissively. 'I just hoped you hadn't taken offence over the way Liz acted. She can be pretty bloody sometimes, and that was one of them. She's really quite charming, when you get to know her.'

Antonia cleared her throat. 'I—I'm sure she is. Really, it's not important. It was your night, after all.'

'What did you think of Reed?' asked Celia suddenly, and Antonia had the suspicion she had been leading up to this all along. 'You spoke with him, didn't you? Isn't he something?'

The daffodils slipped abruptly from Antonia's fingers, and in the confusion of bending to pick them up, Celia's question was left unanswered. 'I must go,' she said, her mind obviously already on other things. She glanced at her watch. 'I'm meeting Daddy in fifteen minutes, and he won't be very happy if I'm late. By—eee.'

'Goodbye.'

Antonia summoned a farewell smile, but after Celia had disappeared out the door, she felt a wave of weariness sweep over her. It seemed more than five years since she had been as young and vital as Celia, she thought. Had she *ever* been that young? she wondered wistfully.

Tuesday brought a spate of accidents at the institute. Heather Jakes stumbled up the steps that morning and

sprained her wrist, thus preventing her from doing
any typing that day; Mark Stephens, the caretaker,
strained his back shifting boxes in the storeroom; and
Mr Fenwick split his trousers on his way to work and
in consequence, didn't appear at all until eleven
o'clock.

'Probably due to all those marshmallows he keeps
eating,' remarked Heather uncharitably, coming into
Antonia's office to deliver the message. She held out her
bandaged wrist for the other girl's inspection. 'It's just
as well really. I can't do much with this.'

'No.' Antonia grimaced. 'I just hope Mr Stephens is
all right, too. He's really too old to be lifting such heavy
weights.'

'Tell that to the governors,' declared Heather airily,
sauntering back to the door. 'They're all for keeping
costs down, which in lay terms means employing fewer
people. You don't know how lucky you were, getting
this job!'

'Oh, I do.' Antonia spoke fervently. 'I have been
looking for a job for a long time, Heather.'

'Hmm.' Heather shrugged. 'Well, I think it's a shame
you had to leave your little girl in Newcastle. The
powers that be should take things like that into
consideration, when they offer a job to a woman.'

'Maybe one day I'll be able to afford to pay someone
to take care of her, when she's not at school,' said
Antonia, voicing her own private thoughts on the
matter. 'Or perhaps, when she's older, and can take
care of herself until I get home she can live with me.'

'Men never have these problems, do they?' Heather
remarked drily. 'If they did, they'd soon find a way to
deal with it.'

Antonia smiled. 'You sound aggressive. Have you
had another row with Peter?'

'Not another row!' Heather laughed. 'Just the same
one. He wants me to agree to give up *my* work if we
have a baby.'

'And is that likely?'

'What? My giving up work? Not on your . . .'

'No. I mean the baby,' said Antonia gently. 'How long have you been married?'

'Two years,' Heather grimaced. 'And the answer is no, on both counts. Not so long as Peter insists on being such a chauvinist!'

By lunchtime, Antonia felt as if she had done a full day's work. There were certain letters that had to be attended to, and with Heather's incapacity, Antonia took it upon herself to do the typing. It wasn't easy. It was years since she had played about on an old typewriter of her father's, and Heather's sophisticated electric machine was unfamiliar to her. To begin with, she pressed too hard on the keys and had rows of letters appearing instead of just one, and when she did succeed in producing an acceptable copy, she discovered she had forgotten to put a carbon between the sheets.

With shopping to do in her lunch hour, she decided to miss out on the salad in the dining hall. Instead, she put on the jacket of her dark grey suit, ran a hasty comb through her hair, and emerged into the pale sunshine flooding the Edgware Road.

The sight of the black sports car, parked carelessly on the double yellow lines outside, would have alerted her, without the added identification of the man leaning casually against the bonnet. Reed Gallagher, for she had no difficulty in discerning his lean, sinuous frame, straightened abruptly at her appearance, and although she started swiftly away along the pavement, he had no problem in overtaking her.

'Hey,' he exclaimed, his hand on her sleeve barely slowing her progress. 'I was waiting for you.'

'Were you?' Taking a deep breath, Antonia halted and turned to face him. 'Why?'

His dark features were surprisingly sombre. 'Why do you think?'

'I really can't imagine.' Antonia tried to quell her rapidly accelerating heart. 'But I'd be glad if you could make it brief. I don't have a lot of time.'

'You do eat lunch, don't you?' he enquired tensely, the errant breeze lifting the collar of the black silk shirt he was wearing. In an equally sombre black leather jacket and black denims, he looked as disruptively attractive as ever, and Antonia's eyes were unwillingly drawn to the brown column of his throat rising from the unbuttoned neckline. 'I was beginning to wonder.'

'What do you mean?' Dragging her eyes away, Antonia endeavoured to maintain an offhand manner, forcing herself to think of Celia, and what this might mean to her.

'I mean I waited yesterday, without any success,' he responded, glancing impatiently up and down the street.

Antonia's lips parted. 'You waited yesterday!' she echoed.

'That's what I said,' he conceded drily.

She shook her head. 'I generally eat lunch in the dining hall.'

'Really.' His tone was sardonic now, and he cast another doubtful look around him. 'I should have thought of that.'

Antonia strove to retain her indifference. 'I don't see why,' she remarked, observing out of the corner of her eye a traffic warden just turning the corner. 'Do you know you're parked on yellow lines?'

'As I collected a couple of tickets yesterday, I should,' he responded briefly. 'Antonia . . .'

'Then I should warn you, there's a traffic warden coming this way,' she interrupted him crisply, closing her ears to the explicit oath he uttered. 'I think you'd better move your car, Mr Gallagher. Unless you enjoy contributing to the Greater London authority.'

Reed's mouth compressed. 'Will you have lunch with me?' he demanded, quickly measuring the distance between himself, the traffic warden, and the car, but Antonia had to refuse him.

'I can't,' she denied swiftly, already moving away from him, and with a gesture of frustration, he turned and strode back to the Lamborghini.

There was an arcade just a few yards further along the street where Antonia generally did her shopping, and resisting the impulse to look back and see whether

Reed had succeeded in his bid to avoid another fine, she turned into the covered walkway. Her heart was still beating much faster than it should, notwithstanding the speed with which she had put some distance between herself and temptation, and she stood for several minutes looking into the window of a newsagent, without actually seeing any of the display.

Why was he doing this? she asked herself over and over. It didn't make sense. He had a beautiful fiancée, who cared about him, and doubtless other opportunities for diversion, should he so desire them, so why was he picking on her? If he wanted sexual excitement, why didn't he simply find another girl of his own kind to feed his ego? A girl who would be flattered by his attentions, and perfectly willing to keep their liaison a secret. Or was it the fact that she was different, that she came from a different sort of background, that provided the stimulation, Antonia wondered. Perhaps he thought she might be easier to cajole, or unlikely to put up too much opposition, so long as she was compensated in other ways. Like ... with a gift of flowers, for example ...

The idea was so abhorrent to her, Antonia had walked out of the arcade again and into the street before she realised she had bought none of the things she had come out for. She was trembling so badly, it was almost an effort to put one foot in front of the other, and she decided to abandon her expedition and go back to work.

'Are you feeling all right?'

The kindly male voice startled her, and she swayed a little unsteadily as an elderly gentleman touched her arm. 'I ... oh ... yes, I'm fine,' she managed, hoping he would not think her stricken expression was the result of his considerate enquiry. Just for a moment, she had thought it was Reed speaking to her, and she didn't feel capable of coping with him right now.

'Are you sure?' The old gentleman was evidently concerned about her, and Antonia struggled to reassure him.

'I must be hungry,' she said, summoning a thin smile, and then her breath caught in her throat as she saw the lean dark figure making straight for them. She should have known Reed wouldn't give up that easily, she thought unsteadily, wondering if she dared ask the old man to protect her. But the circumstances were such, she could not involve anyone else.

Reed reached them seconds later, his keen grey eyes raking Antonia's face with growing concern. 'What's wrong?' he asked, his hand beneath her elbow that much more demanding than the older man's had been, and her erstwhile knight-errant turned to him with relief.

'Your young lady's feeling a little faint,' he declared, clearly identifying Reed as someone he could relinquish his responsibilities to. 'She says she's hungry. Perhaps you should see she gets something to eat right away.'

'I'll do that,' said Reed smoothly, the pressure of his fingers on her arm warning her not to contradict him. He looked down at her with apparent indulgence. 'Sorry I'm late, Antonia. I had some difficulty in parking the car.'

Antonia's jaw quivered with a mixture of impotence and frustration, but when Reed's fingers compelled her to move on, she had little choice but to go with him. She was not strong enough to fight with him, not right now, and besides, a weakening feeling of inertia was sweeping over her. She was tired, and hungry, and the effort of simply sparring with him had robbed her of most of her resistance.

'Why are you doing this?' she exclaimed wearily. 'You know someone might see us. And besides, doesn't it mean anything to you that I don't want to eat lunch with you?'

'If I thought that, I wouldn't be here,' Reed responded, with brutal arrogance. 'Now, I've parked the car in the carpark at the back of here. I suggest we go and find it and . . .'

'No!' With quivering determination, Antonia pulled herself away from him. 'No, I won't go with you!' She shook her head. 'I don't know where you've got the idea from that I might like to have lunch with you, but it's mistaken, believe me! Now, please—go away and stop bothering me!'

'*Antonia . . .*'

'Mrs Sheldon!'

'All right, Mrs Sheldon then.' His lips tightened with the effort to be civil. 'Can you deny that you're in no fit state to be left on your own . . .'

'Because of you!' she interrupted him unsteadily, and he politely inclined his head.

'If you say so,' he conceded, neither denying nor admitting the charge. 'Even so, I'd be one hell of a bastard if I walked off and left you now. So I suggest we find somewhere you can sit down, and I'll buy you a drink or a sandwich or whatever it takes to put some colour back into your face.'

Antonia took a deep breath. 'I'm not leaving here.'

'I'm not suggesting you should.' He glanced round. 'How about that pub over there? They're bound to serve bar snacks at lunchtime. Let me buy you a drink and a ham roll or something.' He paused. 'Just to prove I'm not the villain you seem to think me.'

Antonia sighed. 'And if someone sees us?'

Reed's lips twisted. 'Are you ashamed of being seen with me?'

'You *know* what I mean!'

'Someone *I* know?'

'Yes.'

'So what?' He shrugged. 'I'm only buying you a drink. Where's the harm in that?'

Where indeed? Antonia pondered uneasily, reluctantly following Reed into the bar of the pub. Except that she should have been more positive, instead of giving in to what could only be regarded as a reckless impulse.

The Black Lion turned out to be a favourite haunt of students from the institute, Antonia discovered, and she saw several familiar faces as she made her way to the comparative anonymity of a corner booth. She hoped no one recognised her. As yet, her features were not

well known outside Mr Fenwick's domain. But she had
not taken into account the fact that as a newcomer she
had inspired a great deal of interest among the male
fraternity. Tall and slim, with the full breasts she so
abhorred, she had attracted a considerable amount of
admiration, and more than one of the trainees had
expressed the aspiration to be the focus of her long,
faintly Oriental eyes.

The booths were all occupied, but the one in the corner
had two vacant seats on a banquette, facing a young
couple who were evidently engrossed in one another.
Antonia chose this, sliding on to the cool vinyl pad with
some relief. In spite of her reluctance to spend any longer
with Reed than was absolutely necessary, she was grateful
for the chance to sit down and recover her self-possession.
And surely now she had an opportunity to make him see
he was wasting his time by pursuing her?

Reed had got their drinks, and she lifted her hand to
let him see where she was. He came across carrying the
two drinks in one hand and two ham and salad rolls in
a paper napkin in the other. Setting the drinks on the
table, he slid on to the banquette beside her, and
although she had moved to the farthest extremities of
the booth, his thigh brushed hers as he took his seat.

As usual, he looked perfectly at home in what must
be, for him, unfamiliar surroundings. Swallowing a
mouthful of the glass of lager he had bought for
himself, he surveyed the busy environs of the bar with
casual interest, apparently unaware that the girl
opposite had transferred her attention from her
boyfriend to him.

'What is this?' Antonia asked bleakly, to distract the
girl's assessing gaze, and Reed turned his head to look
at her. This close, the disruptive influence of his darkly
fringed eyes was devastating, and forcing herself to
concentrate on the glass in front of her, Antonia made
her meaning plain.

'It's brandy,' Reed told her, putting down his glass
and pushing hers towards her. 'Drink it. It will do you
good. You look as though you need it.'

Aware that their conversation was being monitored by the young woman opposite, albeit that she had been obliged to return her attention to her boyfriend, Antonia felt her indignation rising. 'What do you mean by that?' she enquired, barely audibly, but Reed's expression revealed he had heard.

'Pale,' he said, lifting his hand and running his knuckles down her cheek, and although she flinched away from him, she could still feel his touch long after it had departed.

Deciding she needed the raw spirit after all, Antonia took a sip of the brandy, catching her breath as it forged its way down into her stomach. But he was right. It was warming. And she took another sip before examining her sandwich.

'They only had ham and salad,' Reed remarked, biting into the crisp roll he had bought for himself. 'I hope you like it.'

Antonia made no response, but she did nibble at her own sandwich, meeting the eyes of the young woman opposite with rather more confidence than before. After all, she could hardly blame her for looking at Reed, she thought. He was good to look at. And nor could she blame her if she was wondering what he was doing with someone like her.

'Is it okay?'

Reed emptied his mouth to take another drink of his beer, and Antonia nodded vigorously. 'Yes, thank you,' she answered politely, not responding to his evident desire for her to look at him, and he turned back to his roll with rigid application.

Antonia could not eat all her sandwich. It wasn't easy eating any of it with the twin disadvantages of Reed, and the girl opposite, observing her progress. But the brandy was soothing, and by the time her glass was empty, she was feeling more herself.

Reed, too, left half his roll, his appetite only lasting so long as Antonia was making an effort. However, without asking her permission he took their empty glasses back to the bar and returned with them filled, his eyes challenging her to refuse him when his presence on the banquette prevented her escape.

To Antonia's relief, the young couple opposite departed a few moments later, and no one else came to take their place. The crowd in the bar was thinning as people made their way back to work, and glancing at her watch, Antonia was horrified to discover it was nearly half-past one.

'I should be leaving,' she said, taking a polite, if hasty sip of her drink. 'Really, I'm due back in the office at a quarter to two.'

'You'll be there,' stated Reed flatly, his gaze flickering over her anxious face. 'There's no point in asking you to take the afternoon off, is there? You're honest and conscientious, as well as everything else.'

Antonia's breathing felt constricted. 'Mr Gallagher . . .'

'Reed.'

'*Mr Gallagher*, I think this conversation has gone far enough.'

'Do you?' His lips curled in sudden mockery. 'Well, yes, I guess you could be right. But that doesn't solve my problem.'

'I don't think you have a problem, Mr Gallagher,' Antonia retorted huskily. 'Please: I'd like to get out now.'

'And if I don't let you?' he countered, his obstruction causing her to meet his gaze.

'I could scream,' she retorted.

'Would you?' His eyes taunted her. 'Wouldn't that just be doing what you're trying to avoid? Drawing attention to us?'

'Please . . .'

'Say: *please, Reed*.'

Antonia closed her eyes against his unquestionable attraction and repeated in a small, tense voice: 'Please, Reed!'

'Okay.'

With a jack-knifing movement, he extricated himself from the banquette, but when he would have given her his hand to assist her, Antonia ignored it. Self-consciously aware that the heat of her body had practically glued her to the seat, she managed to lever herself out of the booth, marching stiffly ahead of him out of the pub.

Outside, she was almost amazed to discover the sun was still shining. The subdued lighting in the bar had given the impression that it was quite dull outside, and it was heartening to discover the day was still bright.

'I'll walk you back to the institute,' Reed said, when she would have nodded farewell and left him.

Antonia straightened her spine. 'That's not necessary.'

'I know it's not,' he responded tersely, falling into step beside her in spite of her denial. 'Tell me: what do you do at this institute? We've had lunch together, and I still know next to nothing about you.'

'I'm sure you wouldn't be interested,' replied Antonia annoyingly, and she sensed his controlled reaction.

'If I weren't, I shouldn't be asking,' he retorted, not quite succeeding in disguising his impatience. 'It's not a state secret, is it? You're not quietly a front for MI6?'

'Hardly.' Antonia felt an insurgent desire to laugh at the idea that Mr Fenwick might be involved in counter-espionage. Picturing the rotund director of the institute in the role of a latter-day James Bond didn't quite fit his image, and her lips twitched irresistibly at this portrayal of her employer. 'As a matter of fact, I work for the institute's director,' she volunteered now, deciding there was no harm in being honest with him 'It's interesting work. I like it.'

Reed inclined his head. 'But you're not from London, are you?'

'No.' Antonia took a deep breath. 'Didn't your fiancée tell you?' she asked, introducing Celia's name deliberately. 'I come from the north of England; Newcastle, to be exact. I've only lived in London for the past two months.'

'And do you like it?' he asked, not taking her up on his fiancée's involvement, and she shrugged.

'I've told you. I like my work. For the rest—well, I miss my family.'

They had reached the institute now, and halting, she turned to say goodbye. 'Thank you for my lunch,' she said, as if she was reciting the words, and Reed thrust his hands into his trouser pockets, as if to prevent himself from actual physical violence.

'I want to see you again,' he said, stepping closer to her, and she could feel, as well as smell, the heat of his body. 'Now, don't give me any nonsense about its not being a good idea, or what will Celia say,' he added huskily. 'Just say yes, for once in your life, without weighing the pros and cons.'

'I can't . . .'

'Oh, for Christ's sake!'

'I can't,' she repeated unsteadily, stepping back from him. With the warmth and the musky male scent of him enveloping her, it was incredibly difficult to refuse him, but the sanity of reason eventually prevailed. 'Look,' she appended stiffly, 'I realise you're probably used to young women falling at your feet, but I can't help it. I have no intention of providing a novelty for you or anyone else, and if you want a *gutter* experience, I suggest you look elsewhere!'

CHAPTER FOUR

THE offices of the Gallagher Trust and Investment Corporation were in a quiet square, just off the Strand. When Reed's grandfather took over the company in 1920, its assets only ran to two floors of a rather seedy tenement building near King's Cross, but the old man had changed all that. With the first Great War behind them, people were eager to invest in anything which would bring them a swift profit, and Reed's grandfather had turned this to his advantage. While other speculators concentrated on the stock market, Declan Gallagher bought property, putting his client's money into solid bricks and mortar, that were still standing long after the crash of Wall Street had left less astute investors penniless.

The business grew and expanded, and in the 1950s Reed's father continued its advance, looking overseas for new avenues to explore. Now Gallaghers, as they were dubbed on the stock market, had shares in diamond mines in Africa, oil wells in Alaska, cattle ranches in South America; they owned an air charter company and a fleet of oil tankers; they farmed 10,000 acres of prime farmland in Somerset and Wiltshire, and their chemical laboratories had produced new and more sophisticated types of fertiliser to satisfy the standards of the stiffest conservationists. In fact, the Gallagher corporation was involved in most aspects of technological advancement, and its board of directors was a comprehensive mix of accountants, scientists, engineers, and statisticians—of which Reed classed himself among the latter.

Since his father's retirement at sixty, three years ago, Reed himself had become the board's chairman. He was young, only thirty when Joseph Gallagher adhered to his wife's advice to retire, while he was still young enough to enjoy life. But in the past three years, Reed had confirmed the confidence his father had had in him and now, at thirty-three, there was little about the company he did not know. He had always been interested in maths and a degree in economics at Oxford had reinforced his natural ability to understand figures. In addition, he had spent at least part of each year visiting the company's operations overseas, and although he had learned how to delegate, his intimate knowledge of each project made him a formidable adversary.

Reed had always loved the company. As a schoolboy, he had spent hours at the office during his holidays, watching the computors, studying the telex machine, as it rattled out its messages from all around the world. He found finance an infinitely fascinating subject, not simply in its capacity to make money, but rather as a means to exercise his mental abilities. It was a challenge to predict trends, to anticipate shortfalls, to try and keep one step ahead of the stock market. Had he not been able to step into his father's shoes, he assumed he would have been an economist or a stockbroker, and sometimes, like today, he wished he had had the choice.

Reed's office, the office his father and grandfather had occupied before him, was on the penthouse floor of the building, and overlooked the nearby recreation ground. At this hour of a Friday afternoon, he could see several joggers, doggedly marking the boundaries of the play area, and gradually the swings and roundabouts were set in motion, as children came from school to fill them up.

Reed glanced impatiently at the narrow gold watch on his wrist. What time was it? he wondered irritably, his mouth compressing when he saw it was only half-past four. Another hour-and-a-half before Celia had said she would arrive, so that they could drive down to Sussex together. Another ninety minutes before they set away for the weekend with Celia's parents in the country.

Reed expelled his breath heavily. He was not looking

forward to this weekend with the Lytton-Smythes. It wasn't their fault; it wasn't even Celia's fault. He was just out of sorts with himself, and the idea of a weekend spent being polite to Celia's parents filled him with depression.

Leaving the window, Reed walked back to his desk, idly flicking over the papers requiring his inspection. He had work he could do, but he was strangely lacking in application, and for the first time in his life he had no interest in whether the storms raging in northern Canada would delay their oil explorations another month, or if the overthrow of a certain central African dictator would facilitate their efforts to gain mining rights. He was bored and indifferent, the restless energy he usually poured into his business dealings lacking its normal direction.

There was no rational reason for his dissatisfaction, he acknowledged now, drumming his fingers on the tooled leather pad. There was no crisis in the company, no especial problem he had to deal with. Even his personal life was exactly as he had wished it. Celia was a beautiful girl, and their relationship was perfectly satisfactory. So what was wrong?

Thinking of Celia, he glanced again at his watch, but it was still only twenty-five minutes to five. Eighty-five minutes to take-off, he reflected broodingly, despising his introspection. Perhaps he needed a drink. Perhaps a small measure of alcohol would help to lift the demoralising cloud that was hovering over him.

Pouring himself a double whisky, he carried the glass back to his desk, and dropping down into his leather chair, he propped his feet on the desk. The alcohol felt good as it found its way down into his stomach, and he decided Ladbroke could drive them down to Five Oaks. He felt like getting drunk, and there was plenty of time before Celia would put in an appearance.

Celia . . .

Studying the spirit in his glass, Reed thought about his fiancée. He had known a lot of woman, before she came along—the natural result of being Joseph

Gallagher's son, he always assumed, his father's wealth overcoming a multitude of sins—but Celia was the first he had actually proposed to. She had seemed eminently fitted to being the wife of a man in his position, and as he was thirty-three, and his parents were eager for him to provide them with grandchildren, he had not objected to their active encouragement.

Besides, Celia was sweet; she flattered his ego; and if he occasionally found her conversation boring, it was no different from that of his friends' wives. He did not want to marry a businesswoman. He found women in the professions were more concerned with advancement than their male counterparts, and while he did not resent their ambition, he wanted a wife, not a business partner. So why was he so out of humour with himself? The answer was one he had avoided thus far. *Antonia Sheldon!*

There was no earthly reason why her behaviour towards him should have bothered him so much; but it did! Ever since Tuesday, he had been brooding over what had happened that lunchtime, and her ugly reaction to his friendly invitation had exposed a raw nerve.

Reed was not normally a violent man. On the contrary, he was known for his good humour, his charming personality, that successfully concealed a brain as acute as one of his own computers. On the whole he was an even-tempered man, used to disguising his innermost feelings, even in the face of extreme provocation. But Antonia Sheldon got beneath his skin; she had the uncanny ability to stir emotions he had not known he possessed, and it was disconcerting to realise that with her he could not always control his feelings.

He had wanted to follow her into that institute where she worked on Tuesday afternoon. The simmering rage which had gripped him at her insolent response had almost overwhelmed his natural discretion, and driving back to his apartment he had entertained himself with visions of her colleagues looking helplessly on, while his fingers round her throat squeezed the life out of her.

Since then, of course, he had endeavoured to put all thoughts of her out of his head, and to a certain extent, he had succeeded. The trouble was, he knew she was still there, whether consciously or subconsciously, and it was her image that was clouding his brain and blighting the coming weekend.

Finishing the whisky in his glass, he swung his feet abruptly to the floor and stood up. To hell with it, he thought savagely. He was going to see her one last time and tell her what he thought of her. Half his frustration came from knowing she thought she had had the last word. He would explain that her isolation had aroused his compassion; that he had felt *sorry* for her; that far from desiring her body, he had been trying to educate her mind, and if she had mistaken his—well meaning— invitation for something else, she had his sympathies.

Depositing the empty glass on his desk, he strode towards the heavy door which gave access to his secretary's office. 'I'm just going out for an hour, Mrs Drysdale,' he informed the efficient middle-aged woman, who had worked for his father before him. 'I should be back before six.'

'But—isn't Miss Lytton-Smythe expected?' Mrs Drysdale exclaimed in surprise, removing her horn-rimmed spectacles to look at him.

'Yes, she is,' Reed nodded, hardly pausing in his progress towards the outer door. 'But not before six, and as I've said, I'll be back by then. Relax, Mrs Drysdale. Everything's under control.'

'Did you sign those letters?'

Mrs Drysdale seemed loath to let him go, and Reed sighed, running a weary hand round the back of his neck. 'I've signed everything of importance,' he assured her crisply, impatient to be off. 'You can go, too, as soon as you're ready. Celia can find her own way into my office.'

'Yes, Mr Gallagher.'

Mrs Drysdale had no choice but to accept his edict, although Reed knew she, of all people, found it hardest to adapt to his ways. His father had always deferred to her, as a matter of courtesy, but Reed was less in awe of her admirable qualifications. In consequence, theirs was a relationship based on tolerance, and there were times he knew, as now, when she could not hide her disapproval.

But Reed had no time at present to consider Mrs Drysdale's feelings. He had exactly one hour to drive across London, speak to Antonia, and drive back again, and that, at the height of the Friday rush-hour, was not going to be easy.

As luck would have it, he made good time to Clifton Gate, and it was only just after a quarter-past-five when he turned into the drive of Eaton Lodge. He knew, from earlier enquiries he had made, that the institute where Antonia worked closed at four-thirty on Fridays, and even taking into account the vagaries of the buses, she should be home by now.

Suppressing the instinct that what he was doing was not only foolish but downright reckless, Reed crossed the forecourt and entered the building. Antonia's door was the first on the left, and without giving himself time to have second thoughts, he knocked firmly on the panels.

Infuriating though it was, as he stood there waiting for her to open the door, a mental image of her pale features suddenly flashed into his mind. As if he was looking at a photograph, he could see every facet of her indignant hazel eyes and stubborn mouth—the way she had looked when he had last seen her. She had a nice mouth, he reflected unwillingly, the lower lip fuller and inclined towards sensuality—when she wasn't being angry with him, of course. When she smiled, her whole face lit up—a dazzling transformation—and her eyes were not hazel then, but green . . .

'Are you looking for Mrs Sheldon?' enquired a vaguely familiar voice behind him, and controlling his impatience, Reed turned to face the caretaker's inquisitive wife. 'Why—Mr Gallagher, it's you!' she exclaimed, her thin features acquiring a decidedly curious expression. 'Miss Lytton-Smythe's not here.'

'I know.' Reed pushed his thumbs into the pockets of his waistcoat, refusing to explain himself to her. 'I—it's Mrs Sheldon I wanted to see. Is she in?'

'Oh—she's gone!' declared Mrs Francis swiftly, and for a bone-jarring moment Reed thought she meant for good.

'Gone?' he echoed, his voice revealing a little of the emotion he was feeling, and Mrs Francis nodded.

'She was catching the six o'clock train,' she confided, folding her arms, as if preparing for a long intercourse. 'Gone home for the weekend, she has. You know: to Newcastle. Said she'd be back Sunday night, if that's any help to you.'

Reed withdrew his thumbs from his pockets, aware of a shuddering sense of relief sweeping over him at her words. It was a debilitating experience, and he could have done with a drink now to restore his equilibrium, but instead, he had to convince Mrs Francis that he was grateful for her assistance.

'Well—thank you,' he said, running his tongue over dry lips. 'It . . . wasn't important.'

'Would you like me to give her a message?' Mrs Francis persisted, clearly sensing some intrigue here and loath to let him go without an explanation. 'I'm sure she'll be sorry to have missed you. She doesn't get many visitors, you know.'

Reed's lips twisted a little in self-derision. He had few doubts that Antonia would welcome the omission, and far from being sorry to have missed him, she would resent his implicating her in what would seem a reckless indiscretion.

'As I say, it's not important, Mrs Francis,' he declared, moving firmly towards the outer door. 'I—I had a message for her from Celia. But as she's gone away, it doesn't matter.'

'Oh, I see.'

Mrs Francis accepted his account with an understanding smile, but Reed could still see the doubtful speculation in her eyes. What the hell was he going to tell Cee, he wondered savagely, nodding a farewell and striding back to his car. Now that Mrs Francis was involved, he was going to have to say something, and his brain buzzed frustratedly as he drove back to his office.

Mrs Lord had brought Susie to the station to meet the train. In spite of the lateness of the hour for her, she was jumping with excitement by the time her mother walked through the ticket barrier, and Antonia bent and gathered her small daughter into her arms.

'Hello, treasure,' she said emotively, burying her suddenly tear-wet face in the hollow of her daughter's shoulder. 'It's so good to be back! Have you been a good girl for Nanna?'

'She's been as good as gold since Tuesday,' declared Mrs Lord drily, returning her daughter's kiss and wiping a recalcitrant tear from Antonia's cheek. 'All I've heard is how many days it is to Friday, and what present might you have bought her for her birthday.'

Her mother's careless mention of Tuesday brought a momentary pang of conscience, but Antonia quickly dismissed it. She was not going to allow Reed Gallagher to spoil her weekend, she told herself fiercely, and concentrated her attention on Susie's description of her birthday cake.

'We're having a party,' she explained, holding tightly to her mother's hand as they walked to where Mrs Lord had left her car. 'Uncle Howard and Auntie Sylvia, and David and Kevin, are coming to tea tomorrow, and Nanna said I could ask three of my friends from school.'

'Super,' said Antonia affectionately, exchanging a wordless look of gratitude with her mother. 'Six seven-year-olds! That's all I need! I can see this is going to be a very restless couple of days.'

In fact, the weekend tended to drag. Even in so short a time, Antonia had lost touch with her mother's life in Gosforth, and although initially they had plenty to talk about, by Sunday there was a definite lack of communication.

On Friday evening, Susie had dominated the conversation, both while she was there and after she had gone to bed. Antonia had been relieved to see her daughter did not appear to have suffered any ill effects from her absence. Susie was just as ebullient as ever, and Antonia was more inclined to accept her mother's assertion of out of sight, out of mind.

Saturday morning started with Susie opening her presents. Antonia had brought her a doll that mimicked many of the actions of a real baby, but although Susie was intrigued by its ability to drink its bottle and wet its nappy, she spent more time playing with the electronic game her grandmother had provided.

'Children are notoriously fickle,' remarked Mrs Lord, as she and Antonia sat in the large, sunlit kitchen, lingering over their mid-morning cup of coffee. 'As soon as you've gone, she'll discover that she likes the doll best of all. You'll see. I'm usually right.'

As Susie disappeared into the garden to play soon afterwards, and her mother departed for a hair appointment, Antonia was left to mooch around the house for the rest of the morning. It was odd, she thought. When she was at the flat, she had longed to be at home, back among the people and the places she knew so well. But now she was here, she was restless. Even the surroundings of her old room, which her mother had never altered, in spite of her marriage to Simon, failed to give her the pleasure she had expected. She found herself missing the constant throb of traffic that it was never quite possible to block out of the apartment, the awareness of a city that never seemed to sleep.

Of course, she was being foolish; and she knew it. The persistent hum of traffic was one of the things she had found hardest to adjust to, and she certainly could not wish to duplicate it here in Gosforth. And as for thinking that London never slept: well, that was true of sections of every capital city and every smaller one, as well. Hospitals; law enforcement; public services; there was always someone working for the good of the community, at all hours of the day and night. There was nothing remarkable about that. She was being ridiculously fanciful in associating it only with London. For goodness sake, what was she thinking of? She had hated it to begin with.

Sitting on the edge of her bed, she drew up one slim leg and rested her chin on her knee. The trouble was, she admitted ruefully, she had been feeling pretty rotten since last Tuesday. No matter how she tried to justify her behaviour, she could not get past the fact that Reed had bought her lunch and she had paid him back by insulting him. Oh, she could find a dozen reasons to exonerate her rudeness—he had no right to send her flowers; he had been given no reason to presume on the flimsiest of introductions that she might be willing to have lunch with him, let alone dinner—but they did not ease her conscience. She had behaved like a timid virgin, embarking on her first date, instead of acting like the mature woman she was, and accepting his friendship in like manner. Men and women could have perfectly platonic relationships, she reminded herself irritably. He probably thought she was a prime example of a raw northern upbringing, a mixture of ignorance and prudery, stodginess and unsophistication.

Antonia's brother and his wife arrived in the afternoon, and the tea-party that followed left little time for conversation or introspection. Howard's twins left a trail of havoc wherever they went, and what with mopping up orange juice and scooping jelly off her mother's carpet, Antonia felt physically exhausted by the time they all went home.

Sylvia, her sister-in-law, did find an opportunity while they were washing up to ask her if she was enjoying working in London. 'I envy you, I do honestly,' Howard's wife averred fiercely. 'I wish I had a reason to dump my kids on your mother and clear off to pastures new! Sometimes I think I'll go mad if Howard doesn't find a way to discipline our Kevin!'

'He's only a boy,' said Antonia reassuringly, even though she didn't like Sylvia's dig about *dumping* Susie.

'I expect he'll quieten down as he gets older Howard was quite a handful, I believe, when he was that age.'

'Really?' Sylvia grimaced. 'Well, that's not what he says. He blames our family for Kevin's unruly streak. I told him—I said, there's no one in our family who behaves like a hooligan every time we're in company. But he doesn't listen. He really gets me mad!'

Deciding this conversation was moving into areas she didn't have any right to enter, Antonia changed the subject. 'I like your dress,' she said generously, admiring Sylvia's plaid smock. 'Is it new? It suits you.'

'I got it in town,' Sylvia replied without enthusiasm. 'I suppose you got that dress in London. You can always tell.'

As Antonia was wearing the cream shirt-waister she had worn to Celia's party, she smiled. 'As a matter of fact, I bought this in the sales last January,' she answered, thrusting back the memories it insistently evoked. 'Sorry to disappoint you, Sylvia, but I haven't bought any clothes since I went to London. I don't need any and, even if I did, I can't afford them.'

Sunday was the worst day of all. Although Antonia knew she would not want to leave when it was time to do so, the morning seemed endless. Her mother, as always, went to church, taking Susie with her. Antonia should have accompanied them, she knew, but in spite of her mother's admonishments, she did not feel up to one of the Reverend Lisle's sermons. Besides, someone had to prepare the Sunday dinner, she said, as they were having it in the middle of the day, even though peeling potatoes and cutting up the other vegetables did not take more than half an hour.

During the afternoon, Antonia packed her bag again, and ordered a taxi to take her to the station to catch the five o'clock train. 'I'd rather you didn't come with me, Mum,' she told her mother gently. 'It will be easier for Susie if she doesn't have to wave me goodbye on the platform. This way, it won't seem so terrible when I've gone.'

Susie, however, saw things differently. 'I want to

come to the station,' she wailed, her face crumpling up when she saw her mother's case in the hall. 'I like going to the station. I like seeing all the trains.'

'There aren't that many trains on a Sunday,' Antonia comforted her unhappily, pulling the little girl on to her lap. 'Oh, don't cry, darling. You know Mummy's got to go back.'

'When can I come to London?' Susie persisted, her lower lip trembling. 'I want to see where you live. You said I could come to the flat.'

'Next holidays,' promised Antonia rashly, exchanging a helpless look with her mother. 'Nanna will bring you down in about a month. You can both stay for a long weekend, and I'll show you the Houses of Parliament and Buckingham Palace, where the Queen lives.'

'Really?' Susie stuck her thumb in her mouth and regarded her mother doubtfully.

'Yes, really,' said Antonia, removing Susie's thumb with a reproving frown. 'So—how about helping me make a sandwich to eat on the train? I shan't be able to stay for tea, and there are no buffet cars on Sundays.'

Later, as the train pulled out of Newcastle station, Antonia had to steel herself not to shed a few tears. But they were not really for Susie, they were more for herself, she reflected ruefully. Susie had her grandmother to turn to; she felt as if she had no one.

It was almost ten o'clock when the train pulled into King's Cross station. The journey, which generally took a little over three hours, had lengthened to nearly five, due to repairs being made to the line at Peterborough. Half-empty, the train had chugged its way through a series of rural stations, stopping at every one, and those passengers who were not reading had fallen asleep out of boredom.

Unfortunately, Antonia had neither the will to read nor the relaxation necessary to go to sleep, and by the time the train reached London, she felt utterly miserable. The flat, which had not seemed so bad from a distance, had lost its appeal by the mile, and she tugged her case down from the rack, wishing for once she had chosen to share an apartment with another girl.

Even Celia Lytton-Smythe shared with Liz Ashford, she reflected, unwillingly thinking of her glamorous neighbours. She wondered what they had been doing this weekend. Not spending five unproductive hours on a draughty train, she was sure. People like Celia and Liz—and Reed, too, she assumed, although she knew nothing about him—went everywhere by car or by plane. They did not waste their time on journeys that could comfortably be avoided.

As soon as the train had stopped, Antonia got out, tugging her suitcase after her. It was not heavy. She had not taken much home with her. But it was cumbersome, and it knocked against her legs as she struggled along the platform.

A collector was waiting to take their tickets as they passed through the barrier. Antonia handed hers over, and then set her suitcase on the ground to loop the strap of her bag over one shoulder, and switch the heavier item to her other hand.

As she did so, she got the distinct impression that someone was watching her, and she looked up in dismay, hoping she was not going to have to fend off some unwanted admirer. After the strain of the last five hours, she felt too weary to be polite, and the first twinges of a headache were probing at her temples.

'Reed!'

Her involuntary use of his name was instinctive. It was the way she had been thinking of him for the past two weeks, if she was honest, and the idea of addressing him as *Mr* Gallagher was far from her thoughts at that moment.

Reed was waiting for her. From his stance, she suspected he had been there for some time, which seemed to be confirmed by the way he came stiffly to meet her. He was unsmiling, his dark features drawn into an enigmatic mask, but he bent and took her case from her, and she was too shocked to prevent him.

'The car's parked over here,' he remarked, gesturing towards the side exit. 'You look frozen. Are you? Or is that just your delight at seeing me?'

CHAPTER FIVE

ANTONIA pulled herself together and hastened after him, noticing inconsequently how well the brown leather jacket sat upon his shoulders. Beneath was a fine wool sweater, also in shades of brown and gold, and a pair of narrow Levis completed his attire. She didn't think of arguing with him; not at that moment. Just finding him here, waiting for her, seemed the most natural thing in the world, and she would have plenty of time later to question her judgment.

Reed deposited her suitcase in the boot of the car and then unlocked the doors. 'Get in,' he said, swinging open the one on the nearside, and Antonia complied, glad she was wearing her corded trouser suit.

The door was closed and Reed walked round the bonnet to get in beside her. Between them, the gear console prevented any accidental contact, but he did not immediately start the car; instead, he half-turned in his seat towards her.

'The train was late,' he observed, his features vaguely discernible in the light cast from the station. 'I enquired, and they said they expected it in at nine.'

'Yes.' Antonia endeavoured to sound as composed as he did. 'There was a diversion. Some repairs being done to the line, they said. I'm sorry. H-have you been waiting long?'

'Since nine o'clock,' he conceded expressionlessly. 'You don't seem surprised to see me.'

'Oh, I am.' Antonia shook her head. 'It's just—well, you're here, and ... and I'm grateful. I was feeling pretty awful when I got off the train.'

'And now?'

'And now——' His eyes looked black in the shadows and she lifted her shoulders helplessly. 'I—I'm glad you came,' she mumbled, turning her face away from him. 'I wanted to apologise anyway. For . . . for what I said on Tuesday.'

'Did you?' She heard his sharp intake of breath at her words. 'Yes— well; you might not have felt that way if you had been at home on Friday afternoon.'

'What do you mean?'

Antonia's hair swung forward as she looked at him, half-concealing her expression behind its silky curtain, and Reed's cold fingers looped it back behind her ear. 'I came round to the flat to verbally tear you to pieces,' he confided with asperity, his hand lingering rather longer than was necessary beneath her ear-lobe. 'Unfortunately, Mrs Francis intercepted me to tell me you were away for the weekend, and I had to invent some asinine story about my delivering a message to you, from Cee.'

Antonia went suddenly still. 'So—so that's why you're here,' she said, all the warmth leaving her voice as things swung sickeningly back into perspective. He had not come to meet her because he wanted to. He had come because he dare not allow her to contradict anything Mrs Francis might say to her.

With a sob rising in her throat, she reached impulsively for the door handle. She didn't need a personal warning. A simple telephone call would have sufficed. She had no wish to hurt Celia, any more than he evidently did, and she wanted to get out of this car and away from him before she made an even bigger fool of herself.

'You're crazy!' Reed's voice behind her was rough with emotion, and there was a rattle of keys as he switched off the ignition without starting the engine. 'Do you really think I'd stand here in the cold for over two hours, just to get you to cover my story?' he demanded, his hard fingers digging into her shoulders, as he compelled her round to face him. 'Oh, Antonia— you don't know me very well yet, do you? But you're going to! Believe me, you're going to!'

'You . . . you said you'd been waiting since nine o'clock,' she protested, her hands against the fine cashmere sweater providing a barrier between them, and Reed sighed.

'I have,' he responded huskily, and in spite of her efforts his lips brushed her temple. 'I didn't say I'd been waiting *only* since nine o'clock,' he amended. 'I've been here since about seven-thirty, I suppose. I didn't know what train you were likely to get, so I compromised.'

Antonia shook her head. 'But you . . . you said you were mad with me,' she exclaimed, as his sensuous mouth touched her cheek, and his warm breath was expelled in a rush of wry amusement.

'I was,' he said evenly. 'But that was on Friday. Since then, I've had a change of heart. Not least because of the shock I got when that old busybody told me you had gone.'

'Mrs Francis,' said Antonia flatly, as Reed's tongue stroked her skin, and he nodded.

'The same,' he agreed, his lips hovering near her mouth, and she abruptly turned her head aside to avoid the inevitable consequence.

'Are you going to take me home?'

'Eventually,' he conceded, accepting the rebuff and removing his hands. 'But first, we'll have some supper. You look half-starved, as well as half-frozen.'

'I don't think we should,' she declared as he turned back to the wheel, and he paused to give her a weary look.

'Well, that's par for the course, I suppose,' he responded cynically, starting the engine. 'But now you've made the statutory protest, can we enjoy what's left of the evening? You're going to have supper with me. Accept it. Call it . . . compensation, if you like, for my perseverance.'

All the way along Euston Road and on down Portland Place into Regent Street, Antonia kept telling herself that she ought to be more forceful. She should demand that Reed take her home this instant, or set her down so that she could catch the bus. It was foolish to pretend he was just being friendly. Friends did not indulge in the kind of interplay Reed had indulged in at the station, and she had no way of knowing what manner of man he was. He could be a sex maniac, for all she knew. Just because he treated Celia with respect, did not mean he treated all women the same. And if she disappeared right now, who would know where she had gone? She'd be just another missing person, one of the hundreds who disappeared in London every year.

She shook her head frustratedly, and saw that they had turned into St James's Street. She didn't honestly believe Reed was dangerous—at least, not in a violent way. But what they were doing was wrong, both ethically and morally, and she was to blame for allowing it to go on.

The sudden descent into a darkened cavern was startling enough to drive all other thoughts out of her head. One minute, they were above ground, and the next the car had thudded over a ramp and swooped down into the bowels of the earth.

The realisation that it was an underground carpark gave her some relief, but the polite acknowledgment of the carpark attendant rekindled her anxieties. Where were they? she wondered, looking doubtfully at Reed's dark profile, and his lips parted in satisfaction as he drew into an empty space.

'Okay. Let's go,' he said, switching off the engine, and thrusting open his door, and Antonia gazed up at him in surprise.

'Go?' she echoed. 'Go where?'

'To have supper, of course,' he said resignedly, walking round the car to open her door. 'Come on. You don't want to create a scene, do you? Harry knows me quite well, and I wouldn't want to upset him.'

Antonia hesitated. 'Mr Gallagher——'

'It's Reed,' he said flatly, his hand beneath her elbow practically lifting her out of her seat. 'And you used it earlier, before you remembered it was *verboten*!'

She let him help her out, partly because she was convinced he would break her arm if she didn't, and partly because, as he had said, Harry was watching them.

'You hurt my arm,' she told him stiffly, as he locked the car, and he permitted her a brief appraisal.

'I'll massage it for you,' he said, his hand in the small of her back directing her towards a bank of lifts, that evidently gave access to the upper floors. 'Stop worrying, can't you? I'm not taking you to a torture chamber!'

Inside the lift, Antonia stood as far away from him as she could, hoping it would stop and other people get in. But he had used a key beside the button which designated the twenty-second floor, and the lift ascended swiftly, leaving her stomach far behind. She assumed, as the twenty-second floor was the penthouse, he was taking her to a rooftop restaurant, but when the doors glided open, only a carpeted hallway and white-panelled door confronted her.

'Out,' said Reed brusquely, compelling her to move forward, and the lift closed behind them as he drew out his keys again.

'Is this—is this . . .?'

'. . . my apartment,' agreed Reed drily, inserting a perforated metal strip below the door handle. There was a momentary pause as the computed key slid into its compartment and then the door swung open. Reed rescued the key again before urging Antonia ahead of him, and although she was indignant, curiosity got the better of her.

The first thing that caught her eyes in the subdued lighting of the entrance hall was the magnificent chandelier suspended overhead. It was not lit. Such illumination as there was, was concealed above the frieze that decorated the walls. But the prisms swung together delicately, like wind chimes, in the sudden draught from outside, drawing Antonia's attention and inspiring her admiration.

She had little time to observe the other appointments of the hall, however. The glossy darkwood table and the antique mirror above received only the briefest of appraisals, before Reed was impelling her past several other doors to the one furthest away from the entrance. The thick beige carpet, which had cushioned her feet in the hall, flowed on into a room already illuminated by a handful of lamps. The enormous, gold-coloured velvet sofas that met her bemused gaze provided oases of comfort in a room seemingly designed for that purpose. Everything in the room spoke of style and good taste, from the bowl of amber lilies occupying a low revolving bookcase, to the exquisitely laid-out chessboard, with its ebony and ivory pieces. The room was spacious, but its size had been tempered by the way the furniture was grouped, creating areas for reading or relaxing, or perhaps to listen to the elegant hi-fi system, cleverly concealed in a mahogany console. One wall was given over to bookcases, carelessly stacked alongside paperbacks and magazines; another comprised shelves of smoked glass, set with an interesting selection of sculptures, that invited a visitor's inspection; and finally the wall opposite was composed of windows, running from floor to ceiling, fluted by long blinds, and flanked by heavy cream velvet curtains.

'Hungry?' inquired Reed softly, lifting the jacket of her suit from her shoulders, and Antonia turned to him bewilderedly.

'This . . . is yours?' she asked faintly. 'You . . . *live* . . . here?'

'When I'm in town,' amended Reed evenly, depositing her jacket on the back of a chair and removing his own. 'I asked if you were hungry. Maria will have left us a snack in the dining room.'

Antonia swallowed. 'Maria?'

'My housekeeper,' Reed informed her tolerantly, loosening his tie. 'Come on. Let's go and see what she's left us. I don't know about you, but I could do with a drink.'

Antonia moistened her dry lips. 'Wh-where do you live when you're not in town?' she ventured, still overawed by her surroundings, and Reed sighed.

'I have a house in Oxfordshire. I'll show you that another day,' he promised, touching her shoulder. 'Now -do we eat, or do I satisfy my other instincts?'

She could feel the strength of his fingers, through the thin material of her blouse, and she moved swiftly out of reach. 'Wh-where is the dining room?' she asked, wondering how she had ever got herself into this position, and with a whimsical smile, he led the way across the living room and through a door that was hidden in the smoky recesses of the shelves.

Like the living room, the dining room had long windows overlooking the lights of London below But the other walls were panelled here, surrounding a gleaming refectory table, capable of accommodating at least twenty people, with matching cushioned chairs upholstered in shades of green.

The 'snack' Reed had referred to, was laid out at one end of the table: a remarkable repast of smoked salmon and salad, rolls of ham stuffed with pineapple and skewered with olives, dishes of various kinds of fondue, with sticks of cheese and celery for dipping, and luscious black caviar, nestling on a bed of lettuce. There were sweet things, too: a meringue gâteau, two different types of cheesecake, and a fragrant dish of fruit salad, filled with every kind of fresh fruit imaginable, and flavoured with a trace of kirsch.

'Help yourself,' advised Reed easily, lifting a bottle of champagne out of its refrigerated bucket and expertly extracting the cork. The chilled liquid tumbled invitingly into long-stemmed glasses, and Reed handed one to her when she hesitantly looked his way. 'To us,' he said softly, touching his glass to hers, and she had swallowed a mouthful obediently before she realised what she was toasting.

'So . . .' Reed put down his glass again and regarded her gently. 'What would you like? As you're apparently not prepared to help yourself, I'll have to serve you.' He scooped a spoonful of caviare on to a round wafer and held it to her lips. 'Come on: taste it. It's delicious. Then you can tell me what you prefer.'

Antonia withstood his offering for only a moment before her lips parted. Reed studied her unknowingly provocative mouth for several seconds before popping the wafer inside, and Antonia's heart was pounding when he turned back to the table.

The caviare was nice, rather salty and distinctively flavoured. The champagne was good, too, much better than the rather indifferent sparkling wine she had had at her wedding. But every new experience underlined the vast gulf that stretched between Reed and herself, a gulf even she had not fully appreciated until tonight.

'Try the smoked salmon,' he suggested now, forking another small morsel for her delectation. 'Like it?' he asked lazily, his eyes on her mouth, and her knees felt suddenly weak and incapable of supporting her.

'I ought to go,' she got out carefully, putting down her glass. 'Really—I'm not awfully hungry, and it's getting very late.'

'It's barely eleven o'clock,' declared Reed persuasively, glancing at his watch.

'But I have to go to work tomorrow,' Antonia persisted.

'So do I.'

She shook her head. '*Do* you have a job?'

'You'd better believe it.' Reed was smilingly indignant. 'I'm not a playboy, if that's what you think.'

Antonia took a deep breath. 'Nevertheless . . .'

'Nevertheless—what?' Reed abandoned his attempt to tempt her with the food and came unnervingly towards her. 'Let's take our glasses and go back into the living room. We'll have another drink, and then I'll take you home.'

'Will you?'

Antonia looked at him doubtfully, and his expression sobered. 'If that's what you want,' he agreed, picking up his glass and the opened bottle of champagne and propping the door open with his shoulder. 'Come on. Maria will deal with that tomorrow.'

'Wh-where is Maria?' Antonia asked, glad of the diversion as she walked past him. Her shoulder brushed the wool of his sweater, and she was intensely conscious of the muscled frame beneath.

'I imagine she's in bed,' Reed replied, allowing the door to swing closed behind him. 'She generally retires soon after ten o'clock, I believe. I think she reads in bed.' He grinned suddenly. 'She devours romantic novels.'

Antonia bit her lip. 'You mean—she lives here, too?'

'Her rooms are on the other side of the kitchen,' explained Reed tolerantly. 'She has her own self-contained apartment, with her own lift. She likes it.' He nodded to the nearest sofa. 'Why don't you sit down?'

'Is—is she young—old—what?' asked Antonia, seating herself on the very edge of the sofa, her glass cradled protectively in her hand.

'She's a fifty-five-year-old German lady, who came to Ireland just after the war as an *au pair*, and has never wanted to go back,' declared Reed, setting the champagne bottle on the carved end table, and reclining on the cushions beside her. 'And that's the last word I'm going to say about Maria Mueller, is that clear? I didn't bring you here to conduct a discussion about my housekeeper's undoubted attributes!'

Antonia pressed her lips together. 'Why—why did you bring me here?'

Reed groaned. 'You know why. To have supper.'

'And that's all?' Antonia looked at him out of the corners of her eyes.

Reed turned his head against the honey-gold velvet 'That's up to you.'

'What do you mean?'

'What do you think I mean?' he demanded, a trace of impatience colouring his tone. Pushing himself up he deposited his glass on the table beside the champagne bottle. 'For God's sake, stop looking at me like I was about to jump on you! I won't.' He paused, and when next he spoke his voice had thickened: 'Not unless you want me to, of course.'

Antonia was never sure whether it was the champagne on an empty stomach or some malicious demon inside her that inspired her next question, but the words were uttered, and she could not take them back: 'Do you want to?'

'Yes,' he said honestly, the fringe of dark lashes giving his face an oddly vulnerable expression, and when a mutual feeling stirred inside her, Antonia sprang abruptly to her feet.

'*You're* crazy!' she exclaimed, throwing his earlier words back at him, but when his hand came up and removed her glass, and then took her fingers to his lips, she could not deny the aching sensation that ran down her back and into her thighs.

'Sit down,' he said, tugging at her arm, and because her legs were so unsteady, she complied. She came down on to the sofa heavily, rocking the cushions, and her breath caught constrictedly when she saw his lazy smile.

'What are you trying to do? Break my sofa?' he enquired with some amusement, trying to put her at her ease. But the unconscious sensuality of her wide wary eyes and parted mouth dispelled his humour, and his hand slid behind her nape to massage the sensitive skin.

'I feel such a fool,' she breathed, realising the hem of her blouse had separated from the waistband of her trousers and trying unsuccessfully to restore it.

'You don't look a fool,' Reed assured her, using his free hand to still her restless fingers and drawing them instead to his lips again. Taking them into his mouth, one by one, he caressed their sensitive pads with his tongue, evoking sensations inside her Antonia knew she had never experienced before.

'Reed, be sensible,' she whispered, prepared to make one final protest, but his finger against her lips silenced her.

'You're sensible enough for both of us,' he responded, bearing her back against the soft cushions, and then the hard beauty of his mouth found hers.

She had guessed he would be as good at this as he was at getting his own way, but nothing had prepared her for her own response. It was as if she had never been kissed before, and certainly Simon, at his most passionate, had never disturbed her as Reed was disturbing her now. The probing pressure of his lips, the sensuous invasion of his tongue, the possessive strength of his hand behind her head, holding her imprisoned in

his grasp—he was arousing emotions she had hardly
known existed, and although she was a mature woman,
a *divorcee* moreover, she felt like an amateur in the
hands of a professional.

Reed shifted, so the muscled weight of his body was
lying half-over her, pressing her down into the cushions
of the sofa. She could feel the sensuous brush of velvet
at her back, where the gap her blouse had made
exposed her bare midriff, and the powerful hardness of
his legs against hers. His shirt was loose at the throat,
and her hands moved compulsively to touch the brown
skin rising above his collar. Her fingers curled
instinctively into the silky hair at the back of his head,
enjoying the unfamiliar intimacy, and he made a sound
of pleasure as she caressed his neck.

She didn't understand it. Simon had kissed her;
Simon had made love to her; they had even had a
daughter together. Yet, she knew now, Simon had
scarcely touched her deepest feelings. His fumbling
overtures had often left her cold, and impatient for it to
be over, and it dawned on her, with increasing certainty
that what she had regarded as her own inadequacy had,
in fact, been his. And had it not been for Susie, she
might never have married him . . .

The sudden recollection of her daughter's existence
was sobering. No matter how attractive the proposition,
Reed's intentions were no different from what Simon's
had been, and what he was doing was, if anything, more
dangerous. With Simon, it had been bravado on her
part, a need to prove she was as liberated as the next
girl—a foolish contention, and one she had learned to
regret. With Reed it was different. She wasn't a girl any
longer; she was a woman, with a woman's needs, needs
Simon had aroused, and just occasionally satisfied.
Now, as Reed continued to kiss her, his lips finding the
palpitating pulse at her temple, his tongue stroking the
delicate contours of her ear, she was reminded of those
needs, and alerted to an awareness of how pleasurable it
would be to allow him to fulfil them. She would like to
sleep with Reed, she realised guiltily; she would like to

feel his skin against hers, without the cumbersome barrier of their clothes. And that was exactly why she had to get away from him, she acknowledged. It was years since she had taken a pill or used any other means to protect herself. At least Simon had wanted to marry her. Reed only wanted a diversion.

'*No!*' she said fiercely, as his hand slid down from her shoulder to touch her breast. His thumb, moving lazily over the swollen nipple already surging against the thin acrylic fibre of her blouse, halted its sensuous exploration, but her eyes were frankly disbelieving when he drew back a space to look down at her.

'No?'

'No,' she repeated huskily, pushing his hand away. 'Reed, I want to go home.'

He drew a deep breath and gently smoothed back the slightly damp hair at her temples. 'You *want* me,' he contradicted her softly, bestowing a disturbing kiss at the corner of her mouth. 'Just as much as I want you. Don't tell me no. I don't believe it.'

Antonia sighed. 'All right, all right,' she said, her body trembling. 'I—I do want you, but—but not on your terms.'

Reed's grey eyes narrowed. 'And what terms are they?' he asked quietly.

'Like—like this,' she stammered, her tongue circling her lips. 'At—at this time of night. Behind your fiancée's back!'

Reed drew back to support himself with a hand at either side of her. 'Might I remind you that you dictated the time,' he remarked narrowly. His lips tightened. 'And as for Cee—what she doesn't know can't hurt her!'

Antonia shrank from his words. 'And that's all that matters? That Celia shouldn't get to know about it?' she demanded contemptuously.

'No.' His cheeks hollowed. 'I'm not saying it's right——'

'What are you saying then?' She wriggled up against the cushions until her eyes were on a level with his. 'That you can't help yourself?'

'Something like that,' he retorted, astounding her. Then he turned abruptly away. 'Okay, okay. I'll take you home. Just give me a minute to—well, to control my baser instincts.'

Antonia hesitated, and then swung her legs to the floor and sat up beside him. She gave him a doubtful look. 'Are you all right?'

'Oh, fine!' Reed gave a short mirthless laugh.

Antonia shook her head. 'You don't understand.'

'I think I do.'

'I'm not a tease.'

'Did I say you were?'

'No, but——' She bent her head. 'You implied it. I can't help it if I'm not like the other women you deal with . . .'

'Wait!' Reed's harsh ejaculation interrupted her. '*What* other women?'

'Well, I assumed . . .'

'You assumed wrong then, didn't you?' Reed countered grimly, getting abruptly to his feet. 'Whatever opinion you have of my treatment of Cee, I *am not* in the habit of making clandestine assignations with other members of her sex. Oh, I admit I've been tempted, but contrary to your beliefs, I have respected my commitments. Until now.'

Antonia stood up also. 'Then—why? Why me?' she asked huskily, her expression revealing her confusion, and Reed's face hardened.

'I've been asking myself that for the past two weeks,' he responded, reaching for his jacket and putting it on. 'Come on.' He tossed her her jacket and turned towards the door. 'Let's go. Before I change my mind and decide to show you you're not as strongwilled as you like to think!'

The journey down in the lift was almost as traumatic as the journey up had been. Antonia kept her eyes averted from his lean intelligent face, knowing that if she looked at him, she might betray her feelings. She was frightened of the power he had over her, the ability he had to arouse her emotions and tug at her heart. He had been so right; she did *want* him, badly, and it was going to be *hell* to try and put him out of her mind.

The Lamborghini soon ate up the distance between Reed's home and the Victorian apartment building she lived in. It was nearly midnight, and the city streets were not busy, even if they were not exactly deserted. Reed drove smoothly, concentrating on the traffic there was, taking evasive action when a driver with probably an over-indulgence of alcohol in his veins swung wildly out of a side-street, and reverting to a crawl when a party of late-night revellers stepped incautiously out in front of him.

Antonia thought he would drop her at the gate, and her hand went out protestingly when he began to turn into the drive of Eaton Lodge. 'Don't,' she said, looking anxiously at his profile. 'Someone might recognise the car. It is rather—recognisable, isn't it?'

'You can't walk up there alone at this time of night,' said Reed doggedly, and Antonia sighed.

'Walk with me then,' she invited softly. 'Though I hardly think anyone is likely to attack me.'

Reed made no response to this. He merely gave her an enigmatic look before getting out of the car, and by the time he had rescued her case from the boot, Antonia was standing beside him.

In actual fact, she was glad he had decided to escort her up the drive. The privet hedge and the shrubs that were banked on either side were a little eerie in the darkness, and at this time of night the area was blanketed in silence. The outer door, which often stood open in daylight, was closed, and Antonia had to find her key to open it. Then, she turned to take her case from Reed.

'I—thanks,' she murmured, reaching out her hand, and he set the bulky suitcase down beside her.

'My pleasure,' he responded tautly, his features vaguely discernible in the half-light from the street lamp a few yards away.

'It—it's goodbye then,' she stammered, wishing he would go, and he nodded.

'Good*night*,' he amended, watching her changing expression. Then, with a groan of impatience, he bent his head. 'I'll call you,' he said, his mouth finding her parted lips with devastating intimacy. 'Sleep- if you can.' His lips twisted. 'I won't!'

CHAPTER SIX

'*Reed!* Are you listening to me?'

He turned, as the petulant tone of his fiancée's voice became a little shrill. 'Yes, I'm listening,' he assured her equably, moving away from his office window and resuming his seat behind his desk. 'You were saying Claire can't go to Paris, because she's discovered she's going to have a baby.'

'*Well!* You might show a little sympathy,' exclaimed Celia grumpily. 'I mean—what is she *doing*, getting herself pregnant! It's not as if *Paul* wants to marry her. He's far too happy running that club of his, to want to settle down to being a *father*!'

'Do you know that?' inquired Reed drily, trying to take an interest in the conversation. 'Aren't you forgetting Claire's a bright, intelligent woman? Paul may be flattered that she wants to marry him.'

'Oh, I don't know that she does,' retorted Celia restlessly, getting up from her chair and pacing about the room. 'She told me she's quite prepared to become a *single* parent. I mean, I ask you: what are her parents going to say about that!'

Reed shrugged, looking down at his fingers playing idly with his pen. 'I doubt if you'd be feeling so concerned if Claire was not letting you down, too,' he remarked flatly, his interest waning. 'Send someone else to Paris. What about Liz?'

Celia came back to the desk and rested her scarlet-tipped fingers on its surface. 'Liz won't go,' she declared ruefully. 'You know she hates flying, and going on her own ... No, she's out of the question.'

'So—what's the alternative?' Reed looked up at her.

Celia grimaced. 'I go myself, I suppose.'

Reed shrugged. 'Problem solved.'

'No, it's not.' Celia's lower lip jutted. 'Will you come with me?'

'No.' Reed's response was final. 'I've already told you——'

'I know, I know. You're going down to Stonor this weekend. But *couldn't* you change your mind?'

'Celia——'

'Oh, all right.' His fiancée lifted her hands from the desk and turned their palms towards him in a gesture of submission. 'I know you don't like fashion shows. But really, someone has to go, and I'm afraid it's going to have to be me.'

'As I said—problem solved.' Reed lay back in his chair and regarded her through his lashes. 'No sweat. I can go to Stonor on my own.'

Celia pursed her lips. 'I was looking forward to it; us being alone for two whole days!'

'Yes.' Reed averted his eyes. 'So was I. But there'll be other weekends.'

'Yes, there will, won't there?' Celia's smile appeared. 'After we're married, I expect we'll spend lots of weekends there.'

'After we're married, we'll be living there,' Reed reminded her tersely. 'Or had you forgotten?'

Celia wrinkled her nose. 'Well—not *all* the time, darling.'

'Stonor's near enough to London to commute,' Reed pointed out evenly. 'And I don't want my children growing up in this polluted atmosphere.'

'Your *children*! Darling, aren't you being just the teeniest bit premature?' Celia uttered a light laugh. 'Honestly, the way you talk, you'd think I was going to spend all my time *breeding*!'

Reed arched his dark brows. 'I did tell you I wanted a family, Cee.'

'I know you did.' Celia shifted beneath his steady gaze. 'But not straight away, surely? We need some time to ourselves.'

'If you say so.' Reed lifted his shoulders. 'We'll wait a year.'

'A *year*!' Celia sounded appalled. 'I thought—five years, at least.'

'That's too long.'

'We'll compromise.' Celia was eager to dismiss the subject. 'Besides, there's absolutely no need to condemn oneself to a rural existence, just because one has a family!'

'I don't want any child of mine left for days on end in the hands of a nursemaid,' retorted Reed curtly, aware that he was being unreasonable, but unable to prevent himself. 'When are you leaving?'

Celia looked sulky. 'Is that all you have to say? You pick an argument at the most inopportune time, and then ask me when I'm leaving, as if my feelings don't matter!'

Reed put down the pen before it snapped between his fingers, and looked up at her again. What a bastard he was, he thought, noticing the tremulous vulnerability of her mouth and the suspicious brightness of her eyes. Dear God, what was happening to him? This was Cee; the girl he intended to marry. Why was he forcing her into a position of confrontation?

'I'm sorry,' he said softly, pushing back his chair and coming round the desk towards her. 'I'm a brute; I know. I guess I'm just a bit disappointed. About tomorrow, I mean.' He put his hands on her shoulders, and drew her gently to him. 'Take no notice of me. I'm feeling my age, that's all.'

'Your *age*!' Celia looped her arms around his neck, and gave him a tearful smile. 'You know that's not true. What is it? Is Gallaghers on the brink of bankruptcy or something?'

'It's nothing,' said Reed, his lips against her cheek. 'Put it down to simple bloody-mindedness. Now—do you want me to drive you to the airport? What time is your flight?'

'*The* flight is at eleven-thirty,' Celia replied, emphasising the definite article. 'And if I go, I'll get Daddy to take me. He's flying off to the Common Market conference in the morning. Besides,' she paused, 'I know you hate driving across town in the rush-hour. Remember?'

Reed brushed her lips with his and then let her go. 'I remember,' he conceded evenly. 'When will you be back?'

'Sunday night. But honestly, darling,' Celia gurgled, 'I'd love to have seen your face when Mrs Francis caught you knocking at Antonia's door. I mean—she must have thought the worst!'

Reed's thick lashes lowered. 'That's not what she told you.' It was a statement, not a question.

'No.' Celia conceded the point. 'She just said what you had told her: that you were delivering a message from me.' She shrugged. 'I don't know why you didn't just tell her the truth. It's not as if Antonia is some sort of *femme fatale*. She surely couldn't think you'd be interested in *her*.'

His instincts were to round on her, savagely, for the patronising way she dismissed the other girl, but he held his tongue. 'It was easier to tell her what I did, than explain that I'd forgotten you'd still be at the shop,' he replied lightly. 'Besides, she'd have wondered why I didn't knock at her door first. I don't suppose she regards herself as a nosey old witch!'

'That's because she's not!' protested Celia, laughing all the same. 'And you *should* have knocked at her door first. I mean—you hardly *know* Antonia!'

'I only wanted to use the bathroom, not invite myself in for refreshment!' retorted Reed flatly. 'I didn't think—Antonia would mind. She seemed a pleasant girl.'

'Oh, she is.' Celia adjusted the neckline of her jacket. 'She's sweet. A little *passé* in the way she dresses, perhaps, but that's probably because she doesn't have a lot of money. I mean—she works at some *institute*, where they teach young people—*skills*; that sort of thing. I understand she's not just a shorthand typist, but I doubt if she's paid *awfully* well.'

Reed walked round his desk again. 'Do you like her?'

'*Like* her?' Celia sounded surprised. 'Well—*yes*, I suppose so. I mean, she's not like us, but she's all right. We don't have much in common. I honestly don't know how she *affords* that apartment! It's small, I know, but prices in that area... Her voice trailed away expressively. Then, as if aware that Reed was waiting for something more, she shrugged. 'Anyway, I don't see much of her. I only asked her to the party because I felt *sorry* for her! And Liz thought I was mad to do it.' She grimaced. 'Actually though, I think that was because Gerry Stockwell seemed so taken with her. Antonia, I mean. Liz was livid!'

Reed pushed his hands into his pockets. 'Stockwell?' he echoed quietly. 'Who is Gerry Stockwell?'

'You know!' Celia fluffed her hair with delicate fingers. 'His father's in steel, or aluminium, something like that. Gerry's the eldest son, *heir* to the family fortune, that sort of thing. Liz says he'll inherit a *title* one day. Anyway, she's been trying to get her claws into him for months, and it was pretty *galling* when he stood and chatted to Antonia for the best part of an hour.'

'As I recall it, she was speaking to several men at once,' Reed remarked levelly. 'No one in particular.'

'No—well, that's true.' Celia outlined her lips with her little finger. 'I mean—you spoke to her yourself, didn't you? Before I realised she was there.'

'No one else was doing so, at that time,' observed Reed drily, flicking back his cuff. Then he drew his features into a polite expression of dismay. 'Heavens, it's nearly five o'clock! Mrs Drysdale will be having fits. I haven't even looked at the letters yet.'

'Oh, aren't you free to go?' Celia looked disappointed. 'I thought you were going to drive me *home*!'

Reed stifled the impulse to refuse point-blank, and made a compromise. 'If you can hang about for another half-hour,' he offered. 'Don't you have to go back to the shop?'

'No. I told Liz I'd go straight home.' Celia sighed. 'Oh, all right. I'll just pop out for a few minutes. There are one or two things I need from the chemist, and that will give you time to sign your letters.'

But after she had gone, Reed did not immediately summon his secretary into the office. Instead, he went to stand by the window—where he seemed to be spending too much time lately, he reflected sourly—and considered the idea, which had entered his head and refused to be dislodged.

The notion of taking Antonia to Stonor with him was a reckless one, he knew. His staff, at his house in Oxfordshire, were trustworthy enough, but he could hardly bring a strange young woman into his home without arousing some comment. It had been different at the apartment. For one thing, Maria had not known who he was asking her to prepare supper for, and even if she had, he acknowledged, she would not have demurred. Maria did not care for Celia. His fiancée's decidedly patronising attitude with people she did not consider her social equal, did not wear well with the German woman, and Maria had already made it clear that she would not be staying on after they were married. Which was a pity, Reed thought, who had known Maria since he was a child at home in Ireland. In those days, she had worked at his family's house in County Wicklow, and he hoped that if she did insist on leaving, his parents might find a place for her again.

He sighed. Maria's future was not in jeopardy for some months yet, and that was not his present problem. What he had to contend with, he acknowledged grimly, was his growing infatuation for a girl who was not his fiancée; a consuming need, that was disturbing his normally easy-going disposition and disrupting his life.

He lifted a hand to massage the muscles of his shoulder with some impatience. He must be crazy, he thought bitterly, recalling all the abortive phone calls he had made to the ground floor flat in Eaton Lodge. During the past week, he had tried to contact Antonia at least a dozen times, and if her phone was not out of order, he could only assume she didn't wish to speak with him.

He shouldn't have warned her, he reflected, remembering his impulsive promise to ring. If she hadn't known he might be phoning, he would have no reason to suspect that she was avoiding him: and the raw frustration he felt every time his calls remained unanswered would have no basis for its inception.

But he had told her, and his inability to get through was beginning to prey on his nerves. He knew he was becoming tense, and irritable, and the conversation he had just had with Celia was an example of his souring temperament. He had never felt so dissatisfied with his lot before, and the extent of his self-pity filled him with contempt. He had to pull himself out of this before he did something really stupid, he told himself severely, walking back to his desk. But it was Antonia's image that filled his mind as he rang for Mrs Drysdale.

Antonia let herself into the flat and leaned back gratefully against the door. The little carriage clock on her mantelshelf informed her it was almost eight-thirty, and she straightened her spine determinedly. She had approximately fifteen minutes to wash and change her clothes, and get herself something to eat, if she needed it. She owed it to Mr Fenwick to turn up for work this morning, even if it was Friday. He had been kind enough to give her the time off to go up to Newcastle. The least she could do was report for work as soon as she got back.

Of course, her mother had suggested she stay over until Sunday. 'There's not much point in going back on a Friday!' she had protested, but Antonia had been adamant. She felt guilty enough as it was, abandoning Mr Fenwick for three days at a stretch. And because he had been so understanding, she didn't want to betray his trust.

Shaking her head, she pushed herself away from the door and walked through to her bedroom. She was stiff, and if she had had more time, she would have welcomed a bath. Eight hours, cramped in the front of her cousin Tony's truck, had left her spine feeling as if she had done it a permanent injury, but she supposed she should be grateful. He had, at least, saved her her train fare.

It was not as if her rushing off to Newcastle had

achieved anything, she reflected, stripping off the
sweater and jeans she had worn to travel in. But when
her mother had rung and said Susie had had an
accident, the three hundred miles between them had
seemed an interminable distance.

As she washed and cleaned her teeth, Antonia
remembered vividly how she had felt when the call had
come through on Tuesday morning. Mrs Lord had
panicked, and the fact that Susie had fallen off a
friend's bicycle and had been taken to hospital with a
suspected fractured skull, had sounded reason enough.

As it turned out, Susie spent Tuesday night in the
hospital, 'under observation', as the Staff Nurse put it,
and returned home on Wednesday, pale, but otherwise
unharmed. It was Antonia's mother who had begged
her daughter to stay on for at least another night. 'Just
in case there are any complications,' she had pleaded,
and realising what a shock Mrs Lord had sustained,
Antonia had agreed. Susie was *her* daughter, after all.
Her responsibility, not her mother's.

She managed to get to work on time, and Mr
Fenwick looked relieved when he walked into her office
and found her already ensconced behind her desk. 'I
was half-afraid you wouldn't get back until Monday,'
he confessed ruefully. 'And I've got those chaps from
the Ministry coming this afternoon.'

'Oh, yes.' Antonia had forgotten the official visit
from the education department which had been planned
for today. 'Well, I'm here now, so you can relax.'

'Yes.' Mr Fenwick smiled. 'And what about your
little girl? How is she?'

'Much better,' said Antonia at once. 'You know what
children are like: down one minute, and up the next.
They kept her in hospital overnight, but there were no
complications, thank goodness. It was my mother who
took it hardest. I think she blamed herself.'

'She would,' agreed Mr Fenwick sympathetically.
'Looking after a six-year-old is quite a responsibility for
a grandmother. Anyway, I'm glad Susie's all right. I
should hate to lose you now.'

'You won't.' Antonia was confident. 'Now—what do you want me to do first? Shall I attend to these estimates, or start on the agenda for next week's meeting?'

Although she had been away and consequently everything in the flat was likely to be stale, Antonia gave up any thought of going shopping at lunchtime. Instead, she collected a sandwich from the dining-hall and ate it at her desk, working right through the break. It was tiring. The disturbed night she had spent in the front of Tony's truck meant she had had little sleep, and it was difficult to keep her eyes open at times. But several cups of strong black coffee served the purpose, and by the time the delegation from the Ministry arrived, she had made some headway with the backlog.

She collected her immediate needs on her way home that afternoon. The buses were full so she walked the distance unhurriedly, enjoying the distinct indications that summer was not as distant as she had thought. The trees were burgeoning with greenness, the birds were twittering in the park; and outside a florist's great bucketfuls of tulips and narcissus nodded their heads as she passed. On impulse, Antonia bought herself a bunch of tulips, inhaling their fresh fragrance as she turned into the gates of Eaton Lodge.

The flowers conjured thoughts of the man, whose image she had been keeping at bay all week, and she permitted herself to wonder if he *had* tried to ring her. The memory of Sunday evening had remained in her subconscious throughout the trauma of the past three days, and while it had not interfered with her anxieties about Susie and her mother, she had not been able to dispel the unworthy suspicion that Reed had played a part in her decision to return so promptly. It was foolish; allowing their association to continue was foolish; but the fact remained, she had thought about him, and to deny it would be less than honest.

The flat looked drab and dusty after its week-long neglect. Tomorrow, she would have to set to and give it a thorough cleaning, she reflected, without enthusiasm, noticing how the sunlight streaming through showed up the murky smudges on the windows. But tonight she was too tired to worry about housework, she decided, pulling out the pre-cooked leg of chicken she had bought for her dinner. After she had eaten, she was going to have an early night. Perhaps tomorrow she would feel more optimistic about tackling her chores.

The sudden knocking at her door interrupted her unpacking of the shopping, and she sighed. Mrs Francis must have seen her come in, she realised wearily. She had had to tell the caretaker she was going away for a few days, and no doubt his wife was curious to hear what had happened.

Suppressing her annoyance, Antonia went to answer the door. It was kind of her to be concerned, she told herself firmly. She ought not to be so ungrateful. But to her astonishment, it was not the garrulous Mrs Francis waiting outside. It was Reed; and her lips parted indignantly when he propelled the door open against her hand and came uninvited into the flat.

'Close it,' he said grimly, when she opened her mouth to make a protest, and she didn't know whether he was referring to her or not. 'The door,' he defined impatiently, and because she really didn't want to attract the caretaker's wife's attention, Antonia complied. But she was furious that he should think he had the right to force his way into her home and it showed.

'Just what do you think you're doing?' she demanded, as he rested against the wall beside the door, and he regarded her with dour intensity.

'That's my question,' he responded, his narrowed eyes moving over her angry face. 'Is your phone out of order?'

'My phone!' Antonia gazed at him blankly. 'I don't know what you mean.'

'Your telephone,' enunciated Reed harshly. 'The instrument people use when they want to get in touch with one another. You do have one, don't you?'

'Of course I do.' Antonia nodded.

'So, why haven't you been answering it?' he enquired oppressively. 'Or does that question require notice?'

Antonia caught her breath. 'You've been *phoning* me!' she exclaimed, suddenly understanding, and he pushed himself away from the wall, a scowl marring his lean features.

'Quick,' he remarked sardonically, his lips twisting. 'I revise my opinion. You're pretty sharp!'

'Oh, don't be so sarcastic!' she retorted, linking and unlinking her fingers. 'I couldn't answer the phone because I haven't been here!'

'No?' He regarded her sceptically. 'Don't tell me they've started a night shift at the institute!'

Antonia flushed at his contemptuous tone. 'No,' she conceded stiffly. 'I haven't been at work.'

Reed expelled his breath heavily. 'So where have you been?'

Antonia held up her head. 'I'm not obliged to tell you.'

'But you will,' he informed her bleakly, moving closer, and her breathing quickened in concert with her accelerating pulse rate.

'Why should I?' she countered, standing her ground. 'It's nothing to do with you.'

'Isn't it?' He was so close now she could see the muscle jerking at the corner of his mouth. 'Not even if I tell you I've been ringing this number constantly since Tuesday evening?'

Antonia moistened her dry lips. 'I didn't ask you to.'

'No.' He conceded the point, his nostrils flaring only slightly as he controlled his temper. 'But the least you could do is be honest with me.'

'I am being honest with you.' Antonia sighed. 'As— as a matter of fact, I went home again.'

'Home?' Reed frowned. 'You mean—to Newcastle?'

'Yes.'

'Oh, come on . . .' He took a backward step. 'You're not trying to tell me you went back to Newcastle on Tuesday, when you only got back from there on Sunday night!'

Antonia blinked. 'Why not?'

He shook his head. 'I wasn't born yesterday, Antonia. If you don't want to tell me where you were, then—I guess I'll have to live with it. But don't *lie* to me!'

'I'm not lying . . .'

'No?'

'No.' She saw his scornful expression and came to a sudden decision. 'My—my daughter had an accident. My mother sent for me.'

Reed's astonishment was palpable. 'Your—*daughter*?'

'Yes.' Antonia straightened her spine. 'I have a child. Now—if you don't mind, I'm very tired . . .'

'Wait a minute.' Reed grasped her arms just below her shoulders. 'You're telling me you've got a daughter? So—where does she live? With your ex-husband?'

'Simon?' Antonia uttered a short laugh. 'No. She lives with my mother. Now, will you please . . .'

'Cool it, will you?' Reed shook her with controlled violence. 'Let me take this in.' He looked down at her impatiently. 'How old is she? What's her name?'

'Susan—*Susie*,' amended Antonia unwillingly. 'And she's six.'

'*Six!*'

'I'm not a teenager, Reed,' she exclaimed, stung by his ejaculation, and his lips turned down ironically.

'I never thought you were,' he assured her drily, and she had to concentrate on the knot of his tie to avoid the disturbing warmth that invaded his eyes. 'I guess I should apologise. For jumping to conclusions, I mean.'

'That's not necessary.'

'Yes, it is.' He sighed. 'What happened? You said she had an accident. Is she all right?'

'She's fine.'

Her tone was as stiff as her spine, and he lifted his shoulders ruefully. 'You don't know what it's been like for me,' he declared. 'I thought you were deliberately ignoring me.'

'A crime, indeed!' she retorted tensely, and his hands slid up over her shoulders to her neck.

'Don't bait me, Antonia,' he advised roughly, his fingers abrasive. 'I mean it. I don't entirely trust my instincts, even if you do look as if you haven't slept for a week!'

Belatedly, Antonia remembered her worn appearance, her pale cheeks and dark-ringed eyes. 'I'm sorry,' she responded bitterly, turning her head aside from his assiduous appraisal. 'This must be quite a shock for you seeing me as I really am! Not to mention discovering I have a child of school age!'

'Antonia——'

His use of her name was a warning, but she paid it no heed. 'What are you doing here anyway?' she demanded wearily, her hands against his stomach providing a necessary barrier. 'Aren't you afraid Celia might see you? Isn't it rather—indiscreet—to come here in daylight?'

'Celia's in Paris,' replied Reed flatly. 'She left this morning and she won't be back until Sunday. Does that answer your question, or would you like more?'

'Oh, no.' Antonia's lips twisted. 'I should have known. You don't take unnecessary risks, do you, Reed?'

'What are you trying to do to me?' he enquired, in a low violent tone. 'What do you want me to say? That I'd come here anyway, and to hell with Cee and our engagement?'

'No——' Antonia coloured.

'Then stop provoking me, will you?' His heated breath fanned her cheek. 'As a matter of fact, I've been sitting out front since about four o'clock, just waiting for you to come home. And that wasn't exactly without hazard!'

Antonia permitted a brief glance up at him. 'You haven't!'

'Oh, I have.' He shrugged. 'Didn't you see the car? It's parked right across the street.' And then he added derisively: 'No. Of course, you wouldn't. I forgot. You were too engrossed in the tulips you were carrying to notice me.'

Antonia shook her head. 'You shouldn't have come here,' she protested, his nearness rapidly overwhelming her objections, as his fingers moved sensuously against her nape. 'You—you should have rung!'

'Again?' he put in wryly, and she had no answer to that.

'Reed . . .'

'Tell me later,' he suggested softly, bending his head to find her resisting lips with his mouth. 'And stop fighting me,' he added, looking down at her splayed palms against his midriff, and with a little moan of helplessness, Antonia slid her arms about his waist.

'We can't do this,' she exclaimed, as his tongue found the delicate cavity of her ear, and he expelled an unsteady breath.

'We're doing it,' he pointed out huskily, his hands sliding into her hair. 'After the week I've had, don't you think I deserve it?'

'I—*no!*' With a supreme effort, Antonia pulled herself away from him, trying to steady her breathing as she ran smoothing hands over her hair. 'Reed—you can't stay here!'

He took a few moments to answer her, but when he did her spirits slumped considerably. 'I don't intend to,' he said, walking round the sofa and subsiding on to the chintz-covered cushions. 'You remember I told you I had a house in the country? I'm going to spend the weekend there.'

'Oh!' Antonia endeavoured not to sound as deflated as she felt. 'I—how nice.'

'It is,' he confirmed, looking up at her with lazily assessing eyes. 'It's just over the Buckinghamshire border into Oxfordshire. Not far from Chalgrove. A village called Stonor's End. My house is just outside the village. Very quiet. Very rural.'

'It sounds lovely.' Antonia forced a note of enthusiasm into her voice.

'Yes.' Reed rested his head back against the upholstery, and sighed. 'It's beautiful at this time of the year. The woods are full of crocuses and there are hundreds of those tulips you admire growing by the lake.'

Antonia moistened her lips. 'There's a lake?'

'Just a small one,' he conceded reflectively. 'We use it for swimming in summer. It's pretty cold, but we enjoy it.'

'We?' Antonia expelled her breath. 'You mean—you and Celia?'

'Occasionally,' he admitted, regarding her through narrowed lids. 'But mostly it's Tricia and her friends who use the place. It's her second home.'

'Tricia?' Antonia frowned. Was she another girlfriend?

'Patricia *Gallagher*,' put in Reed humorously, defining her expression. 'My sister. She's at Oxford. *University*,' he added drily.

'Oh!' Antonia shook her head. 'I see.'

'Do you?' Reed looked sceptical. 'Did you think I kept a harem down there?'

'I never thought about it,' she lied, and he gave her a wry look.

'Anyway, it takes about an hour-and-a-half to get there,' he remarked casually. 'Unless it's the rush hour, and then it can take considerably longer.'

'So why don't you go?' exclaimed Antonia tensely, moving to the hearth to make an unnecessary adjustment to the clock on the mantelshelf. 'It's going to be a fine weekend. At least, that's what Mr Fenwick told me. I'm sure you'll enjoy it.'

'Come with me,' said Reed softly, so softly she thought for a moment she had imagined it. She swung round, her pale face flushed with disbelieving colour, and he pushed himself up from the couch to meet her anxious eyes. 'Come with me,' he said again, pushing his hands into the pockets of his leather jacket. 'Spend the weekend with me. No strings—just a friendly arrangement. I'd like to show you Stonor, and I'd really appreciate your company.'

Antonia blinked. 'You can't be serious!'

Reed sighed. 'Let's not get into another discussion of

what's right and what's wrong,' he said flatly. 'Like I
said, I want your company, that's all. I'm not
suggesting we share a room or anything crass like that.
I like you; and I think that you like me. Why shouldn't
we spend some time together?'

CHAPTER SEVEN

ANTONIA's room was at the back of the house, overlooking the terrace and the tennis courts, with the reed-edged sweep of the lake in the background. Immediately below her windows the flagged terrace had a southerly aspect, and beyond a low-walled boundary, manicured lawns sloped down to the water. The wood Reed had spoken of, formed a backdrop in the distance, but nearer at hand there were spreading elms and bushy poplars, breaking up the landscape with their different shades of green.

Antonia leant her elbows on the opened window, hardly noticing the cool morning air through her thin nightgown. It was all so deliciously different from the smell of London, and she inhaled deeply, half-inclined to believe she was still dreaming.

Behind her, the bed she had occupied beckoned invitingly. It was a huge bed, bigger than any she had slept in, even when she was married to Simon. The mattress was modern enough, firm, but delightfully comfortable, and the night before her tired body had appreciated it. But the quilted headboard was decidedly French in appearance, and very much in keeping with the other appointments of the room. The soft-patterned carpet, in muted shades of pink and grey, blended beautifully with the pale grey silk that lined the walls; there were spindley-legged tables beside the bed; a long polished cabinet, inset with drawers, with a mirror above; a *chaise-longue* covered in pale pink velvet with a matching padded stool; and an inlaid rosewood escritoire, ideal for writing letters.

The dusky pink was picked up again in the curtains at the windows and in the thick satin bedspread, that had been turned down for her the night before. Beneath a downy quilt, pale grey silk sheets were quite shamelessly sensual against her skin, and Antonia remembered how incongruous she had felt putting on her simple cotton gown. Celia, she was sure, would wear silk or lace or satin to sleep in. But then, Celia was used to this kind of treatment; she was not.

Antonia sighed now, turning away from the window and surveying the room with some misgivings. Not for the first time, she wondered what the *real* reaction to her arrival had been among the other members of the household. Last night, Reed had introduced her to his housekeeper, a diminutive woman, by the name of Rose Macauley, who had been very polite to her. But she knew that there were other members of staff—Reed's conversation with his housekeeper had betrayed that— and Antonia couldn't help acknowledging what she would think if she was put in their position. What could they possibly think but the worst? she asked herself unhappily, wondering if anyone would ever believe that Reed had not shared her bed.

Not that Reed himself had seemed at all perturbed. On the contrary, he had got his own way, and in consequence he was very relaxed and very charming. His concern for her well-being, his insistence that she should go to bed as soon as her eyes started drooping, had made her feel someone very special, and although she had been a little doubtful, her suspicions had been ungrounded.

Of course, it had been quite late when they arrived the night before. It was dark when the Lamborghini turned between white-painted gates and followed a gravelled approach to the house. The headlights had illuminated little beyond the grassy verge that sloped away at either side, throwing the row of trees into silhouette, as they formed a shadowy guard along the drive.

After overcoming her opposition, Reed had suggested they had dinner in London before driving out to Stonor's End. That way they would avoid the regular exodus from the city that generally occurred at

weekends, he explained, and because she had still had
doubts about accompanying him, Antonia had agreed.

But after a delicious meal in a quiet, out-of-the-way
restaurant, with several glasses of wine to augment the
cocktail she had had before she started, Antonia was
too relaxed and too sleepy to offer more than a salutory
protest. Besides, her suitcase was in the boot of the
Lamborghini, alongside Reed's briefcase, and the idea
of spending the weekend in London when she had an
alternative was not appealing. Aware of Reed's
satisfaction when she snuggled down in the seat beside
him, she had felt she ought to be more forceful, but it
hadn't lasted long. Lulled by the warmth of the car, the
lazy music on the radio, and the comforting nearness of
Reed's shoulder, she had felt too contented to resist,
and when she opened her eyes, they were miles along
the motorway.

Their arrival at the house had been achieved with the
minimum amount of fuss. Her own appearance—late in
the evening and probably unannounced—was dealt
with without any particular disturbance, Reed issuing
his orders smoothly, and Mrs Macauley expediting
them with every appearance of co-operation. She had
even smiled and asked about the journey as she showed
Antonia to her room, and if she thought the suitcase
she had insisted on taking charge of was rather big to
transport its lightweight contents, she kept her opinion
to herself.

Antonia supposed she might have felt more embarrassed if she had not been so enthralled by her
surroundings. She had thought Reed's apartment was
impressive, but Stonor House, as it was called, was far
more imposing. Silk carpets; panelled walls; a huge
stained-glass window at the first landing of the fan-
shaped staircase; it was difficult to imagine someone
actually *lived* here. Yet, later, when she had joined Reed
for a drink in the library, she had had to revise her
opinion. Although the walls were lined from floor to
ceiling with leather-bound volumes, and the carpet on
the floor was probably priceless, nevertheless, the room

had a lived-in atmosphere. Apart from the familiar smells of alcohol and good tobacco, the squashy leather chairs that flanked the open fireplace had the comfortably worn appearance of having been well-used, and Reed was there to put her at her ease, with all the teasing eloquence of his race.

Thinking of Reed now, she wondered if he was up yet. It was only eight o'clock and she suspected he would still be in his bed. The idea brought a disturbing awareness to the pit of her stomach, and she went hastily into her bathroom before the disruptive seed could take root.

Like the bedroom the bathroom's decoration was predominantly pink, with smoked glass walls to throw back her reflection from all angles. A round, step-in bath had a jacuzzi fitment, but she decided just to take a shower in case she touched the wrong handles.

Afterwards, she dried her hair with the hand-drier provided, and then wrapping herself in the towelling bathrobe she found behind the door, she returned to the bedroom.

Her clothes were through an archway which opened into a dressing area. There were long mirrors flanking a long, fitted closet where she had hung her few garments the night before. Mrs Macauley had slid one of the long doors aside to show her the vacant space, but now, when she opened the door at the opposite end of the unit, she found herself confronted by a colourful array. They were not her clothes, but they were a woman's clothes, and she closed the door abruptly, and slid back the other panel.

They needn't be Celia's, she told herself severely, as she stepped into tight-fitting jeans and a long-sleeved cotton shirt. *But they could be*, a small voice taunted, and she felt a sudden sickness at the thought that Reed might have shared *her* bed with his fiancée.

She was standing at the mirror which hung above the long cabinet in her bedroom, brushing her hair, when someone knocked at her door. 'Yes?' she called tightly, not sure who it was or what she should do, and the door opened slowly to admit a girl scarcely out of her teens. She was carrying a tray, and she looked in some confusion at the bed when she saw that it was empty. But then she saw Antonia, doing her hair, and her homely features softened to expose a friendly smile.

'Mrs Macauley thought you might prefer breakfast in bed this morning, miss,' she declared, in a lovely Oxfordshire drawl. 'Mr Reed said that you were tired and not to disturb you, but Mrs Macauley thought you might like a cup of tea, it being a strange bed and all.'

'Oh, I would.' Dropping her brush on to the cabinet, Antonia turned to the other girl eagerly. 'How kind of Mrs Macauley.'

'You wouldn't prefer to come downstairs, now you're dressed, would you, miss?' the girl asked doubtfully, but Antonia shook her head. 'Then, I'll put the tray here, shall I?' she suggested, setting it down on the table at the nearside of the bed. 'There's some orange juice, and scrambled eggs too, just in case you're hungry. And Mrs Macauley said if you'd prefer coffee, it's no trouble.'

'The tea is fine,' said Antonia firmly, looking at the beautifully laid-out tray with some bemusement. 'And—and everything else,' she added. 'Thank you. Please tell Mrs Macauley I'm very grateful.'

'Yes, miss.'

The girl smiled and departed, and Antonia approached the tray with some amazement. The orange juice was freshly squeezed, and resided in a cut-glass container; the scrambled eggs nestled beneath a silver cover; curls of butter and lightly browned toast jostled a dish of strawberry preserve; and the bone-china teacup and saucer stood beside a squat bone-china teapot, fitted with a padded velour cosy.

Antonia shook her head and sat down on the side of the bed to pour herself some tea. It was years since anyone had brought her breakfast in bed, and never had it been set out so attractively; and although she rarely swallowed more than a slice of toast before leaving for work in the morning, she couldn't resist sampling the orange juice and the eggs.

As she had anticipated, the juice was sweet and palatable, and took no effort whatsoever. The eggs, too, were light and fluffy, and despite her intention just to taste them, she found herself eating with enthusiasm. It must be the air, she told herself wryly, spreading strawberry preserve on a slice of toast. She couldn't ever remember enjoying a breakfast so much.

By the time she had finished the meal, and applied a little make-up, it was after nine o'clock, a much more respectable hour, she reflected. Checking her appearance before leaving the room, she was relieved to see the dark lines that had surrounded her eyes the day before had almost disappeared, and there was actually a little colour in the skin that covered her cheekbones. Her newly washed hair gleamed with health, and although she found her features ordinary, anticipation leant an unfamiliar sparkle to her eyes.

Leaving the tray, and her unmade bed—an unheard-of luxury—Antonia opened her door and looked along the wide corridor. She knew the staircase was to her right. The night before, when Mrs Macauley had shown her to her room, she had taken especial notice of the fact that they had turned left at the top of the stairs so that later, when she wanted to go to bed, she did not need Reed's escort to take her there.

Now, closing the door behind her, she trod the soft cream carpet to the head of the stairs. Several other doors opened off the corridor, and she wondered if one of them was Reed's. If her room was the one Celia used, it was quite likely, she thought, remembering the dismay she had felt earlier, before the maid had brought her breakfast. But as there was a matching corridor at the opposite side of the staircase, it was debatable. Would Reed be so unsubtle as to situate his and his fiancée's rooms side by side, she mused unwillingly, when he must know what interpretation would be put upon it?

The glossy wood of the banister rail ran silkily beneath her fingers as she descended the stairs. Below her, the shining expanse of polished wood revealed a

conscientious attention to duty, the steady tick of a
grandfather clock the only sound to disturb the silence.
Unless one listened hard, she acknowledged; then one
could hear the birds, and the distant barking of a dog,
and even the lowing of cattle, grazing somewhere not
too far away.

'Are you looking for someone, Miss Sheldon?'
inquired a businesslike voice behind her, and Antonia
realised she had been standing on the bottom stair, like
someone in a dream.

'Oh—Mrs Macauley,' she exclaimed, finding the tiny
housekeeper at her elbow. 'I—is Mr Gallagher up yet? I
was just wondering where I might find him.'

'Sure, Mr Reed was up two hours ago, Miss
Sheldon,' responded Mrs Macauley, revealing a brogue
Antonia had scarcely identified the night before. 'He
said you'd be sleeping till mid-morning most likely, but
I thought you might find it strange here, after the
clamour of London.'

'And you were right.' Antonia smiled. 'I should
thank you again for my breakfast. It was delicious. I . . .
er . . . I left the tray upstairs.'

'That's all right, Miss Sheldon. Ruth will get it when
she goes to make the bed.'

'Um—it's *Mrs* Sheldon, actually,' murmured
Antonia, a little awkwardly. 'Do—do you know
where—Reed is?'

Mrs Macauley did not immediately respond to her
enquiry. '*Mrs* Sheldon, is it?' she remarked noncommit-
tally. 'And will your husband be joining us, Mrs
Sheldon?'

'No.' Antonia was obliged to answer her. 'I'm
divorced, Mrs Macauley, and I don't know where my
ex-husband is.'

'Ah . . .' The housekeeper cupped her elbow in the
palm of one hand and tugged thoughtfully at her ear
with the other. 'You're young to be looking for another
husband, Mrs Sheldon.'

'I'm not looking for another husband, Mrs
Macauley,' retorted Antonia shortly, rapidly revising

her opinion of Reed's choice of retainer 'Do you know Mr Gallagher's whereabouts, or shall I look for him myself?'

'Sure, he's been out with the horses since half-past seven,' responded the housekeeper at once. 'And if you're planning on going down to the stables, I should put a coat on, if I were you. The sun's out, but there's still a nip in the air.'

'Thank you.'

Antonia's acknowledgment was decidedly frosty, and the housekeeper smiled. 'Sure, I'm only thinking of the good of—*both* of you,' she observed sagely. 'Wrap up warm now. You wouldn't be wanting to get a chill, now, would you?'

Collecting her pale blue anorak from her room, Antonia had to admit it was difficult to remain aggrieved with Mrs Macauley. The woman said outrageous things, it was true, but Antonia sensed she really did have Reed's well-being at heart. No doubt it was the housekeeper's way of warning her off, Antonia reflected uneasily. And after all, she must be curious as to why her employer had brought a strange young woman into his home. It would be different if there were several guests; but there weren't. There was only her, and the fact that she was divorced led to obvious speculation.

Downstairs again, in the absence of any known alternative, Antonia let herself out of the front door, and pushing her hands into the pockets of her jacket, set off across the courtyard. Mrs Macauley had been right, she thought, as a chill breeze swept her hair back from her face. It was much cooler than it had been the night before, and although the sun was shining, it was not making any impact.

The front of the house faced down the drive they had driven up the night before, and now Antonia could see the imposing sweep of grassland that stretched as far as the distant gateposts. To her right, white rails fenced in a handful of mares and their foals, and further afield, the cattle she had heard earlier grazed a lush green

pasture. Like Reed had said, it was very peaceful and
very rural, and she filled her lungs with enthusiasm as
she breathed the country air.

At one end of the long row of windows that
confronted her, a wall, inset with an arched doorway,
gave access to the garage yard. The Lamborghini was
there, being hosed down by a boy of about sixteen, but
he turned off the water at Antonia's approach, and
arched his brows rather insolently. 'Did you want
something?'

'Yes. Mr Gallagher,' replied Antonia, with some
reluctance. 'I'm looking for the stables actually. Is this
the way?'

'You'd be—Miss Sheldon, is that right?' enquired the
boy inquisitively, squeezing out his wash-leather in a
bucket standing close by, and Antonia sighed.

'Mrs Sheldon, yes,' she agreed, glancing impatiently
about her. 'Can I get to the stables this way?'

The boy hesitated, obviously wishing he could say
more, but unlike Mrs Macauley, he did not have the
confidence. 'Yes,' he said off-handedly, nodding
towards another gateway across the yard. 'If you go
through there and follow the path, you'll see the stables
right ahead of you.'

'Thank you.'

Antonia followed his instructions, aware as she did so
that his eyes followed her until she was out of the gate.
No doubt he was wondering exactly what her
relationship with Reed was, she reflected, wishing she
had anticipated this before she agreed to come.

But then, she thought, she had not realised just how
many people were going to be involved. Her visions of
Reed's country house might have run to a domestic of
some kind, like at his apartment in London. She had
not forseen a country manor, with all its incumbent
employees.

She saw Reed before she reached the three-sided
collection of buildings that made up the stable block.
He was in the yard, talking with an elderly man, who
Antonia assumed must be the groom, and her heart

accelerated annoyingly at the sight of his lean frame. In a suede jerkin and matching moleskin trousers, pushed into knee-length black boots, he looked perfectly at ease with his surroundings. The cream knitted sweater he was wearing, whose rolled collar brushed his chin, accentuated the darkness of his complexion, but otherwise he looked like an English country squire, returning from an outing with the hunt.

The old man saw Antonia first, and apparently he drew Reed's attention to it, for he turned and gave her a casual wave. What did he think he was doing? Antonia asked herself unhappily, slowing her step. How was he going to explain this visit—no matter how innocent—to Celia? And how was she likely to react to the fact that her downstairs neighbour was attracting far too much attention from the man she herself intended to marry? Reed could not expect to keep this a secret. Not when people like Mrs Macauley and the boy who had been cleaning the Lamborghini were so evidently intrigued by her identity. If she were Celia, she would resent it; was she any better than Simon, after all?

Halting at the edge of the cobbled stable yard, she stamped her feet in their dark blue trainers. She shouldn't have come. That was all there was to it. She could fool herself that she wasn't harming anyone, but she really shouldn't have come.

'What are you looking so fed-up about?' enquired Reed tolerantly, detaching himself from the groom, and strolling lazily towards her. 'I didn't think you'd be up yet. Didn't you sleep well?'

'I slept very well,' replied Antonia formally, her shoulder lifting to dislodge the hand he had laid upon it. And, because it was expected of her, she added: 'Did you?'

'No. As a matter-of-fact, I slept badly,' Reed responded softly. 'For which you can take the credit.' His lips twisted. 'Have you had breakfast?'

'Yes.' Antonia made a dismissive gesture. 'Mrs Macauley sent me breakfast in bed. Unfortunately, I was already up when it arrived.'

'I told her not . . .'

'Yes, so the maid said,' Antonia interrupted him tensely. 'But I'm not used to lying in bed until all hours. I'm a working woman.'

'So you keep reminding me,' remarked Reed drily. 'Now—would you like to look round? I don't know if you're interested in horses, but I keep a couple of hunters.'

'A *couple*!' Antonia glanced back over her shoulder. 'I saw at least twice that number in the paddock.'

'They're breeding mares,' responded Reed carelessly. 'Charlie Lomax, he's my trainer, he likes to keep a few mares in foal, just to keep his hand in. He used to run a stud farm, before he came to work for me. I'll show you the foals, if you like. They're very friendly.'

'No. That is——' Antonia looked down at her feet as she struggled to find the words. 'Reed, I'd better go back.'

His grey eyes narrowed. 'Back where? To the house?' He frowned. 'Is something wrong?'

'I mean—back to London,' she admitted unhappily, and he smothered a savage oath.

'For Christ's sake,' he swore, in a low voice, 'I thought we'd settled that!'

'Well, we haven't,' she mumbled, pushing her hair back out of her eyes. 'Reed, I feel such a fraud! I don't belong here.'

'Who says so?' he enquired, his features hardening. 'Did Rose say something? Did anyone else make any insinuations?'

'Well, no—at least, not exactly.'

'What's that supposed to mean?'

Antonia scuffed her toe against the cobbles. 'Mrs Macauley kept calling me *Miss* Sheldon, so I told her I was divorced.'

'And?' His eyes were intent.

'Oh——' Antonia sighed. 'Does it matter?'

'It does to me.' He paused. 'Are you telling me Rose made some comment about you being a divorcee?'

'Well, she said . . . she said I was young to be looking

for another husband,' admitted Antonia at last. 'I don't think she believed me when I said I wasn't.'

'Is that all?' Reed's expression softened again. 'Oh, take no notice of Rose. She's curious, that's all.'

'Wouldn't you be?' exclaimed Antonia, not responding to his mocking smile. 'Reed, can you imagine what these people must be thinking? I'm half-inclined to believe she sent my breakfast to bed to see if we were sharing the same room!'

'What? With me out with the horses soon after seven?' asked Reed teasingly, and her colour deepened. 'Antonia, if we were sleeping together, we'd still be in bed. Believe me, I would not be venting my frustration on a dumb animal!'

Antonia's breath caught in her throat. 'You shouldn't say things like that.'

'Why not? They're true.' His hands descended on her shoulders, and uncaring of the old man still pottering about in the yard behind him, he jerked her towards him. 'Just because I've agreed to your terms, doesn't mean I have to approve of them,' he told her huskily, his mouth warmly insistent on hers. 'Now, come on: stop all this nonsense about rushing back to London, and let me show you the grounds. *I* want you here. That's what's important.' He let her go with some reluctance, and captured her hand in his. 'I'll even let you pick some crocuses in the wood, if you promise to be good.'

Antonia shook her head, but she was weakening, and he knew it. 'Reed—what about Celia? What will she say when——?'

'Let me worry about Celia,' he informed her flatly. Then, observing her uncertainty, he shook his head. 'Stop anticipating something that may never happen.' He smiled. 'Now—do you want to take the dogs? I warn you, they're very affectionate—just like their master.'

It was a wonderful morning. Accompanied by two excitable retrievers, who spent most of their time gambolling in the grass, Antonia walked for miles.

Wearing a pair of rubber boots Reed found for her in the stables, she kept pace with him across the paddock—where the foals dogged their progress—and into the pasture, with its doe-eyed collection of cattle. It didn't matter where she put her feet in the rubber boots, which was just as well in the circumstances, and Reed doubled up when she fastidiously cleaned her boots after every unwary step.

'So long as you don't make a mistake and sit down in it,' he teased her, his hand running possessively over her rear, and she met his gaze in sudden confusion, before brushing his hand away.

They talked a lot; impersonal things mostly, although Reed did tell her a little about the company, and the role he played in it. He was offhand about his own qualifications, playing down the first he had got at Oxford, the agile brain, which had absorbed so much information about the company's operations while he was still in his teens. Yet, Antonia sensed the pride he had in his family's traditions, his admiration for the prestige which his father and his grandfather had maintained, their success in a world where it wasn't always easy just to survive.

She was fascinated by his grasp of investment and finance, but although she listened avidly when he spoke of the company's accomplishments overseas, she was once again reminded of their very different backgrounds. Reed had grown up, secure in the knowledge that one day Gallaghers would be in his control; a multi-million dollar company, with all its incumbent responsibilities. She, on the other hand, was the daughter of a mining overseer from Tyneside, who had been killed in an accident at the pit, when Susie was only a baby.

They had lunch in the breakfast room, an attractive room, overlooking the terrace. After their walk, Antonia's cheeks were flushed with becoming colour, and Reed seldom took his eyes from her as she ate her meal with real enjoyment.

'It's just as well I'm only staying until tomorrow,' she

exclaimed, swallowing a mouthful of the succulent steak
and kidney pie that Reed had explained his cook, Mrs
Braid, had prepared for them. She smiled delightfully.
'I'd get awfully fat! Just like Tuppence.'

'Who is Tuppence?' enquired Reed lazily, neglecting
his own meal and resting his elbows on the table.

'He's a cat,' admitted Antonia ruefully. 'My mother's
cat, actually. Susie torments him unmercifully.'

Reed cupped his chin on one hand. 'I'd like to meet
Susie,' he said, disconcerting her still further. 'Can I?'

Antonia put down her knife and fork. 'How can
you?' she countered, looking down at her plate. 'I've
told you. She lives with my mother.'

'In Newcastle. I know.' Reed stretched across the
table to take one of her hands in his. 'But you go home
sometimes, don't you? At weekends,' he prompted
drily.

Antonia tried to draw her fingers away, but he
wouldn't let her, and looking up at him, she said: 'Why
do you want to meet her?'

'Because she's yours,' replied Reed evenly. 'Because
I'd like to know her, when you talk about her. Because
she's part of your life.'

Antonia sighed. 'Oh, Reed——'

'Oh, Reed—nothing,' he told her softly. 'How about
next weekend? I could drive you up there on Friday
night—or Saturday morning, if you'd prefer it. Don't
worry,' he added, as her eyes grew anxious, 'I'm not
inviting myself to your mother's house. I can stay at an
hotel.' He grinned. 'I presume there are hotels in
Newcastle, aren't there?'

'Of course, there are.' Antonia was indignant, until
she saw his teasing smile. 'But—well, I don't know if
my mother would like that. Your staying in an hotel, I
mean. She'd think—well, you can guess what she'd
think, I'm sure.'

'That her home wasn't good enough?' enquired Reed,
with a grimace. 'Sweetheart, if you invited me to stay
with you, I'd be only too happy to accept.'

'Don't be silly!' Antonia was confused, as much by

his casual use of the endearment as by his outrageous suggestion. What he was proposing was wild; *reckless*; almost as reckless as her being here at Stonor's End.

'Wouldn't you like to go home next weekend?' he asked, playing with her fingers, and she drew an uneven breath.

'What would I tell my mother?'

'Do you have to tell her anything?'

Antonia shook her head. 'How do I introduce you?'

Reed shrugged. 'As a—friend. What's so unusual about that?'

Antonia bent her head. 'A *rich* friend!'

'A *friend*,' he amended harshly. 'Antonia, stop putting the obstacle of my being a Gallagher between us!' He lifted her hand to his lips and she felt his tongue against her palm. 'Let me come with you,' he said huskily. 'Let me meet Susie. I promise I won't do anything to embarrass you.'

Mrs Macauley's arrival with their dessert saved Antonia from making a response. But Reed's eyes were frankly persuasive as they dwelt upon her face, and Antonia snatched her hand away in embarrassment before meeting the housekeeper's knowing gaze.

'Mrs Sheldon approves of your choice of menu, Rose,' Reed remarked incorrigibly, as the housekeeper cleared their plates. 'That's right, isn't it, Antonia? You did enjoy Mrs Braid's pride and joy!'

'I—the pie was lovely,' Antonia conceded uncomfortably. 'I don't think I could eat another thing.'

'I'm sure you'll find room for a few fresh raspberries,' responded Mrs Macauley drily, her sharp eyes missing nothing in their exchange. She set a dish of raspberries and a jug of cream on the table. 'Will you have coffee here, or in the drawing room?'

'We'll have it in the sitting room,' replied Reed, pushing the fruit towards Antonia. 'Help yourself,' he added. 'I like watching you.'

Antonia flushed then; she couldn't help it; and Mrs Macauley regarded her half-sympathetically. 'Take no notice of him, Mrs Sheldon,' she remarked, with the

familiarity of long service. 'If you want some—have
some. He hasn't eaten a decent meal since he came
here.'

She departed on this note, and Antonia looked
doubtfully across the table. 'Is that true?'

Reed grimaced. 'We've only been here since last
night!'

'Didn't you have any breakfast either?'

'I'm not hungry,' he responded quietly. 'At least—not
for food,' he added disturbingly. Then, as if realising he
was getting too serious, he forced a smile. 'Have some
raspberries. Just to please me.'

They spent the afternoon in the sitting room,
listening to music and watching the changing weather
outside. Contrary to Mr Fenwick's expectations, it had
begun to rain while they were having lunch, and now
the drops pattering at the windowpanes enclosed them
in a world cut off from outside influences.

Antonia had found that Reed's taste in music was
similar to her own, a mixture of contemporary bands
and traditional jazz. They both liked China Crisis and
Duran Duran, but they also enjoyed Count Basie and
Duke Ellington, and Antonia discovered other favour-
ites like Elton John and Lionel Richie among the
enormous collection of albums stacked beneath the hi-fi
system.

Curled up on the floor in her jeans and sweater and
without any make-up, she was totally unaware of how
young she appeared. It was only when she looked up
and found Reed's gaze upon her that she realised she
had forgotten to be on her guard with him, and she
brushed her hair out of her eyes in a purely defensive
gesture.

'Relax,' he said, seeing the sudden consternation that
crossed her face at this awareness. 'You're enjoying
yourself, aren't you?'

'You know I am,' she admitted, unknowingly
sensuous as she stretched her arms above her head, and
Reed shifted on the soft rug.

'I'm sleepy,' he said, lowering his length at right

angles to her and depositing his head in her lap. 'Do you mind?' he murmured, but it was a rhetorical question. His eyes were already closed, and she hadn't the will to refuse him.

He did sleep for a while, she thought, his head growing heavier on her legs. With his eyes closed, his face had a disturbing vulnerability, and she couldn't resist the urge to smooth the silky dark hair back from his forehead. He didn't move, the splayed fan of his lashes a dusky arc above his cheekbones. It made her reckless; it made her want to touch him in other places; and her fingers slid daringly over his ear to the heavy roll collar of his sweater.

He stirred then, his eyes opening to look up into hers. Then, lifting his arms, he took her hand and pushed it inside the neck of his sweater, letting her fingers feel his warmth and the lean hard strength beneath his skin. It was an unnerving experience, an unfamiliar intimacy that brought with it a quickening of her pulses and a wash of hot colour to her cheeks. His skin felt so supple, so masculine, the scent of his body unmistakably aroused. For a moment, she held his gaze, feeling her own response like a physical ache in the pit of her stomach. Then, abruptly, she pulled her hand away and scrambled to her feet.

His head thudded on to the rug at her hasty withdrawal, but she didn't apologise. Instead, she went to sit on the seat by the window, and by the time she had controlled herself sufficiently to glance behind her, Reed had resumed his position with his back against the patterned sofa.

The maid who had brought Antonia's breakfast that morning, appeared with afternoon tea at about five o'clock. Antonia, who had spent the last half-hour gazing out at the windswept paddock, abandoned her seat by the window to return to an armchair at the girl's appearance, and Reed smiled at the maid as she set the tray beside her.

'Hello, Ruth,' he said, his tone revealing nothing but a friendly interest. 'How is your mother? Is she any better?'

'Oh, yes, Mr Reed.' Ruth straightened from her task and gazed at him with evident pleasure. 'That holiday really bucked her up. Doctor Michaels says there's no reason why she shouldn't make a full recovery.'

'That's good.' Reed nodded, and Antonia averted her eyes from his attractive face. 'Tell her I was asking after her, will you? Oh, and get George to give you some of those hyacinths out of the greenhouse.'

'Thank you.' Ruth coloured with pride. 'I'll do that.'

'Good.'

Reed regarded her good-humouredly, and with a little nod at Antonia, the girl made a hasty retreat.

Alone again, Antonia forced herself to look at him. 'You like your tea without milk, don't you?' she asked, noticing the slices of lemon residing on a dish.

'Please,' he conceded, putting aside the record sleeve he had been reading. 'You remembered? That's something, I suppose.'

'Reed, please——'

'I know, I know,' he said shortly, evidently finding it less easy to be civil with her. His grey eyes narrowed sardonically. 'I'm sorry. It won't happen again.'

And it didn't. For the remainder of the time they were at Stonor, Reed was on his best behaviour, sustaining a friendly—if impersonal—relationship, that Antonia told herself she wanted, but which was very hard to take after their earlier closeness.

But what did she want, after all, if not to maintain a certain distance between them? she asked herself impatiently, when on Saturday evening Reed abandoned her after dinner, on the pretext of checking on one of his mares that was in foal. How could she expect to go with him, out into the darkness of the stableyard and subsequently, into the warm shadowy intimacy of the stables themselves? she argued fiercely. There would be too many awkward moments, too many opportunities to surrender to the guilty feelings that lay so shallowly beneath the veneer of her detachment. But when, at ten

o'clock. he had not come back and she retired to bed,
there was a hollow feeling in her stomach that would
not go away.

CHAPTER EIGHT

REED drove her back to London on Sunday evening.

It was still light when they left Stonor's End, and Antonia looked back over her shoulder with a helpless sense of despair. It hardly seemed possible it was only two days since he had brought her here. Already she felt an affinity with the house that was going to be difficult to displace.

The day itself had been something of an anti-climax, in that Reed had not appeared before lunchtime. Mrs Macauley, taking pity on her, as she mooched about the downstairs rooms that morning, had declared Reed had been up half the night with the vet, attending to the mare, whose foal had been born feet first. But Antonia had guessed that the housekeeper, too, had her doubts, and one sort of speculation was just as bad as another.

In the afternoon, Reed had spent more precious time talking with George Hetherington, the gardener. Antonia had seen them from her bedroom window, when she had gone upstairs to pack, and she had stood for several minutes watching them, feeling as if her heart was being torn out of her. She didn't want to go; it was as simple as that. She didn't want to return to London, knowing that when she left him, she might never see him again.

The maid, Ruth, had been changing Antonia's bed when she first entered the bedroom, and she had offered to pack for her. 'It's all right; I can manage,' Antonia told her gratefully. 'You go on with what you're doing. I shan't get in your way.'

Ruth smiled her thanks. 'You're leaving today, are you, miss?' she asked, rapidly changing pillow slips. 'Do you like living in London?'

'Not a lot.' Antonia was honest. 'But some of us don't have a choice.'

'No.' Ruth set the pillows squarely against the padded headboard. 'I sometimes think I'd like to live in London, but what with Mum and all, I don't think that's likely.'

'Your mother's been ill?' asked Antonia sympathetically. 'I'm sorry. Was it something serious?'

'Cancer,' said Ruth grimacing. 'She had to have an operation. Then lots of therapy—you know, to make sure all the cells were dead. She was pretty sick over Christmas. My dad didn't think she'd make it.'

'But she did.' Antonia regarded the girl gently.

'Oh, yes.' Ruth's smile reappeared. 'Thanks to Mr Reed. He arranged everything—all the treatment, the nursing home, everything! Then, when she was fit enough, he sent her and my dad out to Barbados for a holiday. Just so's she'd get away from the cold weather.'

Antonia took a deep breath. 'That was kind of him.'

'Well, he is, isn't he?' said Ruth artlessly. 'But I expect you know that. Being a friend of his, and all.'

Antonia had made some comment, she didn't remember what, and soon afterwards, Ruth had finished her task and left her. But her words stuck in Antonia's mind, not least because of their honesty. Reed *was* kind, and generous, and she had never known a man like him before.

The journey back to London was accomplished without any delays, and it was barely a quarter to nine when the Lamborghini drew to a halt outside the gates of Eaton Lodge. Reed had not suggested stopping for dinner on their way, indeed, he had scarcely spoken at all during the journey, and Antonia assumed he would be glad to see the back of her.

However, he surprised her by insisting on carrying her suitcase to her door, dismissing her fears about Mrs Francis with the careless information that she generally went to her daughter's on Sundays.

Struggling to get her key into the lock, Antonia wondered why he simply hadn't dumped her and her suitcase at the gate. He was obviously keen to leave her,

so she didn't offer him a drink. With the door open
behind her, she opened her mouth to express her thanks
for his hospitality, when he suddenly said flatly: 'I
suppose you're not going to invite me to Newcastle next
weekend, are you?'

'I——' Antonia could hardly speak. 'I—do you—still
want to come?'

'I still want—everything,' he told her harshly, and as
the foolish tears welled into her eyes, he backed her into
the flat and slammed the door behind them.

His arms were around her before the latch had
clicked into place, and his mouth found hers with
hungry urgency. Almost without her volition, it seemed,
her arms were around his neck, her fingers sliding into
the hair at his nape, her lips parting under his tongue.
She wanted him; she admitted it to herself; and as he
went on kissing her, all her previous objections melted,
like her bones.

'Oh, God,' he muttered at last, and she realised, with
a pang, that he was trembling, too. 'What are you
trying to do to me?'

'I—I thought you wanted to go. I thought you were
sick of me,' she stammered unsteadily, her lips against
his neck, and he groaned.

'You said—hands off, remember?' he reminded her
roughly, his face grim as he looked down at her. 'If
you'd changed your mind, you should have let me know
sooner.'

Antonia gasped. 'That's a rotten way to put it!'

'What do you expect?' he demanded violently. 'I'm
not used to spending two whole days in a permanent
state of frustration!'

'Oh, no, of course not.' Antonia gazed up at him
bitterly, anger taking the place of submission. 'I forgot.
You're used to an entirely different reaction!'

'Yes, I am,' he told her brutally, and pulling her
unresisting arms from around his neck, he stepped back
from her. 'I'd better go. I've got some work to do
before I go to bed.'

Antonia turned away, unwilling for him to see the

anguish his words had evoked, and she heard the distinctive click as the door closed behind him. '*Damn, oh, damn,*' she breathed, feeling a wave of misery sweeping over her, and after assuring herself that she really was alone, she ran into her bedroom and flung herself on the bed. The things she ought to be doing, like unpacking her clothes, or catching up with the housework she had not done since before she went to Newcastle, were forgotten. Instead, she gave in to the aching need to express the pain inside her.

The depression of the mattress was the first indication she had that she was no longer alone, and a blind panic gripped her as hands touched her body. Catching back a cry, she jerked away, rolling over on to her back in an effort to identify her intruder.

But the cry died in her throat when she saw the man sitting on the bed beside her. 'Y-you!' she got out chokily. 'What—what are you doing here?' She scrubbed her knuckles across eyes which she was sure were red and puffy. 'How did you get in?'

Her key dangled confusingly from his hand, and he dropped the offending article on to the bureau beside her bed. 'You left it in the lock outside,' Reed told her wryly, evading her efforts to keep his hands at bay, and smoothing the damp tendrils of hair out of her eyes. 'It was just as well you did. I'm not much good at breaking down doors.'

Antonia moved her head from side to side. 'You— you left——'

'I got as far as the car,' he contradicted her huskily, his thumbs disposing of two errant streaks of dampness on her cheeks. 'Stop fighting me, will you? I may have saved you from an unwelcome intruder.'

'Who—who says you're welcome?' Antonia demanded, turning her head away, and with a muffled oath, he shrugged off his jacket and stretched his length beside her on the bed.

'I do,' he affirmed, capturing her face with one hand and bringing her mouth to his. 'What do you want me to say?' he added, covering her face with hot urgent kisses. 'That I'm sorry? You know I am. That I've kept out of your way since Saturday because I couldn't bear to be near you and not touch you? You know it's the truth!'

Antonia shook her head. 'I know you shouldn't be here——'

He paused then, drawing back to look at her, the lines of strain sharply etched beside his mouth. 'Do you want me to go?' he asked tensely, pushing his fingers into her hair, his hands moving sensuously against her scalp, and she knew she couldn't send him away again.

'I—*no*,' she admitted honestly, lifting her hand to his lean face and allowing him to turn her palm against his lips. 'Oh, no,' she said again, slipping her arms around his neck, and with a shuddering sigh, he found her mouth once more . . .

Afterwards, it was difficult to remember anything but the intense pleasure he had given her. She knew he had undressed her. She could recall the possessive intimacy of his hands as they had caressed her limbs through the frustrating barrier of her clothes, her breasts swelling and hardening beneath the insinuating brush of his exploring thumbs. She had wanted to tear her clothes from her then, and his from him, but in the event, Reed had disposed of that obstacle with infinite patience.

He had removed his own clothes with rather less deliberation, Antonia's instinctive lips and fingers driving him to abandon his control. In only a few seconds he was beside her again, his lean supple limbs entwining with hers as his mouth sought the provocative arousal of a dusky pink nipple.

His body was every bit as brown and muscled as she had anticipated, and she revelled in the delights of being able to do with him as she willed. The hungry urgency of their passion was tempered by the pleasure they took in one another, and Reed's tongue ravished her mouth in imitation of the possession he was to exact later.

'You're beautiful,' he told her huskily, imprisoning

her arms above her head, and straddling her body so that he could look down at her.

'So are you,' she breathed, her hands straying tantalisingly down over his flat stomach, and with a groan he subsided upon her.

'I want you,' he said unsteadily, his breath moistening her ear, and she quivered.

'I want you,' she confessed, her arms closing convulsively about him, and his mouth crushed hers with hungry passion.

It was strange, she thought now, in the aftermath, how instinctively he had known how to please her. By the time the pulsating strength of his body had penetrated hers, she was aching for his possession, and all the occasions Simon had clumsily taken his pleasure were erased by the simple act of Reed's possession. There was no pain with Reed, no hasty satiation of his senses, no selfish betrayal of her needs as a woman. Instead, he had *made love* to her, something she now realised Simon had never done, and in so doing he had taken them both to the outer limits of human experience.

She knew he had felt the uncontrollable release of feeling, too. The shuddering spasms that racked his body when he attained that final peak with her were proof enough, without the sensual warmth of him inside her. For the first time in her life, she acknowledged the fact that she was not cold or frigid as Simon had accused her of being. She was, instead, a sensitive, passionate woman, who had only just recognised her own sensuality.

It was dark in the room now, and she shivered as the coolness of the air around them chilled her flesh. Wriggling out from beneath the weight of Reed's supine body, she grasped a handful of the quilt and pulled it around her, wondering with an unwilling sense of apprehension exactly what time it was.

'Don't go,' objected Reed sleepily, capturing her hand and drawing it to his lips, but the air was cooling more than just Antonia's skin.

'It's late. *You* have to go,' she told him unevenly, and detaching herself from him. she abruptly switched on the bedside lamp.

If she expected the sudden illumination to embarrass him, she was wrong. Making no effort to cover himself, he rolled lazily on to his back, and lay regarding her unnervingly through the fringe of his lashes.

'Do you want me to?' he enquired at last, propping himself up on one elbow, and Antonia swallowed convulsively.

'It—it's not what I want, is it?' she got out jerkily, hating the need to remind him of that fact, and hating the connotations her words had evoked. 'Your—your car's outside. Anyone can see it.'

'So?' His eyes dwelt sensually on her mouth. 'I told you. I have a key for Cee's flat.'

Antonia shook her head. 'But—you said she's coming back tonight.'

'Let me worry about that,' he advised her huskily, stroking long fingers down the length of her calf, but Antonia stumbled off the bed, dragging the quilt with her.

'You—you're completely unscrupulous, aren't you?' she choked, rounding on him. 'What possible excuse can you produce for your car standing out there all evening? Don't you care what Celia will think of you? Don't you care what she'll think of me?'

'Not right now,' he informed her steadily, and as she struggled to tear her eyes away from his powerful body, he came up off the bed and tugged the protective quilt from her. 'Oh, love,' he breathed, his hands on her hips making her irresistibly aware that he was anything but satisfied at this moment. 'Let me stay. Let me sleep with you. I don't want to go home. I want to make love to you—all night, if that were possible. And you're the *only* woman I've ever said that to.'

Naturally, Antonia overslept. By the time her exhausted eyes opened to take a dazed assessment of the time, it was already after nine o'clock, and the sun was streaming busily through the cracks in the curtains.

Gasping, she struggled up on her pillows, but the imprisoning weight of Reed's arm and the leg that lay confidingly between hers made it an effort.

'Relax,' he grumbled protestingly, opening his eyes to find her face already flushed with her exertions. 'It's early yet.'

'It's a quarter-past-nine,' she contradicted him huskily, her breathing constricting as he bestowed a lingering kiss at the corner of her mouth. 'Reed—I was due at work at nine o'clock. I've got to go!'

He sighed. 'Take the day off.'

'No.' It was a temptation, but she resisted it. 'I—Mr Fenwick was kind enough to give me the time off last week when Susie was ill. I can't let him down again.'

Reed grimaced. 'Okay, okay.' He responded to her panic-stricken efforts to be free by releasing her. 'But——' his hand brushed gently across her cheek, 'I hope he's not as perceptive as I am.'

Antonia paused in the process of sliding out from under the quilt. 'What do you mean?' she asked, and Reed's lips parted in a teasing grin.

'The way you look,' he informed her lazily, and she frowned.

'The way I look?' she echoed. 'Do I look that bad?'

Reed laughed. 'You don't look—bad—at all. At least, not in the sense you mean.'

'Reed!'

'All right.' He sobered. 'You look—ravishing; or should I say ravished?' His lips tilted. 'My darling, you look as if you've spent the night doing what we have been doing. And it suits you.'

Antonia's cheeks were scarlet when she permitted herself a brief glance at her reflection in the dressing table mirror. All she could see were the dark rings around her eyes, evidence of the disturbed night she had spent, and she saw nothing appealing in the vulnerable curve of her mouth.

'I don't want to leave you,' murmured Reed softly, coming up behind her and drawing her resisting body back against his. His hands slid round her body to

cover her breasts, and their peaks hardened automatically. 'I can't let you alone,' he added thickly, and
Antonia's heart pounded heavily in her chest. 'Must
you go to work? I'd like to stay here all day.'

'I—must,' she averred unsteadily, forcing herself to
move out of his arms, and scurrying into the bathroom
before he came after her. 'P-put the kettle on, will you?
If you know how.'

By the time she had had a swift shower, Reed had left
the bedroom, and when she emerged with the towel
wrapped around her, she was able to dress without
interruption. The navy blue suit and cream blouse were
blessedly normal, and sobering, and when she left the
bedroom in search of her houseguest, she felt more
prepared to face the world.

She found Reed in the kitchen. He had put on her
pink towelling bathrobe, and although it was short in
the arms, its generous folds meant he was decently
covered. Its hem also exposed the hair-covered length of
his legs, but apart from the incongruity of the colour, it
did not look too outrageous.

'Tea or coffee?' he enquired, hearing the tap of her
heels and glancing up from the filter he was filling. His
eyes softened as they surveyed her neat appearance and
he gave a rueful smile. 'All present and correct, I see.'

Antonia sighed. 'Reed—you ought to be going.'

'I've made some toast, too,' he remarked, ignoring
her observation. 'Just to prove I'm capable. You can
eat some while I go and put on my clothes.' He ran an
exploring hand over the roughness of his beard. 'I don't
suppose you have a razor, do you?'

'No. And I don't want any toast either,' retorted
Antonia stiffly, as the reality of what she had allowed to
happen swept debilitatingly over her. In the morning
light, she could no longer hide from the scornful
condemnation of her conscience, and she despised
herself utterly for giving in to his persuasion.

'Okay.' Reed was regarding her thoughtfully now, as
if assessing her mood, and with a shrug he sauntered
towards her. 'I'll get dressed anyway,' he remarked, as

she stepped out of his way. 'Then I'll run you to the institute.'

'No.' Antonia swallowed. 'No, there's no need. I can get a bus.'

'Why should you get a bus, when I can take you?' enquired Reed tautly, his voice taking on a sharper edge, and she held up her head.

'Because I have no intention of walking out of here with you,' she responded, her nails digging into her palms. 'You may have no morals. I do. You can leave when you like. I'm going now.'

'Antonia!'

His mouth compressed angrily, but snatching up her handbag, she made it to the door. 'Please be gone when I get home,' she told him huskily, grasping the handle, and she let herself out without a backward glance.

The internal phone rang as Reed was putting the papers he would need in his briefcase. For a moment, his nerves tensed, as the possibility that it might be Antonia occurred to him. But then, remembering the way she had departed that morning, he dismissed the idea. If he had believed she would listen to reason, he would have met her from work that afternoon. As it was, he had this trip to New York to contend with, just when he was needing time to think, and the knowledge that Antonia would have to wait until he got back was something he was finding hard to deal with.

Picking up the receiver, he said: 'Yes?' without much enthusiasm, and then sighed when his fiancée's voice came on the line.

'Darling: I'm downstairs,' Celia exclaimed breathily. 'I know it's late, but I had to come and apologise. Press the button, won't you, darling. I'm waiting to come up.'

Reed made some positive response, and then pressed the switch which would allow the lift to come up to the twenty-second floor. While it made its swift ascent, he closed his briefcase and left his study, opening the door to his apartment as the lift reached its destination.

'Darling!' Celia emerged in a cloud of French

perfume, the hem of her mink coat brushing his legs as she reached up to bestow a warm kiss on his mouth. 'Oh, darling, I'm so sorry I wasn't home last evening as I promised. But I've had the most fantastic time in Paris!'

Reed forced a faint smile to his lips as she swept by him into the apartment, not pausing until she reached the centre of his living room. Then, slipping her arms out of her coat, she dropped it carelessly on to the sofa, and wrapped her arms around herself as Reed followed her into the room.

'I know you must be mad at me,' she exclaimed, before he could say anything. 'When I got home an hour ago, Mrs Francis couldn't *wait* to tell me you'd spent the night at the apartment, waiting for me. But— well, it was just impossible for me to get away yesterday. There was this reception yesterday evening, and Ra—I mean, the *buyers*—all stayed on for it.'

Reed expelled his breath levelly, and thrust his hands into the hip pockets of his trousers, wondering why he hadn't caught the night flight to New York after all. 'You enjoyed yourself, I gather.'

'Oh, *tremendously*!' Celia declared fervently. 'It was great fun! I don't know why I've never gone before.'

Reed nodded. 'Well—good.'

Celia sighed. 'And what about you?' she asked, contritely, slipping her hand through his arm and pressing herself against him. 'I suppose you've had a *rotten* weekend! Did you go to Stonor? But, of course you must have done.'

'Yes.' Reed detached himself without haste, and walked casually over to the drinks tray. 'Do you want a Martini?'

'Pernod, darling, please,' said Celia, subsiding on to a sofa. 'That's what I've been drinking all weekend. Lots and lots of Pernod!'

Reed poured himself a scotch, and than handed Celia her drink. '*A votre santé!*' she toasted him smilingly, lifting her glass, and Reed made some suitable comment before raising his glass to his lips.

Seating himself on the sofa opposite, he made a concerted effort to think of something relevant to say. But the headache he had had earlier in the day had returned to throb at his temples, and it was incredibly difficult to be civil to Celia when his mind was occupied elsewhere.

'So,' she said encouragingly at last, 'what sort of a weekend did you have?'

'Oh—fine.' Reed's cheeks hollowed. 'A rural one.'

'And you spent last night at the apartment,' Celia remarked, returning to her original theme. 'I'd have phoned if I'd known where you were. But I rang Stonor and I rang here, and as you weren't at either . . .' She shrugged. 'I forgot Liz was spending the weekend at her mother's.'

'It doesn't matter.' Reed wondered how he would have explained the fact of his not answering the phone if Celia had rung her apartment. *God*, he thought angrily, he should be feeling one hell of a heel, instead of tearing himself to pieces over a woman who didn't seem to care if she never saw him again!

'Is something wrong?' Not noticeably perceptive, Celia had nevertheless observed the signs of strain in Reed's face, and leaving her seat, she joined him on the sofa where he was sitting. Putting an arm around his shoulders, she rested her cheek against his sleeve, and murmured softly: 'Honestly, I'm sorry about last night. But—well, you might as well know, there was this gorgeous Frenchman, who seemed to find me quite irresistible! I was flattered. I admit it. And that's really why I stayed on. Oh—it was nothing serious. Just a— flirtation. His name was Raoul, and I let him take me to dinner. But that's all.'

Reed turned his head to look at her. 'Were you attracted to him?' he enquired tensely, and Celia shrugged.

'I suppose so.'

'How attracted?'

'Darling, not as attracted as I am to you,' she assured him firmly. 'It was just a—a weekend's flirtation. I told you. You don't have to worry. I wasn't unfaithful, or anything like that.'

Stifling an oath, Reed got to his feet, and swallowing the remainder of his drink, he went to pour himself another. The appalling truth was, he had wanted Celia to tell him she had been unfaithful. Maybe then, he could have excused his own selfish behaviour. With the knowledge that what he was doing was not so outrageous, he might have come to terms with it. As it was, his attraction to Antonia continued to torment him, like an uncontrollable fever in his blood.

'Reed—*darling*——' Celia was behind him suddenly, sliding her arms around his waist, pressing her face into the hollow of his back. 'You're not jealous, are you? You know you have no need to be.'

'I am not jealous!' Reed said the words between his teeth, wishing with an urgency that bordered on desperation that he were. 'Celia, please,' he exclaimed, extricating himself from her hands. 'Look—I've got to tell you, I'm leaving for New York in the morning. I'm sorry, but it's unavoidable. I don't know when I'll be back.'

'New York!' Celia gazed at him petulantly. 'You're not serious! You know it's Daddy's birthday on Wednesday. What about the dinner party? You promised you'd come!'

'I'm sorry.' This exchange was not going at all well. and Reed knew he was to blame. 'Something's come up, quite unexpectedly. And I've got to go myself. I promised my father I would.'

'And of course a promise to your father is more important than a promise to mine,' declared Celia sulkily.

'Cee, it's only your father's birthday. This is important!'

'My father's birthday is important,' retorted Celia sniffing. 'For heaven's sake, why can't you send someone else? Mark Hammond, perhaps. Or Lucas Turner. You always said you could delegate.'

'Not in this instance,' replied Reed flatly. 'I've got to

attend a meeting of financiers. It's not something I can delegate.' He paused, and then said quietly: 'You can come with me, if you like.'

'No, thank you.' Celia shook her head. 'I don't like New York at the best of times, and *I* have no intention of disappointing Daddy.'

'Of course.' Reed inclined his head, despising the relief that had enveloped him at her words. If he had thought she might have accepted, he would not have made the offer, he realised disgustedly. Dear God, what had Antonia done to him? Why couldn't he put her out of his head?

'Oh, well——' Celia, as if sensing his uncertain mood, gave a characteristic sigh. 'There's no point in getting angry, I suppose. You have your work, and I have mine.' She took a breath, and then continued carefully: 'So—you won't object if I don't stay the night, will you? I am—*rather* tired. It's been a hectic weekend.'

Reed, who had been trying to find a reason to make the same excuse, breathed a little more freely. 'I think that's a good idea,' he averred swiftly. 'I've got to leave for the airport early in the morning, and you wouldn't want to eat breakfast alone, would you?'

Celia hesitated, his abrupt acceptance of what had been a tentative suggestion evidently not meeting with her approval. 'I—can stay, if you want me to,' she ventured, but Reed was already lifting her coat from its resting place.

'Not tonight, Cee,' he said evenly, as she rose reluctantly to her feet. 'I'll ring you from New York tomorrow. By the time I get back, maybe we'll both have more time for one another.'

CHAPTER NINE

By Friday, Antonia's nerves were in a terrible state.

It had been a nervewracking week, not helped by the knowledge that once again she had allowed a man to make a fool of her. She must have been crazy to allow Reed to spend the night at the flat, she told herself fiercely. Crazier still, to go to bed with him without taking any precautions to protect herself. What if she became pregnant again? she thought desperately. What if history was about to repeat itself? There was no possible chance that Reed would feel responsible for her. He had got what he wanted, and she doubted she would ever see him again.

It was all so stupid, so *ludicrous*! She had suspected what manner of man he was when he started pursuing her, but instead of sticking to her guns and keeping him at arm's length, she had allowed him to get under her skin. He had used every trick in the book to persuade her—his beautiful apartment, the house at Stonor's End; he had even pretended he cared about her daughter, when all he had really wanted to do was sleep with her. And how he had; and it was over; and she didn't know how she was going to cope with it.

She had thought, at first, that that was what she wanted. When Tuesday and Wednesday went by and he didn't ring, she had managed to convince herself that she was glad it was over. Their relationship had never had any future, she had known that, and in spite of the bitterness his betrayal aroused, she had half-believed she was unscathed by the experience.

But when Thursday came, and then Friday, and she was forced to face the fact that their brief affair really was over, the whole weight of what it meant to her enveloped her like a shroud. It was no use pretending to herself any longer. She was not—she had never been—

the kind of girl who slept around. With Simon, it could
be excused as a youthful indiscretion, an indiscretion
she had paid for with the destruction of her career.
With Reed, there were no excuses of that kind. She was
a woman now, not a child, and she could not console
herself with childish vindications. She knew why she
had let Reed stay at the flat; she knew why she had
made love with him. It was very simple: she had fallen
in love with him. In spite of herself, she had fallen
under his spell, and no amount of self-condemnation
would make it otherwise.

Of course, it was crazy. Even without his so-suitable
fiancée, he was not the kind of man to get seriously
involved with someone like her. The gulf between them
was too wide, both financially and socially. She had
been a diversion, that's all. Something he had wanted,
and got. And the guilt she had felt about Celia, and
which was now absolved, was no compensation for the
rawness his abandonment had created.

'You don't seem well,' said Mr Fenwick, on Friday
afternoon, coming into Antonia's office as she was
clearing her desk. 'Are you going north this weekend? If
not, my recommendation is that you take it easy over
the next couple of days.'

Antonia's smile was thin. 'I'm—not—going north
this weekend,' she assured him quietly. 'And I shall
probably take your advice. I am feeling a bit—under
the weather.'

'I knew it.' Mr Fenwick seemed pleased with his
diagnosis. 'I said to Heather on Wednesday that you
seemed out of sorts.'

'I'm sure it's nothing,' said Antonia, sliding her
blotter into a drawer. 'I—if that's all for today, I'll go
now. I've got some shopping to do on my way home.'

'Of course, of course.'

Mr Fenwick stepped back politely, and Antonia
slung her jacket about her shoulders. 'See you on
Monday,' she said, striving for a bright tone, and her
boss nodded understandingly as she disappeared out of
the door.

The idea of buying food was not appealing to her, but realising she had to eat if she wanted to survive this present disaster, she bought some cooked ham for her dinner. A loaf of bread and some cheese completed her purchases, and deciding to leave the bulk of her shopping until the following day, she made her way to the bus-stop. She could have walked, she supposed, feeling in her pocket for some change. The truth was, she didn't feel as if she had the energy, and she propped herself against the post, hoping she would not have to wait long.

The sleek bonnet of the Lamborghini pulling alongside her brought her up with a start, and her mouth went dry when Reed opened the window and said harshly: 'Get in!'

With a red double-decker bus looming in the distance, and Reed parked in the space where the bus would stop, Antonia did not stop to consider her actions. Pulling open the door, she scrambled into the low vehicle, and Reed drove swiftly away without saying another word.

She thought he would take her home, but he passed the turning for Clifton Gate and drove on through Maida Vale and Kilburn. He seemed to be following the signs for the North Circular Road, she thought blankly, and then abandoned that thought when he turned into the grounds of a small hotel.

Switching off the engine, he half-turned in his seat towards her, but Antonia purposely stared straight ahead. She had no idea why he had come to find her. She could not comprehend what his motives might be. And in spite of his compulsive attraction, she refused to give in to his sexual bribery.

'Are you hungry?' he inquired, evidently noticing the loaf of bread sticking out of her bag, and she shrugged.

'It—it's just some ham and cheese, for—for my dinner,' she replied unevenly.

'Are you mad at me?' he asked softly. 'You didn't seriously think we wouldn't see one another again, did you?'

Antonia shook her head. 'I don't have to think, do I?' she said, in a tense little voice. 'Only—only obey.'

'Oh. for Christ's sake!' With a smothered oath, he moved, his hand sliding possessively beneath her hair, forcing her to look at him. 'What do you take me for. you stupid little bitch?' he demanded savagely. 'I've been in New York. I just flew back this morning. I thought it would give us a breathing space, but damn it, I didn't intend it should fuel that goddamned pride of yours!'

Antonia stared at him. 'New York?' she echoed faintly, and he nodded.

'I had to attend a conference. My father arranged it all. I arrived home this morning; I took a shower, a couple of hours rest, and then I came to meet you. Unfortunately, you had left by the time I arrived.'

Antonia moistened her lips. 'I left early——'

'So your superior told me.'

'You—you spoke to Mr Fenwick?' Antonia was appalled.

'An old guy with a weight problem?' Reed's fingers gentled at her nape, and his eyes softened. 'Hell—have I missed you!'

Antonia drew back. 'Reed——'

'Shut up, will you?' he muttered, without aggression, and before she could protest, his mouth had covered hers.

The console was an irresistible barrier between them, and Reed swore again when she succeeded in using it to her advantage. 'Wh-what excuse did you give Celia for leaving your car outside Eaton Lodge all night?' she got out huskily, deliberately raising his fiancée's name between them, and Reed regarded her broodingly before flinging himself back in his seat.

'I didn't have to give her an excuse,' he retorted harshly. 'She didn't arrive back from Paris until Monday, and Mrs Francis assumed I had spent the night in the apartment upstairs.'

'I see.' Antonia swallowed. 'How convenient!'

'Yes. Wasn't it?' Reed's nostrils flared. 'I'm lucky that way.'

'So—where are you going now?' Antonia enquired carefully. 'To—to see Celia?'

Reed expelled his breath wearily. 'Is that likely?' he demanded. 'As a matter of fact, Cee doesn't even know I'm back in the country. So far as she's concerned, I'm still in the big apple! Does that satisfy you?'

Antonia bent her head. 'So where are you going?'

'I thought—I really thought—we might be driving north,' declared Reed quietly. 'But as you're buying ham and cheese for your evening meal, I guess you haven't any plans for that.'

Antonia gasped. 'You really expected to go to Newcastle?'

'To meet Susie? Yes, why not?'

'After—after what happened?'

'Particularly after what happened,' he retorted roughly. 'Oh, Toni——' it was the first time he had abbreviated her name, except when he was making love to her, and her senses tingled; '—I don't want to forget what happened!' He gazed at her intently, his eyes sensually brilliant. 'I want to do it again! Over and over. Until you can't think or feel or *taste* anyone else but me!'

'You're crazy——'

'About you? Yes, I am,' he conceded emotively. 'Let's go to Newcastle, Antonia. Let's spend the weekend together, at least. Hell, I'll even promise to be good, if you'll just stop fighting me!'

Antonia bent her head. 'We can't——'

'Why can't we?'

'I haven't packed, and we can't go to the flat——'

'Buy a toothbrush,' declared Reed reasonably. 'What else?'

'I haven't told my mother.'

'Phone her.'

'Wh-what can I say?'

'Tell her a friend has offered to drive you up for the weekend, and you don't want to refuse.'

Aware that she was allowing him to railroad her again, Antonia shook her head. 'I can't.'

'Why the hell not?'

Antonia gulped. 'Because you don't care, do you? You don't care about anyone but yourself. So long as you get your own way, you don't give a damn!'

Reed hunched his shoulders, and for several moments there was silence in the car. Then, flatly, he conceded her accusation: 'No,' he said, flexing his neck muscles with weary impatience. 'No, you're right. I'm completely amoral.' He reached for the ignition. 'I'll take you home. I can always tell Cee I gave you a lift from the bus-stop.'

Antonia, who had been expecting another argument, felt her stomach plunge as he spoke. His careless acknowledgment of her words left her with a distinctly hollow feeling inside her, and although she knew if she remained silent he would do as he had promised, her treacherous emotions refused to let it go.

'It's easy for you, isn't it?' she choked bitterly, as the engine sprang to life. 'Off with a mistress, and on with a fiancée! Either way, you can't lose!'

'Is that what you think?' His lips twisted as he looked at her.

'It's the truth! You—you satisfy your—your carnal desires with—with one or other of us, don't you?'

Reed swore then, an ugly word that Antonia could not mistake, and the engine died as he grasped her face between his hands. 'Do you really want to know the truth?' he snarled, and she trembled at the anger in his expression. 'The truth is—I haven't been able to *touch* Cee since that night I took you to the apartment! You say it's easy for me—well, believe me, it's not!' His incensed breath filled her mouth and she tried to look away from him, but he would not let her. 'Let me tell you,' he went on grimly, 'I didn't intend to get involved with you. God help me, I thought I felt sorry for you! I fooled myself into thinking we could be friends! *Friends!*' He groaned. 'Friends don't fill your mind to the exclusion of everything—and everyone—else! Friends don't keep you awake half the night, with the kind of ache I haven't had since I was a schoolboy!' His eyes darkened. 'It dawned on me by degrees, that what I really wanted to do was make love with you, and that's a complication I could have done without!'

Antonia shivered. 'I didn't ask you to——'

'Goddammit, I know that!' he grated heavily, his fingers sliding into her hair. 'But you have to know the way it is!' He expelled an unsteady breath. 'Now—do I take you back to the flat?'

Antonia moved her head helplessly from side to side. 'Oh, Reed! What can I say?'

'You can tell the truth,' he declared huskily, tipping her face up to his. 'You don't want to leave me, any more than I want to leave you. Am I right?'

Antonia closed her eyes against the possessive passion in his and then, slowly, nodded her head. 'I'll phone my mother,' she agreed unevenly, and the searching pressure of his mouth on her parted lips sealed her guilty submission.

Mrs Lord was very surprised to hear that her daughter was phoning from a motorway service area. 'But, who is this man you're bringing home for the weekend?' she protested blankly. 'You've never mentioned him before. Have you known him long? Does he work at the institute?'

'I suppose I've known him nearly a month,' replied Antonia uncomfortably. 'And no—he doesn't work at the institute.'

'Well, what does he do then? And where did you meet him?' Mrs Lord sounded a little impatient now. 'Antonia, you have to be a little more forthcoming. I mean, what do you know about him? Are you sure you want to bring him here? What about Susie?'

'He's quite respectable, Mum,' exclaimed Antonia, half-humorously. 'Honestly, you'll like him.'

'But what does he do?'

Antonia hesitated. 'He—he's a businessman. He owns a company.'

'Owns?' Mrs Lord sounded impressed. 'Well, I must say, he sounds an improvement on Simon Sheldon!'

'It's nothing like that, Mum.' Antonia's tone sharpened. 'We're just—friends. That's all.'

'So why are you bringing him here?' demanded Mrs Lord impatiently.

'To—to meet Susie,' replied Antonia swiftly. 'I must go, Mum. My coins are running out.'

'Wait a minute!' Her mother was not quite finished, and reluctantly, Antonia pushed another coin into the meter. 'Have you forgotten it's my bridge night? I mean, I put it off the night you came home, but you haven't given me any warning this time.'

'That's okay, Mum.' Antonia was quite relieved that Mrs Lord would not be there when they first arrived. 'Lucy's baby-sitting, isn't she? Just tell her we should arrive about ten o'clock.'

Reed was waiting for her in the restaurant, a lean attractive figure in his dark corded trousers and black leather jerkin. 'Did you get through?' he enquired, re-seating himself after she had taken her place opposite, and Antonia swallowed a mouthful of the wine he had ordered for her before nodding vigorously.

'It's her bridge night,' she said, glancing nervously about her. 'Aren't you afraid someone might recognise you? You're not exactly unremarkable!'

'Thank you.' Reed's tone was sardonic. 'But right now, I don't particularly care.' He covered her hand with his and slid his thumb into her palm. 'What are you going to eat?'

Antonia's pulses raced. 'Wh-what are you?' she asked a little breathily, and for a few moments they were absorbed with a consultation over the menu.

But when the waitress had taken their order, and they were alone again, Reed said quietly: 'Tell me about Sheldon: your ex-husband. I want to know about him.'

Antonia lifted her shoulders. 'There's nothing to tell.'

'Don't give me that.' Reed regarded her intently across the lamplit table. 'Why did you marry him? Did you love him? Where is he now? I want to know.'

Antonia bent her head. 'I married him because I was pregnant,' she admitted softly, her cheeks flaming as she felt his gaze upon her. 'I was nineteen. He was twenty-one.'

'Go on.'

She quivered, and drew her hands together in her lap. 'What more is there to say? I had been at university for a year, and I was still a virgin.' She grimaced. 'All my friends thought that I was an anathema. Then, in the summer holidays, Simon started taking me out. He was very popular, and I was very naive. Does that answer your question?'

Reed sighed. 'Did you love him?'

'I thought I did. But—well, after—after *it* happened, I didn't want to see him again.'

'Why not?'

'Oh, Reed!' She shook her head. 'Don't make me have to spell it out.'

'Okay.' Reed's tone was gentle. 'So when you discovered you were going to have a baby, you panicked.'

'My mother did,' conceded Antonia ruefully. 'And— and my father was sick, and I didn't want to hurt anyone . . .' She shrugged. 'It was a long time ago.'

'So you got married.' Reed was implacable, and she sighed.

'Yes, yes. We got married. My parents gave us enough to put down a deposit on a small house and Simon's job at the electronic's factory gave him plenty of scope for overtime.'

'So, what went wrong?'

Antonia turned her head away. 'We—weren't— compatible.'

'You mean he met someone else.'

'Several someones,' admitted Antonia unhappily. 'It was my fault, I suppose. I never did measure up to his expectations of me.'

'What's that supposed to mean?'

'Reed, stop it! I can't talk to you about these things.'

'Why not?'

'Because they're personal.'

Reed regarded her averted face for several seconds,

and then he said softly: 'I guess he accused you of being frigid, hmm?'

Antonia's lips parted and her eyes turned bewilderedly to his. 'How did you know? Am I?'

Reed's laughter was reassuringly intimate. 'Oh, love, you know the answer to that, without me having to tell you,' he answered huskily.

'Then——?'

'It's the usual excuse for a man's inadequacy,' he responded, meeting her anxious gaze. 'Okay, okay. Just one more question. Where is he now?'

'I'm not sure.' Antonia looked doubtful. 'After— after we split up, he left Newcastle. I heard he had joined the Navy, but I'm not sure. He never writes. He never kept in touch at all. I doubt if Susie even remembers him.'

Reed inclined his head. 'I can't say I'm sorry.'

'No.' Antonia allowed a small smile to touch her lips. 'Nor am I.'

When dinner was over, Antonia went into the service shop and bought herself a toothbrush. At least her mother would not be around to observe she had brought no luggage, she reflected thankfully. And she had some old clothes at home she could wear instead of the navy suit.

Sliding into the Lamborghini again, Antonia felt a momentary pang for the ease with which she had accepted this arrangement. The trouble was, she always felt at ease with Reed, and it was this, more than anything else, that warned her to fight his dark attraction. It would be too easy to give in, to be grateful for whatever crumbs of his time he might throw in her direction. She had to always remember he was going to marry someone else, and that no matter how attracted he might be to her, it was Celia Lytton-Smythe who was going to become *Mrs* Reed Gallagher.

To her relief, Reed didn't ask her any more questions, and pretty soon the mesmeric sameness of the motorway uncoiling ahead of them caused her eyelids to droop. She tried to keep awake, chivvying herself with the guilty awareness that Reed, and not she, should be tired. But it was no use. The unhappy week she had spent, worrying over her feelings for the man beside her, had caused many restless nights, and almost without her being aware of it, she drowsed the journey away.

Reed aroused her as they were driving through the outskirts of the city, his rueful smile mirroring his regret at having to do so. 'Which way?' he asked, as they crossed the massive arch of the Tyne Bridge, and Antonia struggled up in her seat to give him hasty directions.

It was only a quarter-to-ten when the Lamborghini turned into the cul-de-sac and Antonia's nerves tightened as Reed drove the short distance to her mother's comfortable semi-detached. Now that she was here, she was intensely conscious of how he might react to his surroundings, and like the first time he came to the flat, she was painfully defensive of her home.

'Do you want me to leave the car on the road?' he asked surveying the short drive to the garage, and Antonia frowned.

'Well—perhaps for the present,' she conceded, wondering who else had observed their arrival. 'My mother's out this evening, and she'll want to put her car away when she gets home. After that, you could park it on the drive.'

'All right.' Reed gave her a wry smile and thrust open his door. 'You think she'll let me stay then?'

Antonia avoided his eyes. 'You're here, aren't you?' she responded, following his example and opening her door. 'Come on. Susie's baby-sitter is expecting us.'

Reed had removed his jacket for driving, but now he looped it over one shoulder to follow her up the path. With his tie pulled a couple of inches away from his collar, and the top two buttons of his dark green shirt unfastened, he looked devastatingly attractive, and Antonia couldn't altogether blame Lucy Telfer for the wide-eyed admiration that followed her opening of the door.

'Hello Antonia,' she said, stepping back to allow them to enter the hall. At sixteen, Lucy was far more experienced than Antonia had been at that age, and she was making no secret of the fact that she found Reed absolutely fascinating. 'Your mother told me you were coming. Did you have a good journey?'

All this was said with her eyes firmly glued to Reed's vaguely amused face, and Antonia found her patience growing increasingly thin. 'It was a very pleasant journey, thank you,' she said, annoyed to hear the edge in her voice. 'I—Reed, this is Lucy. She lives next door.'

'Hello Lucy.' As usual, Reed was completely at ease with his surroundings. 'Is it okay if I hang this here?'

As if he was a regular visitor to the house, Reed draped his jacket over the banister before following the two girls into a comfortable living room. An open fire was burning in the grate, for although the house was centrally heated, Mrs Lord liked the living flame, and a television was playing in one corner. Evidence of Lucy's occupation was there in the glossy magazines residing on the couch, and the remains of the supper Mrs Lord had left for her rested on a tray.

'I'll clear up,' said Antonia shortly, as Lucy would have picked up her tray, and the younger girl grimaced.

'If you're sure,' she murmured, her eyes on Reed again as he stood gazing at the television, and Antonia took off her jacket and dropped it on to a chair.

'I'm sure,' she said, waiting impatiently for Lucy to collect her belongings. 'And—thanks. For baby-sitting, I mean.'

'That's all right.' Lucy was offhand, sensing the older woman's desire to be rid of her and resenting it. She turned to Reed and smiled. 'I might see you again tomorrow—er—Reed,' she murmured, tilting her head provocatively, and Reed dragged his attention from the television to make a polite assention.

Antonia saw her to the door and then came tensely back to the living room. In her absence, Reed had not moved his position, but as she came through the door, he came towards her.

'You don't have to be, you know,' he said roughly, his hands sliding possessively over her shoulders, and she gazed uncomprehendingly up at him. 'Jealous,' he added flatly, resisting her attempts to break away from him. 'You were, weren't you? Dear God, what do you take me for?'

Antonia shook her head, and then with a little moan, she allowed him to pull her closer. Pressing her face against the taut expanse of his chest, warm beneath the fine material of his shirt, she breathed deeply of his clean male smell, filling her nostrils with the scent of him, as his muscled body filled her mind to the exclusion of all else.

'Do you know what you're doing?' he demanded, against her mouth, his hands at her hips making her overwhelmingly aware of his arousal, and with a supreme effort, she broke free of him.

'I—I must tidy up,' she said unsteadily, going towards the tray, and with a groan of impatience, Reed went after her.

It was as well they had their backs to the door, Antonia thought later, remembering the sensuous feel of Reed's palms against her nipples. He was in the process of unbuttoning her blouse to facilitate the invasion of his hands when Antonia heard her daughter's voice, but he released her almost immediately when Susie sidled into the room.

'Mummy?' she said doubtfully, coming round the couch towards them, and Antonia just had time to straighten her clothes before the little girl saw her. 'Oh, Mummy!' she exclaimed, abandoning her uncertainty and rushing into Antonia's arms. 'Nanna didn't tell me you were coming!'

'Nanna didn't know,' Antonia assured her gently, smoothing the silky dark hair out of Susie's eyes and giving her a breathtaking hug. 'I didn't know myself until this afternoon. I—Mr Gallagher very kindly offered me a lift.'

Susie drew away from her mother sufficiently to look up at Reed, standing silently beside them, and her small face grew serious. 'Are you Mr Galla—Gallagher?' she asked, stumbling a little over the word, and Reed came down on his haunches so that she could better see his face.

'Reed,' he amended gently, his lean face creasing into a smile. 'So long as I can call you Susie, of course, and not Miss Sheldon.'

Susie's chin dimpled. 'Nobody calls me *Miss* Sheldon,' she exclaimed, glancing at her mother for support. 'Can I really call you Reed?'

'Do you want to?'

Susie nodded.

'Reed it is, then,' he assured her equably, and Antonia realised he had disarmed the child without her even being aware of it.

'Do you have a car?' Susie asked now, as her mother straightened, and Antonia endeavoured to recover her composure.

'Not tonight, Susie,' she said, pointing firmly at the clock. 'You should be in bed and asleep, not creeping down the stairs and asking questions.'

'Oh, but—*Reed* won't be here tomorrow,' protested the little girl disappointedly, and Antonia drew a breath.

'Yes, he will,' she said levelly. 'He's going to spend the weekend with us. And——' She paused and glanced at Reed, who had now got to his feet again. 'He'll tell you all about his car tomorrow.'

'And give you a ride, too, if you'd like one,' agreed Reed irrepressibly. 'You and your Mummy both. How about that?'

'Really? Tomorrow?' Susie was excited. 'You're sleeping at my house?'

'If your Mummy can find me a bed,' remarked Reed drily, causing Antonia's colour to rise once again. 'Is that all right?'

Susie clasped her hands together. 'I'll never sleep, you know. I don't; not when something exciting's going to happen.'

'Then you'll have to lie awake,' declared Antonia,

reasonably, putting a teasing finger on her daughter's nose. 'Now—say good night to—to Reed. You'll see him again in the morning.'

Susie was loathe to settle down, but the anticipation of the promised outing the following day eventually persuaded her to behave herself. 'He's nice, isn't he, Mummy?' she murmured, as Antonia tucked the covers around her. 'Reed, I mean. Are you going to marry him?'

'Marry him?' Antonia was appalled. 'Don't be silly, Sue!'

'I'm not being silly.' Susie pouted. 'Auntie Sylvia said it was time you thought about getting married again. She said it isn't fair to—to expect Nanna to look after me all the time.'

'Well, there's no chance of me marrying Mr Gallagher,' declared Antonia brusquely, resenting her sister-in-law's careless tongue. 'Go to sleep, darling. We can talk again tomorrow. And don't get up when Nanna comes home, or she won't be very pleased.'

Downstairs again, Antonia found that Reed had discovered the whereabouts of the kitchen for himself, and was presently disposing of Lucy's leftovers into the waste bin. 'You see, I'm quite domesticated,' he remarked, grinning at her surprised face. 'It's what comes of an Irish upbringing. Sure, and didn't I milk the cows and collect the eggs before I was old enough to go to school!'

'You're incorrigible,' she exclaimed, shaking her head, and he dried his hands and came to meet her.

'And you're beautiful,' he told her, burying his face in the hollow at her nape. 'How soon will your mother be back? Or is that a leading question?'

'Any minute now,' said Antonia unsteadily, her bones melting at the sensuous brush of his tongue, and as if to confirm the truth of her statement, she heard the distinctive sound of her mother's key in the lock.

By the time her mother had come into the hall, Antonia and Reed were standing in the doorway to the living room, and Mrs Lord met her daughter's gaze only briefly before transferring her attention to her companion.

'Mr—Gallagher, isn't it?' she observed, not waiting for Antonia's introduction, but coming forward with her hand outstretched. 'I'm Antonia's mother, Mrs Lord. I hope she's made you welcome to our home.'

'I'm delighted to be here, and to meet you, Mrs Lord,' replied Reed gallantly, as Antonia caught her breath. 'And please—my name's Reed. When I'm called Mr Gallagher, I always feel as though my father should be here.'

Mrs Lord smiled, evidently liking his easy courtesy. 'Have you been here long?' she enquired, as Antonia came to bestow a warm kiss on her cheek. 'Where's Lucy? I hope you've sent her home.'

'We have,' said Antonia, taking her mother's coat and hanging it away in the cloakroom. 'Did you have a nice evening?'

'I lost, if that's what you mean,' remarked Mrs Lord drily, passing them to enter the living room. 'Make some coffee, will you, Antonia? I'm sure—Reed could drink a cup.'

Antonia was reluctant to leave Reed alone with her mother, but she had little choice. She guessed Mrs Lord had engineered this to speak with him without her daughter's presence, and stifling her unease, Antonia hurried back into the kitchen.

She need not have been concerned. When she returned some fifteen minutes later with the tray of coffee and biscuits, she found Mrs Lord and Reed talking easily together, and her fears seemed totally groundless when she met her mother's innocent gaze. Ensconced in her favourite position on the sofa, with Reed sprawled in the armchair opposite, Mrs Lord was evidently enjoying herself, and Antonia wondered how Reed had explained his friendship with her daughter.

Reed rose at Antonia's entrance, and set the low coffee table near the sofa so that she could deposit the tray. Then, he accepted the cup she prepared for him, seeming not to notice the anxious look she cast towards him.

'Reed was just telling me he's met Susie already,' remarked Mrs Lord, as Antonia subsided on to the sofa beside her. 'Little minx! I purposely didn't tell her who had phoned, so she would behave herself.'

'I expect she heard our voices,' said Reed lazily, putting his cup aside, and Antonia wondered if he would have preferred something stronger.

'I expect she did,' agreed Mrs Lord, helping herself to a square of shortbread. 'She so looks forward to her mother's visits. It's a pity Antonia has to work so far away. I'm sure you'll agree, a child needs her mother.'

'Mum!' Antonia gave her mother a speaking look. 'Reed's not interested in our ... *personal* problems.'

'Isn't he?' Mrs Lord seemed unrepentant, and Antonia's face burned. 'I'm sure—Reed—understands the difficulties of the present economic situation better than we do. As an employer, he must have faced the problem dozens of times.'

'It's a pity Susie can't live with her mother,' commented Reed, and Antonia turned frustrated eyes in his direction. 'Although, I have to say,' he added evenly, 'London is not a place to bring up children; not if there's an alternative.'

'Do you live in London, Reed?' enquired Mrs Lord innocently, and her daughter wanted to die of embarrassment.

'I have an apartment in town, yes,' he responded, without resentment. 'But I also own a house in Oxfordshire, and I try to spend as much time as I can there.'

'In Oxfordshire!' remarked Mrs Lord with interest. 'How lovely! My husband and I spent a holiday there once. We stayed at Woodstock. Do you know it?'

'I've been there,' conceded Reed, after a moment. 'I hope to spend more time exploring the area in the future.'

'You're not from that area then?' probed Mrs Lord persistently, and Antonia caught her breath.

'Mum, what is this? An inquisition?' She sighed impatiently. 'I think perhaps I should show our guest to

his room, don't you? He just got back from the United
States this morning, and I'm sure he must be tired.'

'A business trip?' suggested Mrs Lord irrepressibly,
as Antonia got purposefully to her feet, and Reed
smiled.

'In a manner of speaking,' he replied, following
Antonia's example. And then, with innate politeness, he
added: 'It's very kind of you to allow me to stay here,
Mrs Lord. I do appreciate it.'

'It's our pleasure,' responded Antonia's mother
charmingly. 'I've put Reed in Howard's old room,
Antonia. I think he'll be comfortable there.'

'Who is Howard?' murmured Reed in her ear, as they
ascended the stairs, and Antonia quivered.

'My brother,' she told him, as his lips brushed her ear.
'He—er—you may meet him tomorrow. He and his
wife sometimes come to tea on Saturdays.'

'I'll look forward to it,' declared Reed mockingly, his
hand at her waist disturbingly possessive. 'Which is
your room?' he added, as they reached the upstairs
landing.

'My room, my mother's room, Susie's room—and
yours,' Antonia pointed out softly, leading the way
across the landing to the door furthest from the stairs.
'And that's the bathroom,' she appended, indicating the
fifth door. 'I'm sorry, but you'll have to share. We
don't have two bathrooms, I'm afraid.'

'I guess I'll survive,' remarked Reed drily, following
her into her brother's old room. There were still
football pennants on the walls, and photographs of
Howard when he was a member of the school rugby
team. But the room was warm and comfortable, and in
the lamplight it did not look too shabby.

'If you're not warm enough, there are extra blankets
in the ottoman,' observed Antonia, gesturing towards
the chest at the foot of the bed. 'My mother doesn't like
duvets, so I'm afraid we're rather old-fashioned when it
comes to bedding.'

'After spending last night in a sleeper-seat, this will
be absolute luxury,' Reed assured her drily. 'Toni, stop

worrying about me. I can take care of myself.' He paused. 'And that includes handling your mother, too.'

Antonia bent her head. 'She's awfully inquisitive.'

'She's a mother,' retorted Reed, putting his hand beneath her chin and tipping it upward. 'Now—I'm going to get my case from the car, before I flake out.' He bent his head to brush her lips with his. 'Okay?'

CHAPTER TEN

ANTONIA awoke to the sound of her daughter's voice chattering away in the room next door. For a moment, she was disorientated, unable to comprehend why Susie should be in Howard's room at all. And then, she remembered who was occupying her brother's bed, and a wave of nervous apprehension swept over her.

In spite of her exhaustion, she had not slept well. She had lain awake for hours after the other occupants of the house had settled down for the night, wondering— in reality *hoping*—that Reed might come to her room. But he hadn't. By the time her mother had allowed her to come upstairs, Reed had had time to wash and undress and get into bed, and there was no sound from his room as Antonia attended to her own toilette.

But now, Susie had evidently taken it upon herself to waken their unexpected guest, and realising she could not allow her daughter to go on making a nuisance of herself, Antonia slid reluctantly out of bed. Pulling on her old woollen dressing gown, she only paused long enough to run combing fingers through her hair before hurrying next door. A proper appraisal of her appearance would depress her too much, she reflected, unaware that without make-up she looked infinitely younger, and more vulnerable.

The door of Howard's room was ajar, and not bothering to knock, Antonia pushed it wider. 'Susie!' she exclaimed reprovingly, discovering her daughter perched on the end of Reed's bed, and the little girl's face took on a rueful expression as her mother advanced into the room.

'It's all right, Toni. I don't mind,' Reed inserted gently, and Antonia was forced to look at the man reclining lazily on the pillows. The darkness of his skin was pronounced against the whiteness of the bedding, and the fine whorls of dark hair that lightly spread down to his rib-cage and beyond, brought a vivid memory of their abrasive texture against her breasts.

'I——' Her breath catching in her throat at the sexual appeal of his muscled body, Antonia shook her head. 'She—she shouldn't be here,' she said, switching her attention back to the safer features of the little girl. 'Susie, you know you don't go disturbing people at this hour of the morning! It's only half-past-seven! Heavens, Nanna isn't even up yet!'

'Reed was awake, weren't you?' protested Susie hopefully, looking to the occupant of the bed for support, and he nodded.

'That's right. I was awake,' he assured Antonia lazily. 'I'm sorry if we disturbed you. Susie was just telling me about falling off Helen's bicycle.'

Antonia pressed her lips together. 'Nevertheless——'

'Did we wake you up, Mummy?' interrupted Susie quickly. 'I've been awake for ages. Reed says he's going to take me out in his car this morning. I've seen it out of the window. It's ever so long and sneaky.'

'Susie——'

'I think perhaps you'd better get out of here, so I can get dressed,' Reed put in swiftly. He gave Susie a deliberate wink. 'We don't want to upset your mother, do we? She might not let you come out with us, if she's mad!'

Antonia gave him an indignant look, but Susie was already scrambling off the bed. 'I'll go and get dressed,' she declared, skipping past her mother. 'Can I wear my new dungarees?'

'Provided you have a thorough wash first,' replied Antonia tersely, feeling decidedly put out. 'And clean your teeth, remember?'

'Yes, Mummy.'

Susie sailed out of the door in high spirits, but when Antonia would have followed her, Reed put out his hand. 'Close the door,' he said softly, his eyes warmly indulgent, and although she knew she was being reckless, she automatically obeyed him.

'Come here,' he said, and with a feeling of helplessness she approached the bed.

'I can't stay,' she got out huskily, but Reed was already drawing her down beside him.

'You shouldn't have come then,' he told her, his hand sliding behind her nape and compelling her insistently towards him. 'Did I tell you, you're the only woman I know who looks good in the morning?'

'And you've had plenty of experience,' she breathed, as his tongue brushed her ear.

'Some,' he conceded modestly, his lips moving sensuously on hers. And then, with consummate ease, the pressure of his mouth hardened into passion, the kiss deepening and lengthening, so that when he drew her down on to the pillows, she had no will to resist. The drugging magic of his mouth was destroying all her inhibitions, and she no longer cared where they were or who might see them, so long as Reed continued his hungry assault.

Her hands slid over his chest, revelling in the feel of his hair-roughened flesh beneath her fingers, and with a little groan, he released the belt of her dressing gown, so that all that was between them was the frail barrier of her cotton nightshirt.

Turning, Reed was above her now, and dragging the covers aside, he gathered her trembling body into the bed beside him. Immediately, she was conscious of the lean strength of his legs, naked as they imprisoned hers, and the swollen pressure of his manhood hard against her stomach.

'I know, I know—we can't!' he muttered roughly, as she started to resist him, 'but just let me hold you for a few moments. Christ, it's bad enough sleeping in the room next to yours and not being able to touch you, without denying me this small pleasure!'

Antonia's fingers curled into the hair at his nape. 'I— I thought you might have——' She broke off discomfortedly, and he buried his face between her breasts.

'Did you think I didn't want to?' he demanded in a

muffled voice. 'Oh, Toni—I didn't feel as if I should. I mean, inviting myself up here; accepting your mother's hospitality. I didn't want you to think that was why I had come.'

'And wasn't it?' she breathed unsteadily, and he lifted his head.

'I wanted to spend the weekend with you,' he told her softly. 'Oh, I'm not denying I want you—really want you, I mean. Here—like this. But I do enjoy just being *with* you, and I did want to meet Susie. It wasn't just a line.'

Antonia touched his mouth with her fingertips, and his lips parted to allow them access. 'I want you, too,' she confessed, unable to hold back the words, her fingers tingling at the sensual caress of his tongue. 'I've wanted to see you all week. I hated myself for what I said to you on Monday.'

'I wish I'd known,' he muttered, lowering his head to nuzzle the peak of her breast, thrusting against the thin covering of her nightshirt. 'When I flew out of London on Tuesday morning, I had a God-awful feeling in my gut, and if I'd thought you wouldn't hang up on me, I'd have phoned you Tuesday night.'

'Oh, Reed!'

'Yes—oh, Reed!' he said thickly, and then, with a sudden change of mood, he compelled her out of the bed. 'I think you'd better go,' he told her harshly, rolling over on to his stomach. 'I can only take so much, and right now, I'm at the limit of my endurance.'

Antonia gathered up her dressing gown and wrapped it about her. 'Are you getting up?'

He glanced over his shoulder. 'Do you have a shower?'

'Yes.'

'Good.' He swung round and sat up, crossing his legs Buddha fashion. 'Can I take one?' He grimaced. 'A cold one, preferably.'

By the time Reed came downstairs, dark and handsome, in mud-coloured Levis and a matching cotton shirt, Antonia was helping her mother prepare breakfast. But her heart flipped a beat when he came into the kitchen and she met the lazy indulgence of his gaze. Dear God, she thought wildly, how was she going to exist when he married Celia? The idea of him sharing the same intimacies with another woman that they had both shared, filled her with desperation, and she tore her eyes away abruptly, wishing she had never brought him here.

'Eggs and bacon all right, Reed?' inquired Mrs Lord, as Susie, having heard his descent of the stairs, came dancing through from the living room.

'That's fine, thanks,' he responded, allowing the little girl to grab hold of his hand, and Susie giggled as she dragged him towards the door.

'Come on,' she said. 'I want to show you how to play space invaders. Nanna bought it for me for my birthday, and I bet I can get more points than you can.'

'I bet you can,' conceded Reed good-humouredly, giving Antonia a rueful grin. 'Okay, okay; I'm coming. But you must make allowances for my inexperience.'

'Susie——' began Antonia doubtfully, but her mother touched her arm.

'Leave her alone,' she advised quietly, forking curls of crispy bacon from the grill. 'Reed's very good with her. Hadn't you noticed? I'd have thought the exchange they were having earlier would have wakened the dead!'

Antonia set out knives and forks on the scrubbed pine table. 'You heard them, too?' she murmured awkwardly.

'And your intervention,' agreed Mrs Lord drily. 'You mustn't blame Susie. She's never had a man to take an interest in her before.'

'You mean a father, don't you?' remarked Antonia tautly. 'Mum, Reed and I—we're not—*serious* about one another.'

'Aren't you?' Her mother cast her a sceptical glance. 'Don't you really mean, he is, but you're not?'

Antonia gasped. 'I don't know what——'

'Yes, you do, Antonia.' Her mother sighed. 'I've seen the way you look at him. And I've seen the way he looks at you. My God, if ever a man was obsessed with a woman, Reed Gallagher is with you!'

'You're crazy!' Antonia dropped the salt cellar, and uttered an imprecation as the fine grains scattered about the floor. She sighed as she bent to sweep them up with a paper towel. 'I wish you'd stop imagining things, Mum. You hardly know the man!'

'Well—I know what I know,' retorted Mrs Lord obscurely, breaking eggs into the pan. 'Put some more bread in the toaster, will you, dear? And just remember—all men aren't like Simon Sheldon!'

After breakfast, Reed drove Antonia, and Susie, into Newcastle, to do some shopping for her mother. They parked in the multi-storey complex at Eldon Square, and then Antonia showed him round the huge shopping arcade, which was reputed to be the largest in Europe. It was easier to keep a sense of detachment in Susie's presence, and if Reed noticed Antonia's efforts to keep the child between them, he politely avoided commenting on the fact. Instead, he generously gave his time to Susie, allowing her to dictate where they went and what they did, and if Antonia's feelings had not been so traumatic, she would have appreciated the efforts he was making.

While Antonia went round the food department at Marks and Spencers, Reed suggested taking Susie into the toy department at Fenwicks, and they met up later to make their way back to the car. Susie was wearing a distinctly smug expression now, and as Reed took Antonia's bags from her, she noticed the suspicious carrier her daughter was hiding behind her back. Oh, well, she thought wearily, if Reed had bought Susie something, she could hardly object. It was his money, after all, and he wasn't likely to see her again after this weekend.

Back at home, Susie was evidently bubbling over with excitement. While Reed deposited the bags of shopping on the kitchen table, the little girl unpacked her own carrier, handing over a separate bag to her mother.

'This is for you,' she said importantly, glancing over her shoulder as Reed came back into the living room. 'It's all right if I give it to Mummy now, isn't it?' she requested. 'You did say I could, once we got back home.'

Antonia pressed her lips together. 'Reed——'

'Take it,' he said flatly. 'It's—well, call it a token of my appreciation for letting me spend the weekend here.'

With Susie looking on with anxious eyes, Antonia felt obliged to open the bag, and her lips parted incredulously as she drew out the silky object it contained. It was a dress, made of fine cashmere, so delicately woven it took up very little space. Its colour was less easy to define—a subtle blend of tawny gold and bronze, that almost exactly matched the colour of her hair. The sleeveless bodice had a deep vee neckline, and the skirt was full and gently flared. It was the most beautiful dress she had ever seen in her life, and her eyes lifted to Reed's in total confusion.

'The sales assistant was about your size,' he remarked carelessly, as the soft material spilled through her hands. 'If you don't like it, I've no doubt you can change it.'

'But you do like it, don't you, Mummy?' exclaimed Susie, breaking the spell that had gripped Antonia ever since she had opened the bag, and she bent her head, nodding a little jerkily as she did so.

'Yes. Yes, it's lovely,' she murmured, fighting back the urge to burst into tears. 'I—I don't know what to say to you.'

'Say you like it,' said Reed quietly, watching her with guarded eyes, and unable to deny it, she covered the space between them.

'I do. I do like it,' she said huskily, looking up at him. And then, gripping his hand tightly, she reached up and kissed his cheek.

Reed's fingers moved to grip hers, and she knew if Susie had not been there, he would have responded far more satisfactorily. As it was, a little of the tension eased out of his face, and forcing himself to speak naturally, he said softly: 'You could wear it tonight. When I take you out for dinner.'

'Am I going out for dinner, too?' demanded Susie, pushing herself between them, and Reed's lazy smile took away her disappointment at his response.

'Not this time,' he told her, lifting the carrier bag out of her hands and extracting the bulky object that was still inside. 'Who is going to show Garfield where he's to sleep, if you're not here to look after him?' he exclaimed, depositing the orange cat in her arms. 'You said he'd probably feel lonely, leaving all those other cats in the shop. You wouldn't go out and leave him, would you? Not on his first night in a strange bed!'

Reed had a gift for Mrs Lord, too; a small pearl brooch, which she was evidently charmed with. 'You really shouldn't,' she said, at lunch, admiring the way it glinted on her lapel. But her reaction on her return from the hairdressers had been all Reed could have wanted, and Antonia dreaded what her mother would say when she saw her dress.

As Antonia had anticipated, Howard and Sylvia and the twins came over in the afternoon. 'Your mother was so intrigued that you were bringing a man home, she couldn't wait to phone us,' declared Sylvia, as she came to find her sister-in-law in the kitchen, revealing that their visit was hardly accidental. 'But I must admit, he's not at all what I expected. However did you meet such a dishy man?'

'What did you expect, Sylvia?' enquired Antonia, setting teacups and saucers on a tray. 'He's nothing like Simon, if that's what you mean. And if my mother's made some allusion to our being—well, involved, forget it!'

'You mean, you're not—sleeping together?' probed Sylvia maliciously, and Antonia's eyes sparkled angrily.

'No, we're not,' she denied, controlling her colour with difficulty. 'And now, if you don't mind, I'll make the tea!'

There was another reason why Howard and Sylvia

had made the journey from Tynemouth to Gosforth, which became evident later in the afternoon.

'Howard's been given four tickets for tonight's performance of the play at the Royal,' his wife inserted at the first opportunity. 'It's supposed to be a very funny play, and they're awfully good seats.' She paused. 'We wondered—Howard and I, that is—whether Antonia and . . . and Reed might like to go with us.'

'How lovely!'

Mrs Lord was enthusiastic, but before Antonia could do more than exchange a helpless glance with Reed, Sylvia had something else to add.

'The only thing is,' she went on, and Antonia wondered why she found the rueful tone her sister-in-law had adopted so suspect, 'we don't have a baby-sitter; and no doubt you're looking after Susie, Mum, so it makes things a little difficult.'

Howard, noticing his sister's expression, said gallantly: 'You can have two of the tickets anyway, Antonia. I mean, whether or not Syl and I go is unimportant, really.'

'You speak for yourself, Howard Lord!' retorted his wife sharply. 'I was looking forward to a night out. We don't get many, goodness knows. We don't have an in-house child-minder!'

'That'll do, Syl,' muttered Howard gruffly, flashing his sister an appealing look. 'The fact is,' he flushed, 'we wondered if the twins could stay here tonight, Mum. I know you've got company, but if Antonia shared with you, the twins could have her bed.'

It was ironic, thought Antonia later that evening, as she applied her mascara. She didn't even want to go to the theatre, and she suspected Reed didn't either. But because of Sylvia, and her complimentary tickets, they were going, and what was more, when they got back, Mrs Lord would be waiting for her daughter to share her bed.

She didn't wear the new dress. It seemed a shame to have to conceal it beneath the woollen coat her mother had lent her, and besides, they were eating at home before meeting Howard and Sylvia outside the theatre.

The twins were as naughty as usual, making Susie cry by hiding Garfield in the dirty clothes basket and driving Mrs Lord wild by chasing madly about the house. Eventually, it was Reed who settled them, threatening them both with corporal punishment if they didn't behave themselves while he and Antonia were out, and softening the blow by promising to take them home on Sunday morning in the Lamborghini, if they made no further nuisance of themselves.

'You'll make a remarkably good father one day,' said Antonia carelessly, as they drove away, and then could have bitten out her tongue at the obvious connotations of her pronouncement. She didn't want to think about Celia—not tonight—and she turned her head away to hide her pained expression.

'I hope so,' Reed answered behind her, as she struggled to get her emotions under control. 'My parents can't wait to have a grandchild. Someone like Susie would suit them very well.'

Antonia moistened her lips. 'I doubt if they'd agree with you,' she murmured, and she sensed his wry amusement.

'Well, I suppose they would prefer for me to be the father of my children,' he conceded softly. 'They'll leave the choice of the mother up to me.'

Antonia's fingers tightened round the slim purse in her lap. 'But it wouldn't do for you to produce a little bastard, would it?' she got out bitterly, and she felt the sudden intensity of his gaze.

'What is that supposed to mean?' he enquired, and her tongue circled her lips once again.

'Well,' she ventured tensely, 'accidents can happen.'

'What are you trying to say?' he exclaimed wearily, and all her pent-up frustrations burst from her like a flood.

'You don't care, do you?' she cried tremulously. 'Oh, I know it's unlikely that that particular stroke of lightning should strike twice in the same place, but it doesn't matter to you, does it?'

Reed brought the car to an abrupt halt and turned

towards her. 'Why are you doing this?' he demanded harshly. 'Why are you saying these things? Who are you trying to hurt? Me? Or yourself?'

Antonia was trembling violently, but when he would have put his hands upon her, she shook them off. 'I can't hurt you, can I?' she choked. 'You wouldn't allow that to happen.'

'Antonia, for Christ's sake!' Reed thrust long impatient fingers through his hair. 'We can't talk about this now!' He shook his head. 'What do you want me to say?'

'Nothing.' Antonia withdrew into her corner, putting as much distance between them as it was possible to achieve. 'Go on. We're going to be late. We don't want to keep Howard and Sylvia waiting.'

'I don't give a damn about Howard and Sylvia,' Reed told her roughly. 'Hell, why did we let them talk us into going to see this bloody play? I wanted to be alone with you—not obliged to make small-talk with your brother and his wife!'

Antonia bent her head. She could not doubt the sincerity of his words, and she knew a blind impatience with herself for precipitating such a scene. 'I'm sorry,' she said unhappily, as he swung back to the wheel, and with a muffled oath, he set the car in motion again.

'So am I,' he muttered harshly, his features set in grim lines, and for the remainder of the journey there was silence between them.

Antonia had even less reason for enjoying the evening when, after a couple of whiskies at the bar in the interval, Howard admitted that it had been Sylvia's idea to get the tickets. 'You mean—they weren't complimentary tickets?' Antonia demanded of her brother, as Reed discussed the first half of the play with Sylvia.

'Syl wanted an evening out,' said Howard placatingly, already realising he had said too much. 'And you know how our mother hates to come out to Tynemouth to baby-sit. It seemed the ideal solution. And you are enjoying the play, aren't you? I'm sure Reed is. He's a good chap. I like him.'

It was supposed to be an apology, but Antonia found it hard to forgive him. Still, she reflected, as she and Reed drove back to Gosforth, Howard was not to know how precious the time she spent with Reed was. And perhaps it was fate, after all, stepping in to prevent her from making another mistake.

The house was dark when they let themselves in, but Antonia guessed her mother would still be awake. Mrs Lord always liked to assure herself that all the occupants of the house were safely home and the doors securely locked before she went to sleep. And when Reed suppressed a yawn, Antonia realised she had selfishly forgotten how tired he must be.

'Do you want a drink?' she asked, adhering to the rules of politeness, but Reed only looked at her with guarded eyes.

'Not tonight,' he responded evenly, loosening his tie and unbuttoning his shirt. 'Would you think me very rude, if I went up to bed?'

It was late on Sunday afternoon when they finally left Newcastle. Susie was tearful, as usual, doubly so because the twins' presence had spoiled the morning for her, and she clung frantically to her mother when Antonia tried to get into the car.

'You're coming to London in two weeks,' Antonia consoled her gently, extricating the little girl's arms from around her neck. 'Less than that, actually, because Nanna's going to bring you down on Friday, and she says she'll stay until Tuesday, how about that?'

'Will Reed be there?' asked Susie innocently, and Antonia cast an awkward look at his dark face.

'We'll see,' she murmured uncomfortably, aware of her mother's eyes upon her, and Susie had to be content with the half-promise.

'Drive carefully,' called Mrs Lord, as the car began to move, and Reed lifted his hand in farewell as they turned out of the close.

To begin with, the traffic in the city took all of Reed's attention, and Antonia lay back in her seat, wondering what he was really thinking. A surreptitious glance at her watch advised her it was already four-thirty, and by her estimation it would be half-past nine or ten o'clock by the time they got back to London. Much too late to have dinner, she reflected, unless he stopped on the motorway. But looking at his grim face she suspected he was eager to reach his destination, and her heart ached at the knowledge that she had generated his mood.

The roads were not busy once they left the outskirts of Gateshead, and paying little attention to the speed limit, Reed's foot descended on the accelerator. The miles were eaten up at a steadily increasing rate, and she dare not disturb his sombre concentration. She was not afraid. Reed drove fast, but safely, and there was a certain exhilaration in passing every other vehicle on the road. Nevertheless, it shortened the journey considerably, and it was barely eight o'clock when Reed suddenly signalled his intentions to leave the M1, and turned instead on to the Aylesbury road.

Antonia, who had been anticipating their arrival at the flat with some apprehension, turned to look at him. 'Where are we going?'

'Stonor,' he said flatly, negotiating a pair of slow-moving vehicles and picking up his speed. 'As you're already prepared for the office, I thought we could spend the night there, and I'll drive you in to work in the morning.'

Antonia's heart fluttered. 'Spend the night at your house, you mean?'

'If you have no objections,' he conceded harshly, his fingers flexing tiredly against the wheel.

Antonia caught her breath. 'I—I thought you were mad at me,' she faltered.

'I am,' he agreed shortly, slowing for some traffic lights. 'But I'm also in love with you, and somehow I've got to convince you of that!'

By the time the Lamborghini turned between the gates of the gravelled drive that ran up to the house, Antonia had convinced herself she must have imagined

Reed's terse words. He could not have said he *loved* her, she told herself fiercely. She was tired, and so was he, and somewhere between his lips and her ears, an error had been made. It was probably her, she chided herself bitterly. She was confusing her feelings with his. Reed didn't love her; he loved Celia Lytton-Smythe. For her he felt a fleeting attraction; it was Celia who was to be his wife.

'I phoned on my way back from Tynemouth this morning,' Reed remarked briefly as Rose Macauley appeared at the door to greet them. Switching off the engine, he thrust open his door and got out, and Antonia was left to acknowledge that she could not have known. Reed had driven the twins home that morning, accompanied only by Susie. The sleek sports car was not built for two adults and three children, and besides, Antonia had not been invited.

'Sure, this is a surprise,' the little housekeeper observed, as Antonia slid out of the car. She smiled at Antonia and then turned her attention back to her employer, as she said: 'I've delayed the meal, just as you suggested, sir. But I'm sorry to have to say, Miss Patricia arrived late this afternoon.'

'Tricia!' Reed cast a rueful look in Antonia's direction, and then shook his head. 'Oh, well,' he remarked carelessly, 'I guess there'll be three of us for dinner, Rose. That doesn't create any problems does it?'

'Not to me,' replied Mrs Macauley meaningfully, and Reed's lean mouth curved into a smile.

'Nor to me, Rose,' he assured her drily, but Antonia's nerve fled at the prospect of meeting Reed's sister.

'Perhaps I ought not to stay,' she murmured, in a low voice, as they walked towards the entrance, and Reed looked down at her half-impatiently.

'I was polite to your brother, wasn't I?' he demanded, his hand in the small of her back compelling her forward. 'Now you can be nice to my sister, even if it is going to be an effort—for both of us!'

Patricia Gallagher met them in the hall. She, too, had

heard the car, it appeared, but her reactions were not as acute as Mrs Macauley's. 'Hi, Reed,' she ventured doubtfully, her grey eyes, so like her brother's, moving swiftly to the young woman beside him. 'I hope you don't mind me inviting myself for a couple of days. I didn't think you'd be here. Aren't you supposed to be in New York, or something?'

'I was,' drawled Reed, slipping his arm carelessly about Antonia's shoulders and drawing her closer to him. 'But—well, I got home sooner than I expected.'

'Yes.' Patricia's smile came and went, and Antonia realised the other girl was as nervous as she was. She was very like her brother: dark hair, grey eyes, a tall, slim body. But her features were much more feminine. The simple jersey tunic she was wearing bore the unmistakeable hallmark of good taste.

'You'll have gathered, this is my sister, Tricia,' Reed said now, resisting Antonia's efforts to break free of him. 'She always turns up at the least convenient moment.'

'And you must be—Mrs Sheldon,' Tricia declared, putting out her hand politely. 'I—Rose told me all about you.' She glanced awkwardly at her brother. 'I gather . . . I gather Celia's not with you.'

Shaking hands with his sister, Antonia knew her face was suffused with colour, but Reed was unperturbed. 'No, Cee's not with me,' he agreed, the look he cast in Antonia's direction turning her bones to water. 'And now, I suggest you let us freshen up before dinner. Which room are you occupying? Your usual one, I suppose.'

'Well, Rose did tell me that—Mrs Sheldon used that room the last time she was here,' said Tricia uncomfortably. 'But she said she didn't think you'd mind if—if your guest occupied the green room. You don't, do you?'

'We can live with it,' responded Reed drily, as Mrs Macauley came in carrying his overnight case and the small hold-all containing Antonia's suit and the dress he had bought her. 'I'll take those, Rose,' he added swiftly, releasing Antonia to take the bags from the housekeeper. 'We'll see you at dinner, infant. I'll show—my guest to her room.'

At the head of the staircase, Reed turned in the opposite direction from the one Antonia remembered. Instead, he escorted her to the fourth door along on the right, allowing her to open the door and precede him into the room.

Dropping his own case outside, he deposited her hold-all on the chest at the foot of the bed, and then retreated to the door. 'You know your way downstairs again, don't you?' he said, propping himself against the jamb. 'Don't be long. Rose will get impatient.'

'Reed—' As he would have left her, Antonia took a step towards him. 'Reed, I don't have anything to wear.'

'Wear the dress I bought you,' he muttered, his brooding gaze raking her slim figure in the simple shirt and jeans she had worn to travel in. 'You have brought it with you, haven't you?' And at her nod: 'I'll see you downstairs in twenty minutes.'

With the door closed behind him, Antonia drew a hasty breath. Twenty minutes seemed such a little time to come to terms with the situation, and her heart palpitated wildly at the prospect of what his sister must be thinking.

She paid little attention to her surroundings as she took a hasty shower in the perfectly matched bathroom. Like the other room, the misty greens and gold of the carpet were picked out in the covers and curtains, and the deliciously warm apartment banished the goose-pimples from her flesh.

Applying a little make-up, she remembered what Tricia had said about her room, and the realisation that the clothes she had seen in the closet there were Reed's sister's gave her an unwarranted lift. It was foolish, she knew, for if Celia did not occupy that room there was no doubt another room that she did. Or did she simply share Reed's apartments? Antonia mused unhappily. Although she had spent the weekend here, she still had no idea where the master of the house slept.

Dinner was served in the small dining room that

opened off the library. It was where she and Reed had had dinner the Saturday evening she had stayed at the house, and beforehand, they had drinks in the comfortable book-lined room adjoining.

'Did you go to New York with my brother, Mrs Sheldon?' Tricia asked, as the two girls sipped glasses of white wine seated on the leather sofa.

'No, she didn't,' Reed interposed briefly, from his position on the hearth. 'And I think you should call her Antonia, don't you?' His lips twisted. 'As our relationship is anything but formal.'

To Antonia's relief, Mrs Macauley's appearance to announce that dinner was served, saved the younger girl from making any response. With an eager: 'Thank goodness!' Tricia followed the housekeeper into the dining room, and Antonia met Reed's gaze with growing apprehension.

'You look beautiful,' he said, his hand at the nape of her neck preventing her from hastening after his sister. 'Just remember that.' His lips brushed her temple. 'Dinner will soon be over.'

She didn't know what he meant, and she was too unsure of herself to probe. Instead, when Rose Macauley appeared in the doorway again, evidently impatient for them to come and start their meal, Antonia took the opportunity to break away from him, and Tricia looked up diffidently as the other two took their places.

The food was as delectable as anything Mrs Braid had produced on Antonia's previous visit. A smoked salmon mousse was followed by a creamy vegetable soup; and medallions of veal, cooked in wine and served with tiny button mushrooms, were a forerunner to the raspberry meringues which completed the meal.

Antonia noticed that for all her slender figure, Tricia had a healthy appetite, whereas she found it incredibly difficult to eat anything. Reed, too, seemed to find the wine which accompanied the meal far more to his taste than his cook's culinary expertise, and Mrs Macauley clicked her tongue disapprovingly as she took their plates away.

'What do you do to him, Mrs Sheldon?' she exclaimed, as Reed's plate was returned to the kitchen virtually untouched. 'Sure, the man must be sick of something to be starving himself like this! Let's hope that by the morning, he'll have more appetite for his breakfast!'

Antonia's face burned, and even Reed gave the old woman an impatient glare. 'Your tongue's so sharp, it will cut your throat one of these days,' he essayed narrowly, as she served the coffee. 'As a matter of fact, we'll be leaving early in the morning, so you can forget the sarcasm.'

Rose grimaced and left them, and Tricia expelled her breath on a rueful sigh. 'She really is the limit!' she exclaimed, looking sympathetically at Antonia. 'You mustn't take any notice of her. She thinks she has the right to say what she likes!'

Antonia forced a faint smile, but she couldn't meet Reed's eyes, and a few moments later he pushed his chair back and got to his feet. 'Look, I think we should all get an early night,' he remarked heavily. 'I've promised to drive Antonia in to work in the morning, and as she starts at nine, we've got to leave here at seven o'clock at the latest.'

'And, of course, you'll still be jet-lagged,' said his sister, nodding. 'You're going to find it pretty difficult to open your eyes at seven o'clock.'

'I know that.' Reed regarded her levelly. 'So—good night then.'

'Good night.'

Tricia smiled up at him over the rim of her coffee cup, and because it would look too suspicious if she attempted to accompany him upstairs, Antonia echoed the younger girl's response.

'See you—see you in the morning,' she offered, trying to sound casual, and Reed inclined his head politely before leaving the room.

Left alone with Tricia, Antonia waited apprehensively for the words of censure she was sure the younger girl wanted to voice. But they never came. Instead, Reed's sister offered her more coffee, and when their cups were filled, she said quietly: 'I'm so pleased I've had this chance to meet you. You're different from what I expected.'

'Am I?' Antonia assumed Rose Macauley had been less than generous in her assessment. 'Well—I hope it's an improvement.'

'It is.' Tricia's lips twitched. 'I think we've all been labouring under a misapprehension.'

'All?' Antonia frowned. 'You mean—Rose; Mrs Macauley?'

'No, I mean my parents,' said Tricia evenly. 'I might as well be honest. It's no accident that I'm here, Antonia. When Reed phoned and said you would be spending the night here, Rose contacted my mother and she contacted me.'

CHAPTER ELEVEN

ANTONIA let herself into her room with an aching sense of weariness. The conversation she had had with Tricia had left her feeling troubled and confused, and although Reed's sister had said nothing to upset her, she was upset nevertheless.

It had been such a shattering discovery to make: that Mrs Macauley should have taken it upon herself to inform Reed's parents of their son's aberrations. She could imagine what the Gallaghers must be thinking. And the fact that she was a divorcee could only have added to their anxieties.

Not that Tricia had said anything of the sort. On the contrary, she had been amazingly casual about the whole affair. 'You must understand,' she had said swiftly, reacting to Antonia's shocked embarrassment at her words, 'we have always been a very—close family. And when Rose informed my mother that you and Reed had spent the weekend here, alone, Mummy was quite disturbed.'

'I'm sure she was.' Striving for composure, Antonia had shaken her head. 'Does she think I'm trying to break up Reed's engagement?'

'Well—she was concerned that Reed hadn't told her about you,' Tricia confessed. 'I mean—Celia wasn't Reed's first girlfriend, or anything like that, but he never used to bring his—well, Celia's the only one who's ever stayed at Stonor. Until now.'

Antonia's face was burning. 'I don't know what to say——'

'Don't say anything,' said Tricia ruefully. 'Reed's probably going to wring my neck for talking to you. But—oh, you know what mothers are. She just wanted to know what you were like.'

Antonia shook her head. 'She doesn't have to worry,

you know,' she murmured uncomfortably. 'Our ...
relationship—mine and Reed's that is—it's not–
important.'

'Don't you think so?' Tricia's eyes were suddenly very
like her brother's. 'You know, I'm tempted to agree
with Rose, harridan though she is. I've never known
Reed lose his appetite before.'

Now, Antonia closed her door and leaned exhaustedly
against the panels. What did it matter what Tricia
thought, she asked herself, or Mrs Gallagher either?
After this weekend, she was determined not to see Reed
again. It was becoming too bittersweet, too painful; too
deceptively easy to fool herself they were hurting no
one. They *were* hurting people, themselves most of all—
or so Tricia would have her believe, if her statement
was true.

Straightening away from the door, she started to
unzip her dress. It was late, and she was tired. The
problem of how to cope with the situation would have
to wait until the morning. Right now, she wanted to
lose herself in oblivion, and forget that he'd ever said he
loved her.

Stepping out of her dress, she turned, and as she did
so, her breath caught in her throat. She had been so
intent in her misery, she had scarcely noticed the fact
that her bed was turned down and that someone was
already reclining between the fine silk sheets. In the
subdued lighting of the bedside lamp, Reed's lean face
had a hollow vulnerability, the sooty fringe of his lashes
resting on his cheeks. He was asleep, his brown body
dark against the pastel green of the pillows.

After what she had been telling herself, she knew she
should wake him and send him back to his own room,
but she didn't. Consoling herself with the thought that
Reed needed his sleep, she went into the bathroom and
removed her make-up. Then, after cleaning her teeth,
she took off her tights and her bra, and came back to
the bed. She had brought no nightdress with her, as she
had expected to be sleeping at the flat tonight, so she
kept her slip on instead.

Folding back the covers, she slid carefully into the bed, trying not to disturb him, and then nearly jumped out of her skin when he said huskily: 'What a hell of a time you've been!'

'You're awake!'

The words were little more than a squeak, and he moved lazily nearer, his arm sliding beneath her head and pulling her towards him. 'Did you really think I wouldn't be?' he demanded, burying his face in the scented hollow between her breasts, and trembling a little, she felt his tongue against her skin.

'You shouldn't be here,' she protested, struggling to maintain a sense of reality. 'Reed, what would your sister think?'

'I don't give a damn what my sister thinks,' he retorted, his impatient fingers sliding beneath the hem of her slip. 'This is my house, and finding an unwanted visitor here, is no reason to spend another frustrated night.' He made a sound of aggravation. 'What on earth did you leave this on for? You're not cold, are you?'

Cold? Antonia drew an unsteady breath. Her body was as suffused with warmth as her face had been earlier, and the sensuous brush of his aroused body against her thighs was bringing a distinct ache to the pit of her stomach.

'Reed—your mother . . . that is, Mrs Macauley *told* your mother you and I had spent the weekend here,' she breathed, as the satin slip was cast aside, and she felt the delicious softness of the sheet against her bare back. 'Reed—are you listening to me?'

'Do you want me to?' he murmured, his mouth devouring hers with sensual abandon, and her senses swam beneath the moist invasion of his tongue.

'Reed——'

'All right. I guessed she might,' he responded carelessly, taking one full breast in his hand and loving the swollen nipple with hungry urgency. 'Oh, love, I don't care what Rose says, or what my mother says, or what anyone says, but you.' He slid lower, his hand

finding the soft inner curve of her thigh. 'You are the
only person I care about. God, don't you believe me?'

The drugging intimacy of his lips suspended all other
thought. Her hands sliding possessively over the
muscled curve of his hips, Antonia couldn't think of
anything else but the immeasurable delight of his
lovemaking, and Reed was not immune to the tentative
sexuality of her caress. With a muffled groan, he moved
over her, crushing her breasts beneath him, and the
pulsating power of his manhood sought its silken
sheath . . .

Reed dropped Antonia outside the institute at five
minutes past nine the following morning. 'Sorry, you're
late,' he remarked softly, as she made to get out, and
Antonia cast him a tremulous glance before reaching
for the door handle. 'I'll call you,' he said, his hand on
her wrist delaying the moment, but Antonia shook her
head.

'Don't,' she said huskily. 'I—I don't want us to see
one another again!' and with this damning indictment,
she scrambled out of the car.

He was tempted to go after her, but the prospect of
trying to reason with her here deterred him. Besides, he
had other things he wanted to do, other things he *had*
to do, before seeing Antonia again, and with a smothered
oath, he let her go, his lungs constricting in his chest.

Dear God, he thought incredulously, when had it hit
him that what he felt for Antonia was more than just a
desire to go to bed with her? Oh, he wanted that, of
course. Just remembering the night they had just spent
brought a disruptive stirring in his groin, but his
feelings went far beyond the physical. Even when he
was making love to her, even when their bodies were
fused in the mindless aftermath of their mutual passion,
he wanted to possess her mind, as well as her delectable
form, and the emptiness he felt whenever he left her,
would not easily be displaced.

He knew she was not indifferent to him. When she
stopped fighting him, her hunger was as great as his,

and he had never known a woman who so exactly matched his moods. There had been other women, lots of other women, ever since he had been old enough to attract the attention of the opposite sex. But, none of them, and most particularly, not Celia, had ever given him the satisfaction—both mentally and physically—that Antonia did. She was so delicious, so delightful, so lovable—so everything he wanted in a woman. It was funny—whenever he had anticipated his marriage to Celia, it had been in terms of their having a family, of giving his parents the grandchild they craved. With Antonia, whether or not they had a baby didn't come into it. He wanted her, he wanted to be with her, and he was selfish enough to enjoy the prospect of sharing her with no one but her daughter.

He reached Eaton Lodge in only a few minutes, and parking the Lamborghini on the forecourt, he thrust open his door and strode into the building. With a bit of luck, Celia would not have left yet for the shop, but if she had, he would just have to make other arrangements. He could always take her out to lunch, he reflected reluctantly, although he did not welcome the prospect of prolonging the agony. He wanted to make a clean break, and as decently as possible. He was not the kind of man to take any satisfaction in what he had to do, and if she wanted to tell their friends she had jilted him, he was quite prepared to go along with it. The way it was done didn't matter to him, just so long as he gained his freedom. How was it Shakespeare had put it, he mused wryly: *if it were done . . . then 'twere well it were done quickly.* He grimaced, and as he made for the stairs, Mrs Francis called his name.

'Mr Gallagher,' she exclaimed. 'You're an early caller.'

Reed paused and turned. 'Good morning, Mrs Francis,' he responded resignedly. 'Yes. Is Miss Smythe still at home, do you know?'

'Miss Lytton-Smythe hasn't left to my knowledge,' the caretaker's wife declared knowingly. 'And I usually hear her go. And Miss Ashford, too.'

'I'm sure you do.' Reed turned back to the stairs, and then had another thought. 'Er . . . Liz, Miss Ashford, I mean; did you say she *had* left?'

'I think she's been away for the weekend,' confided Mrs Francis, with a frown. 'Yes. I believe she was spending the weekend in Leicestershire. With the— Stockwells. Would that be right?'

'You're very well informed, Mrs Francis,' Reed complimented her drily. 'Okay. Thanks. I'll just go up and see if Celia's ready to leave.'

He was conscious of her watching him round the curve of the stairs, and he pulled a wry face. He would be glad to get Antonia out of this place. He did not appreciate having to explain his intentions every time he entered the building.

He pulled his keys out of his pocket as he reached Celia's door, but having second thoughts, he pressed his finger on the bell. As he waited, he extricated her key from the others on his keyring and dropped it into his pocket. Celia could have it back again. He had no further use for it.

It seemed ages before she came, and he had rung the bell several more times before he heard the sound of the slip-chain being removed. It was just as well he hadn't tried to get in, he reflected. Evidently Celia was still locked up for the night. He shook his head. For once, he felt grateful to Mrs Francis. Without her intervention, he would probably have imagined Celia had already left.

The door opened slowly and Celia, a thin silk kimono pulled carelessly about her, peered out through narrowed lids. 'Reed!' she exclaimed faintly, identifying the lean dark individual propped indolently outside her door. 'Y—you're back!'

'As you see,' agreed Reed evenly, straightening from his lounging position. 'I got back on Friday, actually.'

'*Friday?*' Celia blinked, and if Reed had not been so concerned with his own problems, he would have taken more account of the faintly furtive glance she cast behind her.

'Friday,' he confirmed now, aware that their voices could carry down the stairs. 'Are you going to invite me in? I've got something to tell you, and I'd as soon say it in private, if you see what I mean.'

The meaningful look he sent down the stairs was self-evident, and Celia's tongue appeared to circle her parted lips. 'Well, I—you couldn't come back later, could you, darling?' she murmured awkwardly. 'You see—Liz hasn't been at all well. I've been up with her half the night. And I really am—absolutely exhausted!'

Reed could believe it. She looked pale and hollow-eyed, and if Mrs Francis had not been so sure about Liz spending the weekend with the Stockwells, Reed would never have doubted her. But there was a curious smell in the air, a sickly sweetness that Reed had smelt once before in his life, and because he could identify it, his cool grey eyes narrowed.

'Are you sure it's Liz who's been sick?' he enquired tensely, the connotations that immediately sprang to his mind causing him to speak with unnecessary violence. 'For Christ's sake, Cee, why didn't you tell me you were on that stuff!'

'What stuff?' asked Celia indignantly, trying desperately to refute his allegations, but Reed could only see his plans for the future—and Antonia—crumbling about him.

'You're crazy, do you know that?' he demanded savagely, pushing her inside and slamming shut the door with his foot. Thrusting her ahead of him into the living room, his jaw was tight with frustration. How could he tell her now, he was asking himself, when his own responsibility for what had happened had to be acknowledged?

'Reed, will you get out of here?' Celia's voice was rising shrilly with emotion, and he thought she could have no idea how much he wanted to do just that.

'When we've talked this through,' he declared, slamming his hands into his pockets. 'God—I thought you had more sense! Where the hell did you get the stuff?'

'Que se passe-t-il?'

The sound of a third voice brought Reed round with a start, his eyes widening disbelievingly at the sight of the thin dark man who had appeared from the direction of the bedrooms. Barefoot, hair tousled, the bathrobe pulled around him of evidently feminine design, he gazed across the room at them, aghast, and Celia rounded on him in angry protest.

'Raoul!' she exclaimed. *'Es pèce d imbecile! Je t ai dit de rester dans la chambre———'*

'I do speak French, Cee,' Reed put in drily, a faintly sardonic twist lifting the corners of his mouth. Hell, he thought, with rueful self-derision, no wonder Celia had been so reluctant for him to enter the apartment. With Liz Ashford away, how could she explain this?

'You don't understand, Reed,' Celia blurted in confusion, as she saw the dawning comprehension in his face. 'Darling, I only offered Raoul a bed for the night, because it was late when he brought me home. We'd been out to dinner. I thought you were away. You said you'd be away all weekend. Heavens, you don't imagine there's any more to it, do you? Honestly, Reed, would *I* do a thing like that?'

If Antonia had half-hoped that Reed might meet her from work that evening, she was disappointed. There was no sign of the Lamborghini as she emerged from the institute, and she told herself she was glad as she took her place at the bus stop.

There was no sign of the car at Eaton Lodge either, even though she had entertained the thought that he might be waiting for her there. And after all, he had to come and see Celia some time, she acknowledged unhappily. If she was going to carry on with her life in London, she had to accept that so long as Celia lived in the same building, their paths were bound to cross, sometimes.

She was making herself a sandwich when she heard someone knocking at her door, and her heart lifted wildly at the sound. It had to be Reed, she thought apprehensively. No one else was likely to call. And although she longed to see him, she determinedly ignored the summons.

'Mrs Sheldon! Antonia!'

The voice calling her name was definitely not Reed's, and Antonia expelled her breath. It was Celia. She was sure of it. And abandoning the makings of her sandwich, she mentally steeled herself before going to the door.

'Oh, you are in.' Celia's delicately moulded features drew into a relieved smile. 'I thought I wasn't mistaken. I followed you along Clifton Gate.'

'Did you?' Antonia controlled her colour with difficulty, the self-contempt she felt for deceiving the other girl causing her breath to catch in her throat. 'I'm sorry. I didn't see you.'

'No.' Celia glanced beyond her. 'Can I come in?'

Antonia hesitated, and then moved aside. 'If you like.'

Celia nodded, and stepped into the flat. 'Thanks. I won't keep you more than a few minutes.'

Antonia couldn't imagine what the other girl might have to say to her, and her heart palpitated erratically at the thought that Celia might have found out about her friendship with Reed. Friendship! Antonia's pulses raced. The passionate relationship they had shared bore little resemblance to that ineffectual description.

'Cosy,' remarked Celia now, looking round the flat with a faintly patronising air, and Antonia linked her fingers together.

'It suits me,' she said, biting back her indignation. 'I—what did you want to see me about? I have to phone my daughter in fifteen minutes.'

'Your daughter? Oh, yes, Reed told me about her,' remarked Celia carelessly, inspiring a sense of angry impotence in the woman she was addressing. 'She lives in the north of England with your mother, doesn't she? Reed seemed to think she was rather sweet.'

Antonia's features froze. 'He did?'

'Hmm.' Celia moved negligently across the floor, and

took up a position before the empty fireplace. 'You spent the weekend with him, didn't you? Oh, don't look so alarmed; I'm not about to scratch your eyes out, or anything silly like that. Reed told me all about it, and I've forgiven him. You don't imagine you're the first female to catch my fiancé's roving eye!'

Antonia's lips parted. 'I don't believe you . . .'

'No, they never do,' said Celia in a bored tone. 'Reed's girls, I mean. I suppose I can't blame them. They don't want to lose him. Reed really is awfully good in bed!'

Antonia took a deep breath and walked stiffly to the door. Pulling it open, she said tightly: 'I'd like you to leave, Miss Lytton-Smythe. Now. This minute. Or I might scratch your eyes out. That's an alternative you've not considered.'

Celia remained where she was for several seconds more, and then, as if not altogether trusting the gleam in Antonia's eyes, she sauntered back across the room. 'All right, all right,' she said. 'I'm going. But, honestly, my dear, to someone who's only thinking of your well-being, you are responding rather primitively.'

'Get out!'

'I will.' But Celia paused in the doorway nevertheless. 'As a matter of fact, there was another reason why I wanted to speak to you. I wanted to warn you, your lease on this flat won't be renewed at the end of June, as you anticipated. My father owns this building, as it happens, and although I shall be leaving myself in December—when I marry Reed—I refuse to feel your envious eyes spying on us every time we go in and out!'

Even five hours after Celia had left, Antonia was still trembling in the aftermath of what she had said. It had been horrible—*so horrible*—that Antonia knew she would never forget it. Hearing the other girl dismiss Reed's infidelities without turning a hair had been sick and humiliating. Yet, Celia was used to it; she had to be. It was the only explanation for the coolness with which she had spoken of his affairs. Antonia knew she ought to be feeling sorry for Celia, but she couldn't. If

the girl was indifferent to Reed's unfaithfulness, then
perhaps she had her own reasons for overlooking his
transgressions.

Not that this conclusion made the situation any
easier. Antonia had *loved* Reed; she loved him still, if
she was honest with herself. Just because the object of
her affections had not lived up to her expectations of
him, did not automatically reduce her feelings. In every
way, except one, he was still the only man she had ever
truly cared about, and no matter what he did her love
would survive. But it was painful. Even thinking about
how he had deceived her made her want to throw up.
She should never have come to London, she thought
bitterly. This was her reward for abandoning her
principles.

As yet, she hadn't given a lot of thought to Celia's
pronouncement on the flat. She had no doubt that what
the other girl had said was true, but she was too
shocked, too numb, too *vulnerable* at present, to
anticipate what she might do and where she might go.
Those problems would have to wait until she was more
equipped to deal with them. Right now, it was an effort
to look beyond the next twenty-four-hours.

She was in her dressing gown, curled up on the sofa,
trying not to remember where she had been at the same
time the previous evening, when she heard the outer
doorbell ring. It was well after eleven, and although she
knew it could not be anyone for her, she slid off the
couch and opened her door.

Mr Francis had done likewise, and she faced the
elderly caretaker across the width of the hall. 'Someone
must have forgotten their key,' he grunted, emerging
from his doorway to reveal his hair-curlered wife
behind him. 'I suppose I'd better answer it, but you
never know at this time of night.'

'You be careful, Bert,' declared Mrs Francis, turning
an anxious face in Antonia's direction, and because she
felt obliged to do so, Antonia waited to ensure there
was no trouble.

'Why—Mr Gallagher!' exclaimed the caretaker at

that moment, and Antonia turned horrified eyes on the door. It was Reed, brushing impatiently past the startled manager, his eyes on her shocked face as he strode unmistakably towards her.

Without giving herself time to have second thoughts, Antonia immediately stepped back inside her flat and closed the door. She had no intention of speaking to Reed tonight, particularly when he was evidently on his way to see Celia. Let the Francises think what they liked. She was not to blame if they thought she was rude.

She had scarcely slipped the safety chain into place before there was a hammering at the door. 'Antonia!' exclaimed Reed with evident impatience. 'What the hell are you doing? Open up! Come on—I want to speak with you.'

Antonia pressed her back against the panels, as if her weight could add anything to its security, and said steadily: 'Go away, Reed. What do you think you are doing? You have no right to embarrass me like this!'

'Embarrass *you*!' he echoed harshly. 'How do you think I feel, yelling at you through a door? Oh, for Christ's sake, let me in! Before Francis gets suspicious and calls the police!'

'He wouldn't do that.'

'Wouldn't he? Are you prepared to take that risk?' Reed expelled his breath wearily, his .voice losing its aggression. 'Look, I've got to see you, Toni. Don't make me spell it out in front of witnesses.'

Pressing her lips together, Antonia tried to resist the insidious appeal of his voice, but she could not let him tell her lies in front of Mrs Francis. She still had to live here, for another couple of months, at least, and was it really a lesser evil to pretend this had not happened?

Taking a deep breath, she slipped the chain and opened the door. Immediately, Reed widened the space she had created to allow him to step inside, and with an ironic smile at Mrs Francis, still hovering doubtfully across the way, he firmly closed the door behind him.

CHAPTER TWELVE

BACKING away from him, Antonia put the length of the sofa between them before permitting herself to meet his eyes. But the intensity of their expression was hardly tempered by the distance, and she shifted a little nervously beneath the censure of his gaze.

'Would you mind telling me what all that was about?' he demanded quietly. 'I realise it's late, and I've probably got you out of bed, but it surely must have occurred to you that my being here must be important.'

Antonia shrugged, her eyes defensive. 'I—I assumed you'd come to see Celia,' she declared, hiding her shaking hands in her pockets. 'Isn't it a little foolhardy, coming here at this time of night, even for you?'

Reed put up a hand and pulled the knot of his tie away from the collar of his pale grey shirt. The tie was silk, like the shirt, Antonia noticed inconsequently, his suit several shades darker and, as usual, immaculately pressed.

'I suppose I deserve that,' he said, when his collar button was unfastened, and his hand through his hair had made it attractively dishevelled. 'I should have got here sooner, and I would have if the eight o'clock plane hadn't sprung a fault.'

Antonia blinked. 'The plane?' she echoed blankly. 'What plane?'

'The plane from Dublin,' replied Reed, glancing about him. 'Can I sit down? I really am pretty bushed!'

Antonia shook her head confusedly, and then made a hasty gesture of acquiescence. 'You've been to Dublin to see your parents,' she essayed carefully. 'To—explain about our weekend at Stonor.'

'In a manner of speaking,' said Reed wearily, subsiding on to the sofa and resting his head back against the cushions. 'I had to speak to my father. And my mother deserved an explanation.'

'Of course.' Antonia drew her hands out of her pockets and gripped the arm of the sofa. 'I assume they don't condone your profligacy. Or perhaps they do. I'm not very expert when it comes to judging people's characters!'

Reed regarded her blankly, and then he shook his head. 'What old-fashioned words you use,' he remarked, pushing himself up from his lounging position. 'Perhaps you'd tell me what you mean by that assessment. Do I take it you consider my character beyond redemption?'

Antonia shivered. 'I think we should stop playing games.'

'Oh, so do I.' Reed's face was broodingly intent.

'So?'

'So what?' Reed frowned. 'What particular game are we playing now? The same game you've been playing, ever since you realised there was something between us?'

'No.' Antonia flushed. 'There is—nothing between us. You know it, and I know it, so I think you should stop pretending there ever was.'

Reed blinked and then, deliberately, he got up from the sofa again. 'Okay,' he said. 'What's happened? Why are you acting like I was the prodigal son? I know what you said this morning, and I know why you said it, but that doesn't apply any more.' He bent his head, his cheeks hollowing as he sucked in his breath. 'Cee and I are through. We split up this morning. The reason why I went to Dublin was to tell my parents about *us*!'

Antonia's reaction was a disbelieving gasp, and she let go of the arm of the sofa to step further away from him. 'I—I—how can you say such things?' she got out incredulously. 'I spoke to Celia this afternoon, and she told me in no uncertain terms that you were *not* through at all.'

Reed's head jerked up. 'You spoke to Cee this afternoon?'

'I've just said so.' Antonia quivered. 'She told me all

about . . . all about the relationship you have with her! It was what I expected—what I deserved, I suppose— but it really wasn't necessary. I had already decided what I had to do.'

'Had you?' Reed's face was grim. 'And I suppose that's what this little charade is all about! It's your— futile way of demonstrating that you still have a choice in the matter!'

'It's not futile——'

'Isn't it? *Isn't it?*' Without giving her a chance to escape him, Reed obliterated the space between them, grasping her wrists with brutal fingers and twisting her arms behind his back. The action brought her up against him, her shocked reaction coming too late to save her. Using his superior strength, Reed ground his hard mouth down on hers, and as she struggled to free herself, she felt the taste of her own blood in her mouth.

She fought him then, but after that first bruising assault, Reed's lips softened and gentled. With insistent persuasion, his tongue coaxed her lips to part, and the moist invasion that followed made a nonsense of her efforts to resist him.

Sensing her confusion, Reed released her wrists to permit his hands to slide possessively across her back, and arching her body towards his, he allowed a shuddering sigh to escape him. 'Dear God, don't you know I love you?' he muttered, in a voice that was amazingly unsteady. 'Why do you persist in believing anyone else but me?'

Antonia trembled. 'Celia said——'

'Yes, I can guess what Celia said,' he cut in harshly, 'but she was lying.' His fingers slid into her hair and holding her head between his palms, he added emotively: 'Give me a little credit, will you? I was an attractive financial proposition, if nothing else, and Celia was always aware of it.'

Antonia looked up at him uncertainly. 'You're— *not*—going to marry her?'

'Haven't I just said so?'

'I don't know.' Antonia could hardly take this in.

'Are you sure this isn't just another ploy to confuse me?'

'Confuse you?' Reed closed his eyes briefly, and then opened them again to reveal a nerve-shattering tenderness. 'Oh, *love*! If anyone's confused here, it's me!'

'But . . . but Celia——'

'Yes?' Reed inclined his head resignedly. 'Go on. You'd better tell me what Cee said, then I'll tell you what really happened.' He glanced behind him as he spoke, and with a determined expression, he sank down on to the sofa again, pulling her across his knees as he did so. 'But first——' and with devastating thoroughness his lips reduced her protests to a quivering submission. 'Go on,' he added, when her arms were about his neck, and she was weakly clinging to him. 'Before I lose all sense of this conversation.'

Antonia shook her head. 'You don't make it easy . . .'

'Nor do you,' he responded, toying with the cord of her dressing gown. 'Please: let's get it over with.'

Antonia moistened her lips, intensely conscious of the muscular strength of his thighs beneath hers. 'I . . . I . . . she came here at teatime, when I got home from work. She . . . she knew all about—Susie, and about the weekend we had spent together. She said you had told her.'

'I had,' agreed Reed laconically. 'Go on.'

Antonia swallowed. 'Why did you tell her?'

'Why do you think?'

'I don't know.'

Reed shrugged. 'Isn't it reasonable that I'd have to give the reasons why I was breaking our engagement?'

Antonia's lips parted. 'You've—really done that?'

Reed's mouth parted to accommodate hers. 'Do you doubt it?' he demanded, his breath almost suffocating her, and suddenly she didn't.

Almost incoherently she blurted out the rest of what Celia had said, glossing over the worst of her excesses, but leaving Reed in no doubt of his ex-fiancée's bitterness towards her. 'I . . . I suppose we had hurt her,' she finished at last. 'Poor Celia!'

'But you believed her,' he reminded her quietly, his fingertips stroking an invisible line from her shoulder to her waist, and Antonia bent her head.

'Yes,' she said, not excusing herself. 'I . . . I still can't believe that . . . that you could want me and not . . . not her.'

'Is that so?' Reed abandoned his line-drawing to cradle her cheek in his palm. Then, seeing the brilliance of unshed tears in her eyes, he added softly: 'I have to say, you don't deserve me.'

Antonia sniffed. 'Don't tease.'

'I'm not teasing,' he told her huskily. 'I'm just trying to make you see it's not important. All that unpleasantness with Cee, it doesn't mean a thing to us. And we have the rest of our lives to prove it.'

'Do you mean that?' Antonia touched his cheek, and he turned his lips against her palm.

'I'm not in the habit of making extravagant statements unless I mean them,' Reed assured her unevenly. 'And if you'd let me explain before jumping to conclusions, I'd have reassured you on that point.'

Antonia caught her lower lip between her teeth. 'I'm sorry.'

'And will you believe me if I tell you I'm not in the habit of lying—to anyone,' he appended drily. 'Nor did I give Cee any reason for jealousy until you came on the scene.'

'But why me?'

'Do you think I haven't asked myself that question?' Reed demanded ruefully, nuzzling her nape. 'My life was so carefully mapped out. There was never any question but that I would take over my father's position in the company, and Celia seemed a suitable addition to my status. I was fond of her, and we seemed compatible enough. It was only when I met you, I started questioning my complacency.'

'A most—unsuitable complication,' put in Antonia softly, and his hand ran possessively down her throat.

'Well, I will admit I fought it,' he muttered roughly. 'My feelings for you were anything but complacent, and

I didn't want the aggravation. Unfortunately, I didn't have much choice in the matter.'

Antonia hesitated. 'Are you sure?'

'Am I sure of what?' He turned her face towards him. 'Am I sure of what I'm doing? Oh, yes.' His mouth brushed hers and then he drew back to look into her face. 'Or do you mean, am I sure I love you?'

Antonia drew a trembling breath. 'Are you?'

'Let me put it this way,' he murmured, his tongue tracing the delicate contours of her ear, 'I don't know what you've done to me, but I can't contemplate my life without you. Does that answer your question?'

'Oh, Reed——'

She tightened her arms around his neck, and she felt his instant response to the lissom provocation of her yielding body. 'Oh, God, I want you,' he groaned, sliding the dressing gown off her shoulders and uttering a frustrated sound at the enveloping folds of her nightshirt beneath. 'Why do you always wear so many clothes!'

'I didn't know I'd be sleeping with you, did I?' Antonia responded huskily, assisting his removal of the offending nightgown, and Reed gave a sigh of approval when she was naked in his arms.

'Help me!' he said, shrugging off his jacket and tugging off his tie, and her fingers moved obediently to the buttons of his shirt.

But when he gathered her warm body against his, he didn't carry her into the bedroom as she had anticipated. 'I want you here—and now,' he told her thickly, wrapping his lean flanks about her, and Antonia discovered there was something rather erotic about making love on a sofa...

It was weeks later before Reed told her all of what had occurred the morning he visited Celia's apartment. And by then, he and Antonia were married, and spending their honeymoon on the exotic island of Tahiti in the south Pacific.

Everything had happened so quickly, sometimes

Antonia had to pinch herself to ensure she wasn't dreaming. But she wasn't. It was all marvellously real, and since the night Reed had talked his way into her flat, they had never been apart. She had moved out of the flat and into Reed's apartment the day after he had visited his parents in Ireland, and although she continued working at the institute until they were married, they had spent every free moment together.

The weeks before their wedding had flown. Antonia had had a long telephone conversation with her mother as soon as she was settled in the St James's Street apartment, and Mrs Lord had adopted a very knowing tone when she heard her daughter's news. But it had been Susie—and Reed's parents—who presented the biggest obstacle, and Antonia had not looked forward to her first visit to his family's home in County Wicklow.

And at first, there had been a certain restraint on the part of Reed's mother and father. It was to be expected, Antonia told herself, knowing she was marrying into a staunchly Catholic family, to whom her divorce from Simon made a church wedding out of the question.

But somehow, she didn't quite know how, the visit had not proved to be the disaster she had anticipated. Maybe, as Reed had intimated, when he came to her room that night, his parents could see that she was making *him* happy, and in the days that followed, Antonia had come to accept his assessment of the situation.

It was Tricia who eventually told her that it was much more simple even than that. 'They like you,' she said, pulling a wry face at her brother. 'They were always a little doubtful about Celia. She was never quite relaxed when she came to stay in the country.'

Susie's reactions had been reassuringly uncomplicated. She already liked Reed, and the knowledge that when her mother married again they would have a proper home life once more was a very persuasive factor.

'Will we live in the country?' she asked Reed, the first

weekend they took her and Antonia's mother to Stonor, and he had smiled.

'Would you like to?' he asked, and at her nod, he continued: 'Then, we'll have to see about finding you a pony, so that you can get about more easily,' and her whoop of delight had made her mother shake her head.

'Bribery and corruption,' she had teased Reed, and he had waited until later to exact a sweet punishment.

Waking on the morning of their last day in Tahiti, Antonia lay for several minutes without stirring, just looking at the man who had made her world so complete. It hardly seemed possible it was less than four months since they had first met. Now, she couldn't remember a time when he had not been an integral part of her life.

'What are you thinking?'

Reed's eyes had opened as she lay musing, and Antonia snuggled nearer to deposit a lingering kiss at the corner of his mouth. 'I was thinking how much I love you,' she admitted, shifting so that his possessive arm could close about her. 'I wish we never had to leave here.'

Reed's eyes were openly caressing. 'I thought you might be eager to get back home. That you might be missing Susie.'

Antonia sighed. 'Well, I do miss her, of course, but I know she's happy.' She ran her hand across his chest, loving the fine whorls of hair that curled confidingly about her finger. 'Your parents have been absolutely marvellous. Letting her stay with them.'

'Well, she seemed to take to them,' remarked Reed modestly, and Antonia's lips tilted.

'They spoil her,' she declared, remembering Susie's excited voice, the last time they had spoken to her on the phone. 'A pony *and* a dog of her own. She's never going to want to leave Drumbarra.'

'I think that's their idea,' said Reed, allowing a lazy laugh to escape him. 'Still, at least that takes the onus from us. They've got the granddaughter they always wanted.'

Antonia nodded, wondering how to phrase her next words. 'But would you mind?' she ventured carefully, watching his expression, 'if we added to our family rather sooner than you expected?'

Reed levered himself up on one elbow to look down at her. 'You're pregnant.'

'Hmm.'

'God!' He bent his head to give her a very disruptive kiss. 'How long have you known?'

'Since about the first week we were here,' admitted Antonia reluctantly, and his eyes widened incredulously.

'So why didn't you tell me?'

'I didn't want to—spoil our honeymoon.'

'How could that spoil anything?' demanded Reed huskily, his eyes running possessively down her body. 'Hell, we've been here four weeks, and you've known all that time!'

Antonia ran her fingers along the roughened curve of his cheek. 'Well, not definitely,' she murmured, colouring. 'These things take time.'

Reed shook his head. 'Do you mind?'

'Do you?'

'That's a crazy question,' he muttered huskily. 'Of course I don't mind! Just so long as you don't shut me out.'

Antonia moistened her lips. 'I—Simon was never interested' she confessed, by way of an explanation. 'When I told him I was going to have Susie, he asked if I wanted to get rid of it.'

'I'm not Simon,' said Reed forcefully, brushing back the silky hair from her temple with caressing fingers. Since their wedding, Antonia had allowed her hair to grow, and now it tumbled softly down her back. 'And—as it happens—I have something to tell you, too.'

'You do?' Antonia was apprehensive. Her eyes darkened. 'What is it?'

As if sensing her uncertainty, Reed lowered his length beside her and gathered her closer to him. 'Don't look so worried,' he told her softly, as anxious anticipation feathered along her spine. He brushed her lips with his thumb. 'I heard from my father a week ago, as you know. But I didn't tell you everything he wrote.'

Antonia's tongue circled her lips. 'It's not—Susie, is it?'

'No.' Reed was very definite on that point. He paused. 'Do you remember, we tried to contact Sheldon to organise the adoption order?'

'Yes.' Antonia held her breath.

'Well—I didn't want to tell you sooner, but Toni—love; Sheldon was drowned in the South China sea more than six months ago.'

'I think we should have a second honeymoon,' declared Reed, coming into the bedroom at Stonor with a towel draped carelessly about his hips. 'What do you think? Would you let Maria and my mother take care of our son as well as our daughter?'

Antonia, who was seated before the vanity unit in the master bedroom, rhythmically brushing her hair, lifted her slim shoulders. 'I thought you had that deal with the Canadians to attend to,' she reminded him. 'Didn't you tell me Cohen and the others were coming to dinner on Tuesday?'

'Well, yes, I did.' Reed came behind her, running possessive fingers under the thin straps of her slip and sliding them off her shoulders. 'But I've learned to delegate,' he added drily, bending to stroke sensuous lips across her soft skin. 'Wouldn't you like to spend a couple of weeks in the south of France? It's marvellous there at this time of the year.'

Antonia lifted her shoulder to facilitate his caress, and shivered in pleasurable anticipation. 'Reed, the Turners will be here in fifteen minutes,' she protested, when his questing hands slid beneath the lacy bodice to find the swelling fullness of her breasts, and he tossed the towel aside before drawing her up into his arms.

'They can wait,' he told her huskily, pressing the slip down over her hips. 'You did say Miss Forrester had taken the children to bed, didn't you?'

'I did say that, yes,' Antonia conceded laughingly, winding her arms around his neck. 'Oh, Reed, can we really take another two weeks to ourselves? Won't your parents think I'm a very indifferent mother?'

'My mother will be overjoyed to have charge of our family once again,' her husband assured her firmly, drawing her gently, but insistently towards their enormous four-poster. 'We went along with her wishes and had a second wedding in the church at Drumbarra. How could she deny us a second honeymoon?'

Antonia sighed reminiscently. 'It was a lovely wedding, wasn't it?' she murmured, remembering the tiny church at Drumbarra; the white surplices of the choirboys; the fragrant perfume of the flowers. 'I didn't think when you sent me that gorgeous bouquet last year that this year the same flowers would remind me of our wedding.'

'You did get them then,' remarked Reed drily, pulling her down on to the bed beside him and crushing her slender form beneath the muscular weight of his body. 'You never told me.'

'Didn't I?' Antonia's slim fingers entwined in the hair at his nape. 'No—well, I didn't want to encourage you, did I?'

'That's the truth,' murmured her husband ruefully. 'Be thankful I didn't take no for an answer!'

'Oh, I'm very thankful for that,' responded Antonia fervently, and then gave herself up to the blissful possession of his mouth . . .

PALE ORCHID

PALE ORCHID

BY
ANNE MATHER

MILLS & BOON LIMITED
Eton House, 18–24 Paradise Road
Richmond, Surrey TW9 1SR

*First published in Great Britain 1985
by Mills & Boon Limited*

© Anne Mather 1985

Australian copyright 1985
Philippine copyright 1985
Reprinted 1985
This edition 1989

ISBN 0 263 76400 1

Set in Monophoto Times 10 on 10pt.
19–8904 – 59806

Made and printed in Great Britain

CHAPTER ONE

THE wide-bodied jet taxied into its unloading bay, and the extending arm of the disembarking gangway was fitted into position. Across the tarmac, another plane was just taking off, its wings dipping to starboard as it executed the manoeuvre which would take it out across the blue waters of the Pacific, skirting the beach at Waikiki before heading back towards California.

Watching the American Airlines jet climb into the late afternoon sky, Laura Huyton wished, with an urgency bordering on desperation, that she could be aboard that plane, heading back to San Francisco, and on to London. Seven thousand miles was a long way to come to face probable humiliation, and she wondered if she would have set out so confidently if she had known where her quest would lead her.

Most of the other passengers waiting to disembark were holidaymakers, bound for one or other of the many excellent hotels Honolulu boasted. Some, unlike herself, were only stopping off in Oahu, *en route* for other islands in the Hawaiian group, but all of them, it seemed to Laura, were looking forward to their arrival. There had been a definite air of excitement in the aircraft, ever since it left San Francisco, and the stewardesses in their long Polynesian dresses added their own particular colour to the trip.

'This your first visit to Hawaii?' inquired the rather stout matron, who had been sitting beside her all trip, and who had tried on several occasions to engage Laura in conversation—without any success.

'No.'

Laura's response was monosyllabic, but she couldn't help it. She didn't want to talk about Hawaii; she didn't want to be here; and had it not been for a brutal trick of fate, she doubted she would ever have come here again.

'You've been before then?' persisted the woman, as the door to the plane was opened and passengers started to block the gangways in their haste to disembark.

'Yes.' Laura slipped the strap of her bag over her shoulder and gathered together the book and magazines she had bought to read on the journey. Then, feeling obliged to say something, if only to get the woman to move out of the aisle seat, she added briefly, 'I used to work here some years ago. It's not a place you forget.'

'Absolutely not,' exclaimed her inquisitor enthusiastically, getting to her feet, and although she would obviously have liked to continue this discussion, she was compelled to move ahead. 'Have a good time,' she added, as Laura slipped into the queue some spaces behind her.

'I intend to.' Laura allowed a small smile that gave her pale features animation. A good time, she reflected ruefully, was the last thing she was likely to have; but that was her problem and no one else's.

The pretty Polynesian girls who waited in the arrivals hall had almost exhausted the supply of flower garlands they handed out to holiday visitors. The *leis*, as they were called, were very popular with tourists, and Laura could still remember her delight when, on her first visit to the islands, she had received the symbolic welcome. Today, however, she sidestepped the smiling throng and hurried on down the escalator, to take her seat on one of the articulated buses, which transported passengers between the arrivals hall and the terminal buildings.

By the time she had collected her luggage from the carousel and summoned a cab, the sun was sinking and, giving the address of the small hotel she remembered, just off Kalakaua Avenue, she settled back to enjoy the ride. Through the open windows of the cab, the air was deliciously warm and pungently familiar. Even before they crossed the Kapalama Canal, she could smell the Dole Canneries, and the water tank, painted to resemble a pineapple, rose like a huge yellow dome, sprouting its prickly stalk.

To her right, the less attractive aspects of the island's

economy gave way to the waving masts of the yacht marina. Dozens of sailing craft, from modest dinghies to ocean-going schooners, were moored in the basin, and Laura couldn't help but wonder if Jason still owned his schooner. Not that it had any relevance, she assured herself impatiently, determinedly turning her attention to the exotic elegance of a floating restaurant moored at the quay. How Jason Montefiore might or might not be conducting his private affairs was no concern of hers.

The cab was approaching Kalakaua Avenue, and Laura gazed out at the towering hotel blocks. There seemed more than she remembered, even the 'Pink Palace', as the Royal Hawaiian Hotel used to be called, was overshadowed now by the looming curve of the Sheraton. But the market place was still there, where Jason had once bought her a string of real pearls and the engraved gold medallion, she still carried in her handbag.

Just beyond the imposing towers of the Hyatt Regency, the cab turned into a side street and a hundred yards down, past an intersection, came to a halt outside the modest façade of the Kapulani Reef Hotel. Laura climbed out, dragging her suitcase after her, and handed over the necessary dollars. Thank goodness she had remembered the name of this place, she thought, looking up at its faded exterior. The paint was chipping on the balconies, and the sun had yellowed its colour-washed walls. But so far as she knew, its reputation was still intact, and one of the girls at the agency used to recommend it. Of course, that was more than three years ago now, but it could not be helped. Hotels in Waikiki were expensive, and those Jason had taken her to were quite beyond her means. The Kapulani used to be both clean and reasonable, and she did not have a lot of choice in the matter. Besides, with luck, it might only be for a couple of nights.

She had 'phoned ahead from San Francisco, and she was expected. A polite receptionist had her sign in, and then a Chinese porter was summoned to take her to her room. The lift transported them three floors up to room number 409, and Laura felt obliged to tip the man, even though his manner was anything but friendly. Still, he had carried her suitcase, she reflected, as she took a proper look at her surroundings.

It was clean and neat, she had to admit, the bed one of the wide divans she had become used to during the time she had worked in Honolulu. There was a chest of drawers and a fitted closet, a round glass-topped table and a chair, and the ubiquitous colour television, standing by the open balcony doors. There was also a telephone, the one object Laura most wanted to see, but she put her immediate impulses aside and walked into the adjoining bathroom.

Fifteen minutes later she emerged, considerably cooler and fresher after a shower. Wrapped in a towel, she threw her soiled clothes on to the chair, and then rescued the key to her suitcase from her handbag and deposited the case on the bed.

There was a definite disorganisation to the contents of the suitcase, but it couldn't be helped. For the past three days, she had thought little about her appearance, and the garments she had packed with reasonable care in London, were now muddled beyond belief. That they were not more creased was due to the resiliency of modern fabrics, and she drew out the short-sleeved shirt and pants that were first to hand.

Running a brush through the fine silky hair, that she generally plaited and wore in a single braid for working purposes, Laura contained her impatience and walked out on to the balcony. It was getting dark, but the air was as soft and velvety as a moth's wing. The temperature stayed balmy most of the time, only becoming hot and sticky in the summer when the wind called the *kona* blew. Usually, the climate was perfect, a delicious blend of sun and trade winds, that made the islands a garden paradise.

Away to the right, Laura could hear the sound of the surf, as it creamed along the shoreline, and she was tempted to leave what she had to do until the morning and go for a walk along the beach. It would be so nice to forget her troubles for a while, and enjoy the exotic

beauty of her surroundings. But then, the memory of
Pamela, lying in the hospital in San Francisco, returned
to haunt her, and putting the brush aside, she quickly
threaded her hair into its neat *queue*.

Crossing the room to where the 'phone sat, on the
low bureau beside the bed, Laura reflected that even
that image was not as disturbing as the scene which had
met her eyes on her arrival in San Francisco. If she
hadn't responded to Pamela's 'phone call so promptly,
if she hadn't ignored Pierce's complaints about her
ingratitude, and taken the first available flight from
London, she might never have found her sister alive. As
it was, Pamela had been unconscious, the terrible
meaning of the empty bottle of sleeping tablets on the
table beside her, telling their own tale. Laura shivered,
even now. Without her unexpected intervention, Pamela
would be dead—and all because of Mike Kazantis.

Before picking up the 'phone, she reached for her
bag, and drew out the handful of letters she had found
scattered about her sister's body. Without them, she
might never have learned the name of the man who had
caused her sister so much heartbreak. Pamela could
have refused to tell her. Indeed, at first, she had denied
any connection between the letters and her attempted
suicide. But when the doctors at the Mount Rushmore
Hospital had informed Laura that her sister was
pregnant, she had immediately understood the situation.

Of course, Mike Kazantis's name would have meant
nothing to Pamela. It was less than two years since she
had applied for a nursing post in Sausalito, and her
work with the elderly, and very rich, Mrs Amy
Goldstein, had seemed far removed from the commercial
success of Jason Montefiore.

Naturally, after her own experiences in the United
States, Laura had tried to persuade her younger sister
not to leave England. But short of explaining exactly
why she had returned to London, there was little she
could say; and besides, it had seemed unlikely that
Pamela would make the same mistakes.

Laura shook her head now, and reached for the

'phone. It was not a situation she had ever expected to have to deal with. When she was making her arrangements to accompany Pierce to the Camargue at the beginning of March, Pamela had been writing, saying how happy she was, and there had been no mention of her relationship with Jason's brother-in-law. Had she known he was married? Was that why she had not mentioned his name to her sister? The little Laura had read of *his* letters, gave no evidence one way or the other. All that was clear was that the letters had ceased, approximately six weeks ago. The most recent postmark was March 14th, and Laura had had no difficulty in making the association.

She rang the club first, guessing that as it was after six o'clock Jason was most likely to be there. If he was in Honolulu, of course, she reflected, crossing her fingers. There was no absolute guarantee. Just her own recollection of his movements, and the fervent hope that this trip to Hawaii had not been a fool's errand.

A man answered, a man whose voice she didn't recognise, and adopting her most confident tone, she asked to speak to Mr Montefiore. 'It's a personal matter of some urgency,' she explained, hoping that by mentioning the personal nature of her call, the man would at least be curious.

'Just a minute,' he said, and the line went dead, indicating she assumed that she had been dealt with by a switchboard, and that her call was receiving more serious attention. *Come on, come on*, she urged impatiently, running first one, and then a second, moist palm over the knees of her trousers. Jason wasn't the Pope, after all. What on earth could be taking so long?

'Yes?'

Another male voice had taken the place of the switchboard attendant, and Laura tried to identify the brusque address. It wasn't Jason, that much was certain, but there was something vaguely familiar about that clipped inquiry.

'Oh, hello,' she said again, swallowing her uncertainty. 'I—er—I'd like to speak to Mr Montefiore, please. This—this is Laura Huyton.'

'Laura!' The voice definitely exhibited surprise now, and the warmer vowels gave her her first clue.

'Phil?' she ventured, and hearing his swift intake of breath: 'Phil Logan? Yes, it's me; Laura.' She took a gulp of air. 'Is Jason there?'

'Where are you, Laura?' Without answering, he turned the question against her. 'You sound pretty close. Are you here, in Oahu?'

Laura hesitated, and then she replied resignedly, 'Yes. I arrived a couple of hours ago. Phil, I need to speak to Jason urgently. If he's there, I'd appreciate it if you'd get him to the 'phone.'

There was silence for a few seconds, and then Logan spoke again. 'Does Jason know you're coming?' he inquired, his tone almost imperceptibly cooler now. And at her swift denial, 'What are you doing in Honolulu, Laura? I have to tell you—I don't think Jason will agree to see you.'

Laura's lips compressed. 'What I'm doing here I'll tell Jason, and no one else,' she retorted. 'Don't you think you should at least give him a chance to refuse? It is important. You can tell him that.'

Again the silence stretched between them, and Laura could feel the nerves in her stomach tightening unpleasantly. She had eaten little since that morning, and the hollow feeling she was experiencing was partly due to her emptiness. But, she couldn't deny a certain irritation at the attitude Phil Logan was adopting, and although she knew she had no right to expect anything of Jason, she resented being thwarted by one of his employees.

'I can't ask Jason to speak to you, because he isn't here,' Logan announced at length, and Laura expelled her breath on a sigh.

'You mean—he's at the apartment?'

'Mr Montefiore doesn't live in Honolulu any more, Laura,' he responded reluctantly, his deliberate use of Jason's surname creating a barrier even a fool could not overlook; and Laura was no fool. 'He . . . er . . . if you'd like to give me the address of the hotel where you're staying, and your 'phone number, I'll pass your message on. That's the best I can do.'

Laura's jaw quivered, and she clamped her teeth together to arrest the weakness. But it was anger, not emotion, that caused her breathing to quicken and the blood to run more thinly through her veins. How dare Phil Logan behave as if she was some pitiful hanger-on, desperate for a hand-out? she thought furiously. When had she ever treated him with anything less than courtesy, even when she had been living in Jason's luxurious penthouse and Logan had been pulling beers in the nightclub bar?

'Thanks,' she said now, deciding there was no point in pursuing her frustration with him. 'I'm staying at the Kapulani Reef Hotel. It's on Haleiwa Avenue——'

'I know where it is,' responded Logan swiftly, evidently taking it down, and Laura contained her resentment at his tone.

'Room 409,' she added, just for good measure, and then rang off before he could make some comment about her choice of accommodation.

But with the receiver replaced on its cradle, Laura found that she was shaking. Somehow, she had never expected Jason's employees to treat her like a pariah. Phil Logan had acted as if Jason had thrown her out, instead of the way it really was. Was that what Jason had told his men? That he had thrown her over?

Getting up from the bed, she walked nervously across to the open windows, rubbing her palms against the unexpectedly chilled flesh of her upper arms. So much for speaking to Jason tonight, she thought bitterly. He might not even get the message. If she didn't hear from him within the next twenty-four hours, she would have to think of some other method of finding him. But how? Logan hadn't even told her where he was living. He could be on the mainland for all she knew. Over two thousand miles away, and as remote as he had ever been.

She supposed she ought to go downstairs and find the coffee shop. Maybe, with something to eat and several cups of coffee inside her she would feel more

capable of handling the situation. Right now, she had
the horrible suspicion that her journey had been a waste
of time, and she couldn't help remembering that Pierce
had threatened to fire her if she didn't return within the
week.

Stepping out on to the verandah, she rested her
hands on the iron rail and looked down at the street
below. There were few people walking, but there were
plenty of cars using the connection between Kalakaua
Avenue and Kapiolani Boulevard; long expensive
limousines, driven by the more affluent members of the
community, through to topless beach buggies, rattling
along at a reckless pace.

But Laura hardly saw them. She was thinking about
Pierce and his objections to her trip. Of course, he had
not known before she left exactly what she would find
in San Francisco, any more than she had. Even so,
when she had 'phoned him from Pamela's apartment
after her sister had been taken to the hospital, he had
not shown a lot of sympathy. Pierce Carver was used to
getting his own way, and that did not include losing his
secretary at a significant point in his latest book.

Laura sighed. As the author of some fifteen novels,
and popularly regarded as the doyen of psychological
thrillers, Pierce would survive, whatever happened.
Pamela might not. For the next few days, he would have
to persevere with the dictaphone he had acquired some
years ago, and if that was not satisfactory, he would no
doubt make other arrangements. Whether those
'arrangements' would involve her dismissal, Laura
could not be absolutely sure. Pierce was artistic and
temperamental, and he tended to say things in anger he
did not actually mean. Not that she considered herself
indispensable, of course. No one was that. But she had
worked for him for almost three years, and she knew
his idiosyncrasies so well.

She remembered his dismay when she had told
him about Pamela's 'phone call. 'But you can't just
walk out on me, Laura,' he had wailed. 'We're at the
most crucial stage of the book. Whatever slough of
despond your sister has got herself into cannot—*simply*

cannot—be allowed to interfere with your obligations to me. Heavens, the girl's not a child, is she? She's over twenty-one. You're her sister, not her mother!'

There had been more of the same, but Laura had had no time to listen. She had been too busy making 'phone calls of her own, to the airport, to the mini cab service, and packing her belongings, to give him her undivided attention. She was sorry she had to leave him in the lurch. She knew how he depended upon her. But Pamela depended on her, too, and the apprehension she felt about her sister over-ruled her remorse.

She was so relieved they had been in England when the call came through. For the past four weeks, she had been staying in Aix, at the villa in Provence, which Pierce had rented to write his latest novel. Had he not grown bored with his surroundings, had he not felt the need for a change of scenery, he would not have suggested flying back to London, and there was no doubt now he regretted his decision to return home.

'You know how much I enjoy *our* sessions,' he had protested, when the issue of the dictaphone had been raised. 'Without your reactions, how will I know if I'm on the right track?'

'You managed perfectly well before I came on the scene,' Laura had pointed out swiftly, but in so doing, she had given Pierce the opening he was looking for.

'So I did,' he had remarked acidly, folding his arms as he was prone to do in moments of stress. 'So I did. Beware I don't decide I can manage without you. There are plenty of out-of-work secretaries simply panting to take your place!'

He was right. Laura knew that; and it had been with a certain amount of trepidation that she had told him she was taking a week's leave of absence with or without his consent. Pierce could be vindictive at times, and he might just decide to be awkward. She could only hope he would find it less easy to choose a replacement than he imagined, and that absence would achieve what reasoned argument could not.

With a feeling of anxious frustration, Laura

abandoned this particular line of thought, and walked back into the bedroom. The hospital, she thought suddenly. She ought to ring the hospital and find out how Pamela was progressing. It had been eight o'clock, San Francisco time, when she last made an inquiry, and despite the doctor's assurance that her sister would pull through, her mental state was so precarious, Laura couldn't quite believe them.

The night staff at Mount Rushmore were reassuring. Pamela had had a reasonably good day and she was sleeping. The toxic level of her blood was falling, and if her psychological report proved satisfactory, she might be allowed to go home in a couple of days.

'There's no physical danger then?' Laura persisted, remembering articles she had read about toxic hepatitis and stomach bleeding.

'It seems unlikely,' replied the charge nurse smoothly. 'I think your sister's mental state is what we need to monitor. You do realise, don't you, she could always try this again?'

She realised, Laura reflected tensely, replacing the receiver. That was why she was here, in Honolulu. That was why she had agreed to contact Jason, on her sister's behalf. Naturally, she hadn't told Pamela of his relationship to Mike Kazantis, but after her sister confessed that Mike was no longer using the address he had put on his letters, there had seemed no alternative but to ask Jason's assistance. She had reassured Pamela with the conviction that if Jason could help, he would, but she had not really believed it. Still, she was prepared to do anything to take that look of desperation from her sister's face, and if it meant humbling herself before Jason Montefiore—and his brother-in-law—she would do it.

Unable to stand the inactivity any longer, Laura gathered up her bag and left the room. It was obvious Jason was unlikely to call this evening. Even if he got her message, which was by no means a foregone conclusion, he would evidently be in no hurry to contact her. If Phil Logan's attitude was anything to go by, he might not even acknowledge her call, and the prospect of having to tell Pamela she had failed was not something she wanted to contemplate.

The coffee shop was crowded and deciding she couldn't stand to wait, Laura left the hotel and headed towards the floodlit brilliance of Kalakaua Avenue. After the comparative quiet of her room, Waikiki's main thoroughfare was decidedly noisy, but she welcomed the activity to numb her anxious brain.

Finding a fast-food establishment, she ordered a burger and some coffee, and then carried her tray to a plastic booth and tried to swallow the sandwich. It wasn't easy. She realised belatedly a bowl of soup or some salad might have gone down more smoothly, but it was too late now to have second thoughts. Picking sesame seeds from the roll, she wondered if Phil Logan would tell her how she might get in touch with Mike Kazantis if Jason's whereabouts were *verboten*. Or had he orders to avoid *any* awkward inquiries? It was always possible that Jason had known of Mike's involvement with her sister, and obviously he would not want *his* sister to be upset. Laura cupped her chin on one hand. Whatever happened, it was unlikely that either Mike or his wife lived in the islands. Mike worked for Jason's father, and so far as she knew, Marco Montefiore's interests did not encroach on his son's territory.

Laura's lips twisted. How on earth had Pamela got herself involved with the Montefiore family? The brief conversation she had had with her sister had not elicited that kind of information. Besides, so far as she knew, Pamela did not know of Mike's connection with the Montefiores, and it was possible, that as Mrs Goldstein's private therapist, they could have met socially. Even if her sister had known the truth behind Laura's own break-up with Jason, she could still have become infatuated with Kazantis. There was nothing to connect him with Laura's abortive liaison, and if Kazantis had known of the association, he was unlikely to mention it to Pamela, for obvious reasons.

Pushing the burger aside, Laura lifted the plastic beaker containing her coffee and thoughtfully sipped the fragrant brew. American coffee was always so good, she mused inconsequently. Even the unimaginative container could not spoil the taste of its contents.

Gazing blindly out through the open doors on to the busy street beyond, she wondered again what she would do if her efforts to reach either Jason or his brother-in-law proved useless. And why—even if by some chance she did get to speak to Jason—did she think he might be able, or willing, to help her? What did she really expect him to do? What *could* he do? Mike Kazantis was his sister's *husband*. Surely, it was the height of arrogance to believe he might put Pamela's well-being before that of Irene.

It seemed an insoluble problem, and her brain ached with the effort of trying to solve it. She was not at all convinced that approaching Mike Kazantis was the right thing to do. If Pamela had been more reasonable, if she had been prepared to go back to England, as soon as she was fit, Laura was sure they would have found a way to sort things out. One parent families were not so unusual these days, if Pamela wanted to keep her baby. And if not, there were always adoption agencies eager and willing to find the child a good home.

But Pamela had not been reasonable. Her unwilling return to consciousness to find her sister at her bedside and, it transpired, in possession of all the facts of her case, had elicited an entirely different response. 'There must be some mistake,' she had insisted, the faith she had lost so drastically returning now that Laura was there to listen. 'Mike wouldn't just abandon me. He wouldn't! Something must be wrong. Perhaps he's been taken ill, or had an accident. If only there was someone we could ask. Someone who could give us a clue to his whereabouts. Is there no one you know, Laura? No one you met while you were over here?'

Whether Pamela knew exactly what she was asking, Laura had no idea. Certainly she had never confided the true facts of her relationship with Jason Montefiore to her sister. But perhaps Pamela sensed, or suspected, that there had been more to Laura's abrupt return to England than the casual explanation that she had grown tired of living so far from London. Whatever,

Laura had felt compelled to use what influence she had
to try and set her sister's mind at rest, and that was why
she was here in Hawaii, facing the increasing conviction
that she was wasting her time.

The situation seemed hardly brighter in the morning.
Laura had not slept well, and after ringing the hospital
and ensuring herself that Pamela was still making
progress, she considered what her next move should be.
She could ring the club again, she supposed, although
the prospect was not one she favoured. Besides, only
the cleaning staff were likely to be there at this hour of
the morning, and none of them would risk their jobs by
giving out private information. And perhaps she was
being overly pessimistic anyway. Jason might telephone.
There was still time.

The telephone rang while she was in the shower, but
although she dashed out of the bathroom to take the
call, a towel wrapped hastily around her dripping body,
it was an early morning call meant for someone else.
'*Aloha*, this is your wake-up service,' announced the
mechanical voice, and Laura slammed down the
receiver, feeling the painful ache of tears behind her
eyes.

Dressed again, in the cotton pants and shirt she had
worn the evening before, she stood in front of the
mirror to plait her hair. She had no particular desire to
look at her reflection, the evidence of the disturbed
nights she had spent since Pamela's call a visual
depressant. But she couldn't help assessing her
appearance with Jason's critical eyes, and her conclusion
was not flattering. Too tall, too thin, and too plain, she
thought bitterly, wondering, not for the first time,
whatever it was he had seen in her. She was certainly
nothing like the girls who had worked in his club or
hung around the bar, hoping to attract his attention.
They had all had one thing in common: an unswerving
faith in their own desirability, whereas Laura had
always doubted her appeal.

She sighed now, her hands falling limply to her sides.
From the very beginning, she had been bemused by

Jason's interest in her, and perhaps that was why he had succeeded where other men had failed. If she had not been so naïvely flattered by his attentions, she might have recognised him sooner for what he was, instead of learning too late how easily she had been deceived.

She shook her head. It was too late now to change the past. And in spite of her experiences, she had succeeded in making a new life for herself with Pierce. There had actually been days when she had not thought about Jason Montefiore and the devastating influence he had had on her. Until Pamela's 'phone call, that was, and the inescapable connotations it had aroused ...

It was barely eight o'clock when she went down to the coffee shop and ordered some coffee. The menu didn't interest her, but realising that starving herself would help no one, she chose scrambled eggs and toast. Trying to do them justice, she surveyed her fellow diners enviously. How nice it would have been to have nothing more momentous on her mind than what bikini she would wear to the beach, Laura mused wryly. With her pale skin, she was definitely a rarity, and it was not a distinction she enjoyed.

After the waitress had taken away her half-eaten plate of eggs, Laura sipped her third cup of coffee and wondered what she ought to do now. She supposed she should stay around the hotel, if only to be on hand should Jason make an attempt to contact her. On the other hand, if he had not 'phoned by lunchtime, she could surely discount his doing so, and then she would have to decide whether or not to try the club in person.

Her decision made, she told the receptionist at the desk she was expecting a call, and then joined the other holidaymakers congregating beside the small pool. Seated in the shade on a padded lounger, she made an effort to appear as nonchalant as the other guests, but she was acutely alert to the paging call of the receptionist's voice.

From time to time, a lissom Polynesian girl, dressed in a flowered bikini, with a matching kanga looped about her waist, came to offer cocktails, fruit drinks or coffee. But Laura always refused her lilting inquiry, and when a shadow fell across her for the fourth time, she lifted her head impatiently.

'Thank you, I don't want ...' she was beginning rather tersely, when her throat dried and the words choked to silence in her mouth. 'Heavens—*Jason*!' she got out disbelievingly, scrambling hastily to her feet, but her knees felt ridiculously unsteady as she faced the man across the width of the lounger.

CHAPTER TWO

'HELLO, Laura.'

Jason's voice was cool and polite, his tone detached and incurious, as if her arrival in the islands was no surprise to him. On the contrary, there was a cynical gleam in the depths of his pale gold eyes, and his expression was resigned and only slightly guarded.

'I ... er ... I thought you'd ring,' Laura stammered now, caught unaware by her own unwelcome response to his dark magnetism. She had thought she had recovered from that unhealthy infatuation, but it seemed she had been premature in dismissing his attraction.

'I did,' he replied briefly, shifting his weight from one foot to the other, and she noticed, inconsequently, how much older he looked. The lines that etched his dark features were deeply ingrained, and the hair that lay so smoothly against his head was distinctly threaded with grey. 'You were not available,' he added, glancing behind him to where two other men were lounging by the pool bar.

Realising he had not come alone, Laura felt a resurgence of the resentment which had sustained her through the long weeks following her return to England. Of course, she thought bitterly, a man like him would need a bodyguard. He must have many enemies, not just here, but on the mainland.

'I rang yesterday evening,' he continued, observing her changing expression with impassive eyes. 'Logan said it was urgent. I presume he exaggerated.'

'I ... why ... *no*!' Laura gathered her wandering thoughts, and adopted an air of concentration. 'He— Logan, that is—doubted you would wish to speak to me. I'm afraid I went for a walk. You should have left a message.'

Jason expelled his breath evenly. 'Yes,' he said flatly.

Yes, I expect I should. Well—I am here now. I suggest we find somewhere we can talk.'

'Oh—yes.' Laura looked about her awkwardly, realising for the first time that their conversation was being observed by at least a dozen pairs of curious eyes. And why not, she reflected drily. They must be wondering what a man like Jason Montefiore could possibly want with a pale-skinned English girl of nondescript appearance, when he could evidently have his pick of any of the golden-skinned beauties lining the pool.

'I assume you have no objections to coming with me?' Jason inquired, as they walked towards the hotel entrance, and Laura cast him a sideways glance.

'Coming with you?' she echoed faintly, acutely aware of the shortcomings of her outfit compared to the fine silk of his beige suit.

'I thought we might use the yacht,' he essayed politely, allowing her to precede him into the hotel. 'We can hardly talk here.'

'Why not?'

Laura's braid swung over one shoulder as she twisted her head towards him, and his lips parted in a thin smile. 'I think we will use the yacht,' he responded, striding lithely through the lobby and pushing wide the swing door for her to precede him out on to the front steps of the building. 'You initiated this meeting, Laura,' he added crisply. 'The least you can do is to allow me to choose its venue.'

Aware of the two men from the bar following them, Laura had little choice but to step out into the sunlight. Rubbing her palms against her upper arms, she saw the sleek silver Mercedes waiting at the kerb, and her heart beat a little faster in spite of her misgivings.

Jason went ahead of her down the steps, and she saw him loosen the button beneath his tie and pull the knot away from his collar. So even he felt the heat, she reflected tensely, glad of the small imperfection. Then, as the doors opened behind her, she descended the steps, just as a uniformed chauffeur emerged to open the car doors for them.

'Get in,' advised Jason briefly, his eyes already looking beyond her to the two men behind. She did so, with reluctance, closing her ears to the terse instructions Jason was issuing, not looking his way again even when she felt the depression of his weight on the cushioned seat beside her.

The door was closed, and immediately the air-conditioning inside the car chilled her flesh. With the glass screen between front and back raised, they were enclosed in a world of smoked glass sophistication, and Laura couldn't help remembering the last occasion she had ridden with him. There had been antagonism between them then, as there was now, but also a compelling familiarity—an addictive intimacy Laura had found it so hard to live without. She had known him so well—or at least she had thought she had—and there were times in those early days when she had wondered how she had ever found the strength to leave him, even after what she had learned. The truth, she had discovered to her cost, was that love did not always conform to a code of ethics. It was headstrong and unpredictable, and it had taken many months and many sleepless nights to get Jason Montefiore out of her blood . . .

'You flew in—when? Yesterday?' he inquired now, and she was forced to withdraw her attention from the leather strap hanging by the window.

'Yesterday afternoon,' she agreed, giving him a swift look of appraisal. He had lost weight, she noticed unwillingly, but the deeply-set eyes and thin-lipped mouth were still as disturbingly sensual as ever. His cheeks had hollowed, but the skin stretched tautly over his bones gave his dark face the strength and character she remembered, his Italian ancestry only evident in the burnished darkness of his hair.

'From London?' he persisted, raising one leg to rest his ankle across his knee, and the fine cloth of his pants tautened across his thighs.

'No,' she responded shortly, turning her eyes away from his unconscious sexuality, and concentrating on the back of the chauffeur's head. Evidently the two other men were riding in a separate car, for there was only themselves and the driver in this one. After all, what use had Jason for a bodyguard with her? He was perfectly capable of subduing her, should he so wish.

She thought he might pursue his questions, but he didn't. As if deciding he could wait if she could, he lounged a little lower in his seat, resting one lean-fingered hand on his drawn-up ankle and gazing broodingly out of the tinted window.

It didn't take them long to reach the marina. Jason's driver evidently knew the city well, and in only a few minutes they had reached the basin where dozens of yachts had their mooring. The Mercedes drove into the parking area, but before he could get out to open the door for his passengers, Jason had already taken care of it.

'You can pick me up at four o'clock,' he told the man, flicking back the cuff of his brown silk shirt and glancing at the narrow gold watch circling his wrist. 'If I need you before, I'll call.'

'Yes, sir.'

The chauffeur touched his cap with exaggerated courtesy, and Jason's lean face displayed the first trace of humour Laura had seen since his appearance. 'Okay, Ben,' he acknowledged drily, jerking open Laura's door and offering her his hand to alight. 'I'll see you later.'

Laura got out without any assistance, and Jason's hand fell to his side without comment. Slamming the door behind her, he waited until his driver had moved away before starting off towards the boardwalk, his long stride covering the ground easily so that Laura had to hurry to keep up.

He was one of the few men who did not make her conscious of her height, she thought reluctantly, his lean frame overtaking hers by a good six inches. It was one of the first things she had noticed about him; that, and the lazy brilliance of his eyes. The fact that he had been at least ten years older than she was had not registered. Despite the fact that until then she had never been interested in older men, her attraction to Jason had been immediate and overwhelming. Was that how it had been with Pamela? she wondered, struggling manfully to remember exactly why she was here.

Jason's yacht, the *Laura M*, was moored at the end of the jetty. Laura had thought he might have changed the yacht—or changed its name—but the 84 foot schooner was exactly as she remembered it, its trim white lines gleaming as it nudged against the boardwalk. A man in white shorts and a knitted cotton shirt was already on board, leaning on the rail, talking to a member of the crew of the adjoining craft. But he quickly straightened when he saw Jason, and Laura's lips parted as she recognised Alec Cowray, the captain of the *Laura M*.

'Good morning, Mr Montefiore,' he greeted Jason politely, lifting his cap and then pushing it back on his bald pate. 'I didna expect ye to be coming aboard this day.'

'I didn't know myself, Mr Cowray,' responded Jason drily, stepping on to the deck. 'Don't disturb yourself. I shan't be staying longer than a few hours. I gather we do have some food on board?'

'No problem,' averred the stout Scotsman, his expression mirroring his confusion, and then he saw Laura. '*Christ!*' he exclaimed, forgetting to moderate his language. 'I don't believe it!'

'Hello, Mr Cowray. How are you?' asked Laura awkwardly, following Jason towards the forward hatch. 'It's good to see you again.'

'It's good to see you, too, miss,' declared Alec Cowray fervently. He looked helplessly towards his employer. 'Will that be lunch for two, Mr Montefiore?'

'Provisionally,' replied Jason crisply, giving Laura a thoughtful glance. 'Don't go to a lot of trouble, Alec. Miss Huyton may not be staying.'

Laura pressed her lips together to prevent herself from voicing an indignant comment as she followed Jason down the gleaming stairway. She was more convinced than ever now that he knew exactly why she had come to the islands, and she fed her resentment in an effort to dispel the effect her surroundings were having on her. He had brought her here deliberately,

she thought, knowing what association it would have
for her. The first time Jason had made love with her
had been aboard this yacht, and she averted her eyes
determinedly from the panelled doors to his stateroom.
She knew the craft so well—she knew there were three
suites; an upper and lower saloon; and a well-equipped
galley aft. Yet, for all its size, a crew of three could
handle it, using the powerful diesel engines when the
sails were not in use.

Jason led the way into the forward saloon, a
beautifully furnished living area, with cushioned
banquettes, panelled walls, and a soft carpet underfoot.
From its windows on three sides, one had an
uninterrupted view when the craft was sailing, and
Laura remembered moonlit evenings, after she and
Jason had dined alone, sitting here and enjoying the
starlit beauty of the night . . .

'Will you have a drink?'

While she had been absorbing the saloon's familiarity,
Jason had opened up the fitted bar and was presently
examining its contents. 'Gin? Scotch? Vodka? Or would
you like me to mix you a Chi-Chi?' he inquired,
mentioning the island cocktail which had once been her
favourite.

'Nothing, thank you,' she responded tautly, seating
herself on the low banquette and imprisoning her hands
between her knees. 'I—well, I'd like to get this over
with. I believe you know why I've come.'

Jason poured himself a scotch, despite the early
hour, and after adding several cubes of ice, looked at
her over the rim of the glass. 'I have a fairly good
idea,' he conceded cynically, swallowing a generous
mouthful. 'I suppose you assume my agreeing to see
you gives you the edge. Well—I shouldn't bank on it,
if I were you.'

Laura felt the colour pour into her cheeks at his
scathing words, and it was all she could do to remain
sitting. But standing would be equally as perilous, and
she didn't want him to see how nervous she really was.

'I have no—preconceptions,' she declared now,
holding up her head and concentrating on the tasselled

cord securing a fall of velvet curtain. The words stuck in her throat, but she had to say them: 'I'm—grateful—you agreed to see me.'

Jason lowered his glass. 'Did you think I wouldn't?' he inquired mockingly, and she bent her head to study the tightly clenched bones of her knees.

'I thought it was possible,' she agreed carefully. 'As I said before, Logan didn't seem to think . . .'

'Phil Logan was only doing his job as he saw it. He knows we split up. I guess he got the wrong idea.'

Laura quivered, and when she lifted her eyes to his, the resentment she was feeling was mirrored in their depths. 'You mean—he thought you got tired of me, don't you?' she demanded painfully. 'Did you disabuse him?'

'You're here, aren't you?' remarked Jason flatly. 'That should mean something, even to Logan.'

Laura absorbed his words with a troubled frown. 'You're—very generous,' she murmured unwillingly. 'I—don't know what to say.'

'I'm sure you'll think of something,' retorted Jason tersely, finishing the scotch in his glass. 'I suggest you tell me what you've been doing since you left. I know; but I'd like to hear it in your words, just so we understand one another.'

Laura caught her breath. 'What do you mean?' she exclaimed, shaking her head. 'You—*know*—what I've been doing?'

Jason sighed. 'Must we go into this right now?'

'Yes, I think we must.'

'Okay.' He set down his glass, and came to stand in front of her. 'But first, I think I should sample the merchandise, don't you? I mean, it has been three years, and I may have overestimated your appeal!' And before she could move or even comprehend his meaning, he had circled her wrist with his fingers and jerked her to her feet.

The warm strength of his lean fingers on her nape, as he drew her unresistingly towards him, was the last coherent awareness Laura had before his lips descended on hers. Disbelief; resentment; *panic*; all were briefly subdued by the hard pressure of his mouth, and her shaken disconcertment opened her lips to his tongue.

His free arm slid around her, drawing her closer into his embrace, and it was the sensuous abrasion of his shirt against her fingers that brought her a returning measure of sanity. But although she fought free of him without too much effort, his shocking behaviour had disturbed her, and she knew he had sensed her involuntary response.

'How—how dare you?' she got out, when her breathing had steadied, and she saw the wary gleam that entered his eyes at her words.

'How dare I?' he asked, echoing her question. 'What did you expect? An apology?' He shook his head. 'I'm sorry. I don't feel I have anything to apologise for.'

Laura blinked. 'What are you talking about?'

Jason expelled his breath heavily. 'Laura, let's stop playing these games, shall we? You know why you're here, and I know why you're here. Okay—maybe I did precipitate matters a little, but you can't deny you wanted it, just as much as I did.'

Laura gulped. 'There's some mistake . . .'

'Is there?'

'Yes.' Her tongue circled her lips with increasing rapidity. 'I . . . I don't know what—kind of an advantage you think Pamela's situation gives you, but—but so far as I am concerned . . .'

'Wait a minute!' Jason's harsh voice broke into her stammered outburst, and she broke off at once, staring at him with troubled eyes. 'Run that by me again,' he said grimly. '*Who* is Pamela?'

'You know who Pamela is,' she exclaimed. 'Pamela Huyton. My *sister* Pamela. Don't pretend you don't know about her and Mike!'

Jason fell back a step, still regarding her with distinct incredulity. 'Your sister Pamela?' he repeated blankly. 'What the hell would I know about your sister, for Christ's sake? And Mike? Mike who?'

'Mike Kazantis!' declared Laura quickly, trembling a little as she struggled to take the initiative. 'You know who Mike Kazantis is, don't you? Or are you going to deny all knowledge of his identity, too?'

Jason's mouth thinned. 'Are you trying to tell me that your sister is in some way involved with Mike Kazantis?' he inquired tautly, and Laura nodded.

'But you know,' she said bitterly. 'You know you do. Else why did you agree to see me? Unless you thought you could gloat over our misfortunes!'

Jason's dark features lost all expression, and the lines that bracketed his nose and mouth looked that much more pronounced. 'Is that the opinion you have of me?' he said sombrely. 'Well, well! You really thought I would do a thing like that?'

Laura was not a little confused by now, and in spite of her determination not to let him get the better of her, his quiet words had more than an element of truth in them. But why—if he hadn't known about his brother-in-law—why had he said he knew why she was here?

'Wheth—whether you knew or not, you do now,' she said, forcing herself to go on. 'Pamela is in the hospital in San Francisco. She took an overdose of sleeping tablets. She'll live, but I don't know for how long.'

Jason's nostrils flared, and with a curious inclination of his head, he moved away towards the bar. Then, swinging round, he poured himself a second glass of scotch, tipping his head back to drink it before turning again to face her.

'It . . . it's barely eleven o'clock,' Laura exclaimed abruptly, unable to prevent the words from spilling from her lips. 'Is it wise to—to drink so much?'

Jason's lips twisted. 'Not wise at all,' he conceded sardonically. 'But that's my problem, not yours. So. Go on about your sister. Why don't you think she'll survive?'

'Because she's pregnant!' Laura pressed the palms of her hands together. 'And Kazantis has deserted her.'

'Deserted her?' Jason considered the phrase. 'What an old-fashioned expression! You mean, I suppose, that as soon as he discovered your sister had a problem, he took off.'

Laura blinked. 'He doesn't know about the baby.'

She frowned. 'At least, I think he doesn't.' It was something she had not thought to ask her sister.

'I'd guess he does,' retorted Jason drily. 'If indeed it is Mike's.'

'What do you mean?' Laura was indignant. 'Pamela wouldn't lie about something like that!'

'And she says it's his?'

'Yes.' Laura drew a trembling breath. 'Do you know where he is?'

'Kazantis? Right now?' Jason shrugged. 'I'd say— Europe.'

'Europe!' Laura blanched. 'Where in Europe?'

'Italy.' Jason dropped his empty glass back on to the bar. 'At least that's where Irene is, so . . .'

'Italy!' Laura's shoulders sagged. 'Oh, God! Why did he have to be there?'

'I'm not saying I know it for a fact,' said Jason evenly. 'But, like I said, Irene is there right now, visiting my grandparents. And, knowing my father's ideas about his women, I'd say he'd insist she didn't go unescorted.'

Laura sank down weakly on to the banquette behind her. 'For how long?' she asked helplessly. 'When will they be coming back?'

'One month, maybe two. Who knows?' Jason lifted his shoulders in a dismissing gesture. 'I'm not my sister's keeper.'

Laura shook her head, resting her elbows on her knees and cupping her cheeks in her hot palms. 'Oh, God!' she said again, feeling the emptiness of despair gripping her insides. 'What am I going to do?'

It was only partly a rhetorical question, but the sudden breeze through the open door alerted her to the fact that Jason had left her. She was alone in the green and gold beauty of the saloon, alone with her unwilling memories, and with the terrifying realisation that there was nothing she could do.

She supposed she should leave. After all, Jason had done what he could. He had told her where Kazantis was, and he had not disbelieved her story. The anger he might have displayed at the news that Pamela had evidently been having an affair with his sister's husband had not materialised, and she was simply wasting her time, and his, by pursuing the matter further. Somehow, she was going to have to find a way to tell Pamela that Mike Kazantis was married; that there was no point in her threatening to kill herself again, because he could not marry her. Not unless he got a divorce from Irene, of course, and if Jason was right and he was with his wife, in Italy, that did not seem at all likely. Besides which, Laura had met Irene, and she knew her to be a very beautiful young woman. It had been an outside chance at best that her marriage to Kazantis had floundered. Remembering what she knew of him, Laura doubted anything would prise him away from the wealth and influence that came from being Marco Montefiore's son-in-law, and contacting Jason had been her last resort.

Which brought her back to that other puzzling development: why had Jason assumed he knew why she was in Hawaii? Was there something she had overlooked? Did he know something she didn't know? And why had he kissed her? She had been prepared to face his anger, not his passion.

With trembling fingers, she traced the bare contours of her lips. She wore little in the way of cosmetics, just eyeliner and mascara, and occasionally a shiny lip-gloss to frame her mouth. But what little make-up she had been wearing had been erased by his caress, and she couldn't deny the unwilling awareness that his touch still had the power to melt her bones. If only . . .

His reappearance with an enamelled beaker which he held out to her arrested her guilty thoughts. 'Here,' he said, pushing it into her hand. 'You look as though you could use it.'

'What is it?' she asked foolishly, while the aromatic odour of ground beans floated to her nostrils, and Jason's mouth pulled down.

'Just coffee,' he replied drily, taking off his jacket and pulling off his tie. 'Laced with heroin, of course!' He grimaced. 'Drink it, for God's sake! I'm not reduced to drugging my women yet!'

Laura obediently sipped the fragrant beverage, recovering a little of her composure in the time it took her to drink it. Jason, she noticed, tossed his jacket and tie aside and flung himself on to the wide velvet cushions at the broad forward end of the cabin, crossing his legs as he had done before and staring broodingly out on to the sunlit dock.

'So, tell me what happened,' he said at length, when he had given her time to compose herself. 'How did your sister meet Kazantis?'

'I don't know.' Laura caught her lower lip between her teeth before continuing: 'She works—*worked*—in Sausalito, but she has an apartment in San Francisco.'

'Since when?'

'Oh eighteen months, I suppose. She qualified as a physiotherapist in London, but she wanted to travel. I tried to dissuade her from coming to the United States, but . . .'

'. . . she wouldn't listen?'

'Right.' Laura looked down into her cup. 'She always seemed so much younger than me. It's only two years, I know, but—well, I've always felt much older.'

'And you didn't want her to venture out into the bold bad world!' remarked Jason wryly, running his hand inside the opened neckline of his shirt and in so doing loosening several more buttons. 'So—she met Kazantis. Why didn't you warn her?'

'Warn her?' Laura looked across the cabin at him, uncomfortably aware of the sensuality of his exploring hand. The skin of his chest exposed by his careless movements was as brown and smooth as she remembered, his nipples taut, an arrowing of fine hair only lightly roughening his flesh. 'I didn't know.'

'She didn't write to you?'

'Well, yes. Yes, of course, she wrote.' Laura dragged her eyes away, and tried to keep her mind on what she was saying. 'She just didn't mention her relationship with Mike Kazantis, that's all. And . . . and after all, she wouldn't know who he was.'

'Who he was?'

'Yes.' Laura shifted a little restlessly. 'Your brother-in-law; Irene's husband! I . . . she . . . we never discussed your relations.'

Jason regarded her intently. 'But she knew of me? She knew we were living together, didn't she?'

Laura moistened her lips. 'She knew we were . . . close, yes.'

'But did she know we were living together?' persisted Jason insistently, and Laura wondered if he already knew the answer.

'It's not important,' she said, shaking her head, but he did not agree.

'Perhaps, if you'd been more honest with her, she would have felt more able to confide in you,' he commented brusquely, and Laura met his relentless gaze with hastily-summoned indignation.

'Are you saying it's my fault?' she exclaimed, using anger as a means to avoid his questioning, and he shrugged.

'I'm saying you were afraid to tell your sister the truth. Why should you be surprised if she feels likewise?'

Laura sniffed, and buried her nose in the beaker. 'That's a simplistic way of looking at things,' she said, in a muffled voice.

'I'm a simplistic person,' he responded carelessly, and she thought how ironic it was that he should say a thing like that.

'You're the least simplistic person I know,' she retorted childishly. 'Oh, for heaven's sake, does it matter what I did or didn't tell her? Pamela's pregnant, right? And if I hadn't arrived when I did, she would have been dead!'

Jason considered her for a few nerve-racking moments, then he said quietly: 'Exactly why did you arrive in California?'

'Pamela 'phoned me.' Laura cradled the beaker between her palms and gazed into space. 'I'd just got back from Aix . . .'

'The South of France, I know.'

'. . . and when she rang . . .' Laura paused briefly, as the import of what he had said reminded her of something he had said earlier—'when she rang, I sensed something was wrong.'

'Just sensed?'

'No. No.' Laura spread a helpless hand. 'Pamela sounded strange—desperate! I don't know why, but I knew she had to have rung for a purpose.'

'A cry for help?' suggested Jason drily, and Laura looked at him sharply.

'Don't you believe me?'

'Oh, yes.' He tilted his head back against the dark green velvet and studied her through narrowed eyes. 'But, objectively, I'd say that perhaps your sister wasn't as desperate to kill herself as you might think. I mean, she did rig herself a lifeline before jumping over the side, metaphorically speaking, of course.'

Laura sat up straighter. 'That's a rotten thing to suggest!'

'It's something for you to think about,' retorted Jason flatly. 'Laura, I hear of people over-dosing every day. Most of them do a better job of it than your sister appears to have done.'

'You ... you swine!'

Laura set down the cup and got unsteadily to her feet, but before she could make it to the door, Jason was there before her. 'The simplistic view, remember?' he said, his back against the panels successfully blocking her exit. 'Laura, I'm not saying Pamela did this to gain attention, but it has been known. Remember that.'

'Will you get out of my way?'

Laura's hands clenched at her sides as she waited for him to move, but he didn't. 'Eventually,' he averred, his tawny eyes resolute between the dark fringe of his lashes. 'Go sit down. We haven't finished our conversation.'

'I have.'

'Do you want me to use force?' he inquired lazily, his eyes moving down over her high small breasts thrusting against the thin material of her shirt, to the slender curve of her hips outlined by the tie-waisted cotton pants, and she immediately abandoned her mission.

'I don't know what else we can possibly have to say
to one another,' she exclaimed, moving back into the
middle of the floor and wrapping her arms about
herself, as if for protection. 'You've made your position
very clear. Why won't you let me go?'

Jason straightened away from the door, but he didn't
shift his stance. 'What are you going to do?' he asked.
'Now that your attempt to find your sister's lover and
speak with him has failed, what are you going to tell
Pamela?'

'I don't know.' Laura shook her head a trifle wearily.
'I'll think of something. If I can persuade her to come
back to London with me...'

'And if you can't?'

'Oh, please!' Laura turned away from him, gazing out
through the window, across the blue waters of the yacht
basin. 'Why should you care? Our lives mean nothing to
you!'

'Yours does,' he retorted crisply, and she turned her
head and gazed at him over her shoulder as if she
couldn't believe her ears.

'What did you say?'

'You heard me,' he responded tersely, folding his
arms across his chest. 'Why else do you suppose I've
had your movements monitored, ever since you ran out
on me? I know all about your life in London, and that
creep, Pierce Carver, you've been living with for the
past two and a half years.'

Laura half turned, her lips parting incredulously. 'I—
am not *living* with Pierce,' she protested, indignation
vying with disbelief. 'I work with him, yes, but that's
all. Your investigator was wrong if he told you there
was anything between us.'

'You live at his house!'

'I have a room there. I also have a flat of my own,'
retorted Laura hotly, and then anger quickly enveloped
her. 'But that's my business. I don't have to explain
myself to you! It's nothing to do with you! I said it
before and I'll say it again: how dare you?'

Jason regarded her beneath lowered brows. 'Why
didn't he come with you to San Francisco?' he

demanded harshly. 'Doesn't he care about your sister?'

'Why should he?' Laura was trembling with resentment. 'Oh! I can't believe this, I really can't! You've actually been having me followed ever since I left Hawaii?'

Jason shrugged, making no immediate response. Then he said flatly, 'I want you back, Laura. But you should know that. I didn't want you to leave. That was why I thought you'd come back to Hawaii. I—foolishly, I now realise—imagined you had had second thoughts; that the feelings you used to say you had for me had overwhelmed your much vaunted scruples. I was wrong. I admit it. But that doesn't alter the situation. I still want you—for the present, at least. Seeing you again has only confirmed that belief. And I'm prepared to go to practically any lengths to get you—even if it means involving your sister!'

CHAPTER THREE

LAURA felt as if someone had just delivered a gasping blow to her midriff. Her throat felt tight, and her breathing was suspended, the stunning reality of what Jason had said resounding in her head like the clanging of a bell.

'You're—not—serious!'

'But, I am.' Jason's expression was faintly self-derisive now. 'How could you doubt it? No one—but no one—walks out on Jason Montifore!'

'So that's it!' Laura caught her breath. 'Your pride was hurt!' she accused him bitterly, the shuddering intensity of his announcement tempered now by his mocking confession.

Jason inclined his head. 'If it pleases you to think so,' he remarked carelessly. 'I won't insult your intelligence by protesting I'm in love with you.'

'No. Don't.' Laura hunched her shoulders with sudden loathing. For a moment, for a brief space of time, she had half believed there must be some feeling behind his impassive pronouncement. But his taunting expression dispelled that assumption, and made a mockery of her sympathetic response.

'Nevertheless, I am prepared to do what I can to help you, providing you are equally prepared to do the same.'

Laura swallowed disbelievingly. 'Are you threatening me?'

'Threatening you? No. How could you think it?' he responded, in that same half mocking tone. 'I'm offering you a way out, an alternative your sister may find more appealing than a depressing plane ride back to London.'

Laura shifted uneasily. 'I don't understand you.'

'You will.' Jason shrugged. 'Stay and have lunch with me, and I'll explain.'

Laura moved her head from side to side, but it was a futile gesture. 'I don't see what you can say to appease Pamela's state of mind,' she insisted. 'She feels desperate and afraid . . .'

'Because she's alone and pregnant, and she has no future means of support,' said Jason levelly. 'Wouldn't you say that covered her immediate situation? That and her professed desire to see Kazantis again?'

'Well, yes . . .'

'Good.' Jason's arms fell to his sides and he gestured politely towards the cushioned seat behind her. 'So. Sit down. I'll go tell Alec we'll eat in fifteen minutes. You do like lobster, don't you?' His dark brows arched, and a faintly humorous gleam entered his eyes. 'Oh, yes, of course you do. How could I forget?'

As he pulled open the door behind him and went to inform the yacht's captain of his intentions, Laura curled one leg beneath her and sank down unhappily on to the soft banquette. It seemed he had all the answers, she thought bitterly, her fingers tugging convulsively at the fringe of braided silk that edged the cushions. And if he wasn't threatening her exactly, he was certainly using Pamela's condition to get what he wanted.

But why her? she brooded helplessly. Why was he prepared to go to such lengths to get her back? Was it only because she had walked out on him? Was he really so vain, that he couldn't bear the implications of her action? It was not an adjective she would have associated with him once, but how well had she really known him, after all? Once, she would have said she knew everything about him—his likes, his dislikes; his fairness, and his humour; the things that made him laugh, and the things that aroused his anger; his integrity in business, and his probity in justice. The men who worked for him and with him, respected him as well as liked him, and until experience had taught her differently, she had never had cause to doubt him.

Of course, she had been in love with him then, madly and irresistibly in love with a man she had never dreamed might be attracted to her. When she first went to work for him, as a temporary replacement for his own secretary, the other girls at the agency had teased her about his lean good looks, and the fact that he was one of the wealthiest men on the island. Naturally they, like her, had never imagined he would take any interest in a long-legged English girl, whose only claim to beauty was the silvery fair hair that fell almost to her waist. The rest of her features were totally ordinary, she knew: blue eyes, that watered when the sun was too strong, a straight nose that was not the least bit retroussé, and a wide mouth, whose lower lip was just the tiniest bit fuller. She discounted the length of her lashes, whose tips required mascara to be seen, and the slender curves of her figure. In her experience, men preferred smaller women, with fuller breasts, women who nestled into the curve of their arm instead of meeting them on eye-level terms.

Not that she had ever been able to say that of Jason. His height, and the lithe muscularity of his body, had always made her aware of her own femininity, and he had always maintained he preferred taller women. There had been plenty of them, goodness knows. Before she had figured in his scheme of things, he had had other mistresses, and there were several would-be supplicants all willing to inform Laura of how precarious her position was. Not to mention his ex-wife, Regina, and their daughter, Lucia . . .

She shook her head, banishing the unwilling memories of the emotions he had aroused. It was ridiculous, she told herself desperately. How could she even consider his demands? She couldn't stay in Hawaii. She couldn't abandon Pierce in the middle of the new book. Her life was in England now. Her job was in England. She had to make him understand she could not abdicate her responsibilities.

Three years ago, things had been different. Pamela had been training at a good teaching hospital in London, and sharing a flat with several other nurses. When Laura had been given the opportunity to spend six months in the Honolulu branch of the international secretarial agency in Bond Street, where she had worked at that time, it had seemed a marvellous break.

It had been no wrench to give up her bedsitter, put the few belongings she was not taking with her into storage, and fly off to Hawaii. But not now. Now, she had her own flat, in Highgate. She had put down roots, and she was no longer the carefree twenty-two-year-old she had been when Jason first met her. Besides which, she didn't want to lose her job with Pierce. She liked working for him. The job was interesting, and it had given her a chance to travel, as well as providing a very generous salary. She couldn't give that up, not at the whim of a man who she despised. She should not have come here, she acknowledged belatedly. She should not have allowed Pamela's desperate plight to drive her into a situation she obviously could not handle. But then, she realised bleakly, she had had no way of knowing how Jason would react to her plea for help. She had never suspected he might have plans of his own.

'I've told Alec to have the awning erected.' Jason's lazy tones interrupted her reverie, and she turned her head to look at him. 'I thought we might eat on deck,' he continued. 'It's cool enough in the shade.'

Laura wanted to say she didn't want to eat lunch with him, but she bit back the words. There was no point in antagonising him, she decided weakly, ignoring the fact that the longer she allowed this charade to continue, the harder it would be to convince him she could not be blackmailed.

'All right,' she said now, indifferently, sliding her curled leg off the cushions and giving a little shrug. 'But I'm not very hungry.'

'Nor am I. My appetites run in an entirely different direction,' responded Jason unemotionally. 'But unless I miss my guess, you're not exactly in a mood to take advantage of them, are you?'

A wave of warm indignation swept over her skin at his careless words, and as if that was answer enough, Jason's lips twisted. 'I thought not,' he essayed, turning back to the bar. 'I suggest a cocktail instead. Something crisp, but not too sharp. I wouldn't want to sour what promises to be an ... interesting association.'

Laura looked up at him tensely, and then, giving in

to a wholly ungovernable sense of panic, she sprang to her feet. 'I ... I can't go through with this!' she exclaimed unsteadily. 'I don't care what you say, I won't let you blackmail me! If you can't help me find Mike Kazantis, I shall fly back to San Francisco tonight.'

Jason turned from pouring white rum into a metal mixer. 'Strong words,' he remarked, his expression wiped of all humour. 'However, much as I hate to say this, you came to me, Laura. I didn't invite you here. And as you have given me the means to keep you here, why should I let you go?'

Laura swallowed. 'You can't force me to stay.'

'No. I can't do that,' he agreed, adding a measure of orange curacao to the flask. 'Nor do I intend to do so. I shall just make it—difficult for you to go.'

Laura gazed at him disbelievingly. 'How could you do that?'

Jason shrugged, his attention fixed on the remaining ingredients needed to complete the cocktail. 'Sit down,' he advised evenly. 'Wait until you've heard what I have to say. And stop looking so anxious.' His tawny eyes lifted to her troubled face. 'The prospect of going to bed with me used not to frighten you that much!'

Laura gulped and turned away. 'You're ... despicable!'

'Why?' He fastened the cap on the container and shook it energetically. 'Isn't it the truth? I seem to remember you were not exactly opposed to our making love.'

'It was *not* love!'

'Would you know the difference?' he demanded cynically, and then he expelled his breath on a heavy sigh. 'Look. I don't want to argue with you, Laura. It's obvious we've got a lot of ground to make up. Right now, I suggest you have a Mai Tai and stop worrying about your fate. The future will take care of itself. It always has, and it always will.'

The crushed ice frosting the glass he held out to her was very appealing, and without really knowing why, she accepted the cocktail. Perhaps she needed the

support the alcohol could give her, she thought
miserably, sipping the chilled liquid. But it was
delicious. She had to admit that, if only to herself.
Jason had lost none of his skill . . . in any direction, she
added silently.

Out on deck, two white-coated stewards had just
finished laying the table. Its glassy surface was spread
with bamboo place mats and shining silver cutlery,
pristine white napkins reflected in the polished gleam of
delicate cut glass. From somewhere, a centrepiece of
star jasmine and scarlet frangipani, called plumeria in the
islands, had been arranged, and a bottle of Dom
Perignon was residing in an ice bucket. Set beneath the
striped awning, it was at once open to the soft trade
winds, yet protected both from the sun, and the
inquisitive glances of others users of the marina. A
millionaire's retreat indeed, though Laura, following
Jason across the white painted boards. And how had
Alec Cowray accomplished so much in such a short
space of time?

'Is everything satisfactory, Mr Montefiore?' inquired
one of the stewards politely, while his companion
subjected Laura to an intent scrutiny. Laura had never
seen either of them before, but she could guess what
they were thinking. In her cheap pants and shirt and
without any make-up, she was not at all the glamorous
kind of female they were no doubt used to seeing. Had
Alec Cowray filled them in on her previous relationship
with Jason, she wondered. She didn't know which was
worse: the idea that they knew she had once been
Jason's mistress, or their avid speculation that she
might be hoping to assume that role.

'This is fine, thank you,' Jason was saying now, his
smile perfunctory but polite. He waited until Laura had
taken the chair the steward held out for her before
dismissing a similar attention and taking his own seat.
'We'll serve ourselves,' he added, his crisp tone
tempered by his manner, and the two men departed,
evidently disappointed that their services were no longer
required.

A prawn cocktail, arranged on pink-fleshed bases of

papaya, had been served as an appetizer, and although Laura had not felt hungry when she sat down, the sun and the breeze, and the succulent aroma of the food were seductive. While Jason was uncorking the bottle of champagne, she took a spoonful of the juicy concoction, and it was so delicious that she took another. There were warm rolls, wrapped in a cloth and residing in a basket, and creamy curls of butter, cool on a bed of ice. With a feeling of resignation, she gave in to the temptation to taste the bread, too, and by the time her glass was filled with the effervescing liquid, she was actually enjoying her meal.

Jason, she noticed, ate little, and she was relieved to see he was not drinking much either. He seemed quite content to lounge in his seat, set at right angles to hers, playing with the stem of his wine glass and watching the antics of a pair of dinghies, tacking backwards and forwards across the blue expanse of Mamala Bay.

The stewards appeared briefly to clear away the dishes already used and to set two silver-domed tureens before them. Inside, Laura discovered two whole lobsters, halved and filled with a delicious thermidor sauce, with tempting mounds of saffron rice to accompany them. 'Help yourself,' advised Jason, offering her the serving tools, and with a little sigh, she lifted half a lobster on to her plate.

'Do you want some?' she asked nervously, feeling obliged to make the gesture, and he inclined his head.

'Thank you,' he said, allowing her to serve him also, and in spite of her apprehension, she managed not to spill any in his lap.

Forking a white piece of lobster meat into her mouth, she eventually said quietly, 'Don't you think this has gone far enough?' She paused, and then added tensely, 'You don't really expect me to move back into your apartment, do you? I mean—why would you want me to? There are plenty of other women who would be only too——'

'I don't want *plenty* of other women,' retorted Jason smoothly, laying his fork aside. 'I want you.' He met her eyes squarely, and she was jolted by the unguarded passion in the depths of his. 'I'm being very civilised about this, Laura, because I sense that if I move too fast I'll have you running scared. But don't doubt my determination. It's there. Believe me!'

She did. With her throat closing up suffocatingly, she found her appetite which had flowered so unexpectedly, closing up too. 'But why?' she demanded imploringly. *Why?*

Jason did not dignify her plea with a reply. 'I don't live in an apartment any more, Laura,' he replied, pouring more champagne into her glass. 'I have a house, approximately two hundred and fifty miles from here, on an island called Kaulanai.'

Laura stared at him. 'Kaulanai?' she shook her head. 'I've never heard of it.'

'You wouldn't have.' Jason's expression was indifferent. 'It's only a small island. Approximately fourteen miles long by seven miles across. But it's beautiful. And it belongs to me.'

'To you?' Laura's tongue circled her dry lips. 'It's your island?'

'For my sins,' agreed Jason wryly. 'You would agree with that, I assume.'

Laura's hands curled together in her lap. 'And—and you expect me to live there?'

'Not all the time,' he assured her drily. 'I still own the apartment in New York, and I keep a suite in one of the hotels here in Honolulu always available.'

Laura took a trembling breath. 'And what is your plan for Pamela? An expensive abortion?'

'Of course not.' Jason's tone hardened in response to her sarcasm. 'Though if that's what she wants, it can be arranged.' He paused. 'But no. Your sister losing her baby was not part of my plan. I'm quite prepared to support her as well as you.'

Laura shook her head. 'She'll never agree.'

'Won't she?' Jason put his glass aside and rested his elbow on the table, supporting his chin on his palm. 'Right now, Pamela is alone and desperate. She has no job and she has no money . . .'

'How do you know she has no job? Mrs Goldstein

hasn't fired her. Pamela's a good physiotherapist . . .'

'I'm sure she is.' Jason shrugged. 'However, an attempted suicide is not something easy to live down. And this Mrs Goldstein, did you say? She's unlikely to want to go on employing someone with such . . . psychological tendencies.'

'You make her sound like a mental case!'

'No. I'm only saying she may find it difficult to take up where she left off, even should she want to. And you yourself suggested persuading her to go back to London.'

Laura sighed. 'All right. So she's in a difficult situation. I know that.'

Jason abandoned his confiding stance and lay back in his chair again. 'Okay. So we agree on something,' he remarked drily. 'Let me put it to you that your sister would find life far more appealing without any money worries, without any responsibilities—except to look after herself and be happy. And you have to admit, the climate here is a little more appealing than London.'

Laura's palms felt damp and she rubbed them hastily over the knees of her pants. 'You're suggesting we both live in your house on Kaulanai?'

Jason's lips twisted. 'Well—not quite as it sounds,' he commented sardonically. 'And I shall require you to do a little more than—*live* in my house.'

Laura trembled. 'You're disgusting!'

Jason shrugged, his expression sobering once again. 'We'll see,' he said flatly. 'Well? Is it a deal? Or are you still going to insist on flying back to San Francisco tonight?'

Laura pushed back her chair and got to her feet. 'You're crazy!'

'Am I?' Jason lifted one shoulder. 'I thought it was an eminently sane solution to your problems.'

'To Pamela's problems, perhaps!' Laura was bitter. Even in her distressed state, she could see the advantages for her sister. 'And what happens after the baby is born?'

Jason expelled his breath carelessly. 'That's for her to decide. She can always find another job, here in Hawaii.

There are plenty of rich old ladies, one of whom is bound to need a personal physiotherapist.' He paused. 'I might even employ her myself.'

'You!' Laura was contemptuous.

'Why not?' Jason looked up at her levelly. 'A hotel could do worse than employ a house masseuse.'

Laura blinked. 'You own a hotel?'

'I took over the Ridgeway complex, remember?' Jason reminded her expressionlessly, and she wondered how she could ever have forgotten.

With a little shake of her head, she moved to the rail, resting her elbows upon it and gazing out across the water. Dear God, she thought despairingly, what was she going to do? He was right. He was not forcing her to do anything, not physically at least. But he was putting the whole responsibility for Pamela's happiness on her shoulders, and if anything should go wrong . . .

The brush of his sleeve against her bare arm made her shudderingly aware he had come to stand beside her. The heat of his flesh burning, even through the texture of his shirt, startled her into an involuntary movement away from him, but his fingers curving over the fine structure of her shoulders arrested her.

'Is it such a hard decision to make?' he murmured, the warmth of his breath against her ear, revealing he had bent his head towards her. 'You've lost weight,' he added inconsequently, feeling the fragility of the bones beneath his hand, and just for a moment she gave in to the urge to say what she was really thinking.

'So have you,' she countered, turning her head to look at him, only to discover his face was only inches from hers.

'I've missed you,' he told her huskily, the flavour of his breath, lightly scented with alcohol, not unpleasant to her nostrils. The pale gold beauty of his eyes was very disturbing, and she felt her resistance ebbing beneath that sensual appraisal. It reminded her of mornings she had wakened to find him propped on his elbow gazing down at her, and the subsequent aftermath of his possession. It reminded her of the sexual pleasure he had given her—the pleasure they had given one another—but it also occurred to her to wonder, with a shrinking heart, how many women he had pleasured since she had been gone, and that brought her to her senses.

Jerking her head away from him, she exclaimed chokingly, 'I haven't missed you!' And, less truthfully: 'I haven't thought about you at all. I enjoy my work, and I was enjoying my life, until your brother-in-law got Pamela into this mess! I've been happy these past three years. However hard that may be for you to believe!'

'Oh, I believe it!' he responded harshly, putting some space between them, and she felt an unwilling sense of deprivation at the loss. 'And I could add that your sister might be equally to blame for this mess, as you put it! However, that is not at issue here. What is, is what you are going to do about it. Have you come to a decision?'

Laura caught her breath. 'How can I?'

'What do you mean?'

'Jason, I have a job in London . . .'

'I know that.'

'. . . and . . . and Pierce won't keep it open for me.'

'Why should he?' Jason was suddenly very still. 'You won't be going back. At least not in the foreseeable future.'

As he spoke, he looped one arm over the rail, and her eyes were drawn to the sweat-moistened muscles of his midriff, bared by the careless opening of his shirt. And it was as if that negligent gesture crystallised in Laura's mind all that he expected of her. It was one thing to remember the way it used to be between them—the urgent, powerful emotions he had aroused so easily, his hungry passionate possession of her body. She had been in love with him then; what they had done had been the irresistible result of their need for one another. The rights and wrongs of their relationship hadn't seemed to matter. He had wanted her, and she would have done anything to please him . . .

But not now. Now, what they were really discussing was a subtle kind of revenge he was going to exact upon her. For three years, he had waited for such an opportunity, and she—fool that she was—had inadvertently given it to him. She couldn't believe he cared about her, and he certainly didn't care about Pamela. He just wanted to prove he was still her master.

Pursing her lips, she said brokenly, 'You can't do this to me!'

Jason shrugged. 'I'm not doing anything to you, Laura. It's your decision. You must choose.'

'Between the serpent and the staff?' she demanded painfully. 'It's not much of a choice, is it?'

'Is that how I really appear to you?' he mused softly. 'A serpent?' He made a dismissing gesture and walked back to the table. 'Very well. I'll give you until tonight to think over what I have said.' He emptied the remains of the champagne into his glass and raised it to his lips. 'I'll 'phone you at eight o'clock precisely. Be there!'

CHAPTER FOUR

'FASTEN your seat belt, Miss Huyton. We'll be landing in fifteen minutes.'

The voice of Clark Sinclair, the co-pilot of Jason's Learjet spoke to her as if from a distance, and Laura dragged her thoughts back to the present to acknowledge his instruction.

'Thank-you,' she said gratefully, feeling down the sides of the comfortable leather armchair for the meshed straps. 'I was miles away. I'm sorry.' She looked up into his fair good-looking face. 'Did you want something else?'

'Just to ask if you'd enjoyed the flight,' he responded easily, squatting down beside her. 'I guess you're going to be pretty tired this morning. Hawaiian time it's just approaching midnight.'

Laura forced a smile and nodded. 'It's been a long flight. When I flew out, I spent a few days in San Francisco.'

'Yes.' Clark evidently knew about that. 'A twenty-four hour stopover is not the same, I know. You should have gone to bed like Julie suggested. A couple of sleeping tablets, and you wouldn't have noticed the distance.'

Laura shook her head, making some deprecating comment. She could hardly tell Clark Sinclair that the reason she had not used the luxurious sleeping compartment of the aircraft was because, like so many other things, it brought back memories of sharing it with Jason. Time enough to think of those things when she was on her way back to Hawaii. Right now, she faced the prospect of telling Pierce of her decision, and the poignant task of closing up her flat and handing over the keys to someone else.

The sleek executive jet landed at Gatwick, and the customs formalities were soon dealt with. The fact that

Laura was a returning British national made her entry simple, and after arranging the details of the return flight with the pilot, Frank Danielli, she wished the three members of the crew goodbye, and took a train into the city.

London was reassuringly familiar, although she felt a distinct sense of chill after the warmth of Hawaii. April was not the most predictable month in England, and she was not surprised to see specks of rain against the train's windows as they pulled into Victoria station. She emerged from the station, hailed a taxi and told the driver to take her directly to Highgate. She knew she was putting off the moment when she would have to speak to Pierce. It hardly seemed possible it was little more than a week since she had left him. Her whole life had been altered since she flew almost blithely out of Heathrow, *en route* for San Francisco.

The flat felt chilled when she opened the door, even though the heating was run from a central generator. In her absence, no one had turned the thermostat up, and she guessed it confirmed her theory that spring had not truly arrived yet. There were letters in her small lobby, bills for the most part, and she realised that was something else she would have to deal with. She would arrange with the post office to have her mail sent on at regular intervals. There was not likely to be much. Apart from a few odd aunts and cousins here and there, the two girls had no close surviving relatives.

Examining the contents of the fridge, Laura found an unopened carton of milk and filled the kettle to make herself some tea. It was strange to think that if she had still been in Hawaii, she would be in bed at this moment. Clark was right; it was disorientating; but she had made the transition one way, she could make it the other.

While she drank her tea, she flicked through the mail, setting the bills aside for immediate payment. Apart from an invitation to a party, being given by one of Pierce's friends, and several envelopes containing advertising, there was nothing of any interest, and she eventually pushed the clutter aside and rested her chin on her upturned palms.

She had a week, that was all, a week to tie up the ends of her life here and fly back to California. By then, Pamela would be ready to accompany her to Hawaii, and together they would make the comparatively short trip to Kaulanai.

The island was some two thousand miles off the American mainland, two hundred and fifty miles southeast of Oahu. According to Jason, it could only be reached commercially from the air, a telling factor she was sure when he first considered its advantages. A reef surrounded it on all sides, only negotiable at high tide by craft with a very shallow draught. Certainly, the *Laura M* could never navigate the reef, and it provided a natural barrier to any would-be intruder.

Not that Laura had been particularly interested in his description of the island. So far as she was concerned, Kaulanai was fast assuming the proportions of a prison, and the fact that there were no bars, did not make it any less confining. Just because Pamela had reacted to Jason's offer with the first trace of animation she had shown since Laura had found her, unconscious in the flat, did not make what she was doing any easier. She felt bruised and resentful, and totally incapable of accepting his aspirations for her future.

Pierce was equally appalled at her decision. 'You can't be serious!' he exclaimed, the silver cigarette holder, which he used as an affectation, falling unheeded to the carpet. Putting the cigarette he had been about to light between his lips, he gazed at her disbelievingly. 'My dear girl, I know I may have been a bit miffed at you swanning off like that, and maybe I was a little too forthright in my objections, but surely you know I have great respect for you, as a person! I don't want to lose you, Laura. There—now you've really got me over a barrel!'

Laura shook her head, sinking down into the chintz-covered armchair at one side of the elegant marble fireplace. She knew Pierce's house almost as well as her own home, and she had often stayed in his spare room after working with him long into the night. Often Pierce's best inspiration had come after darkness had fallen, and she had enjoyed their midnight sessions, and the sense of chill his books always evoked.

'I'm sorry,' she said now, as he took the seat opposite her, coiling his long angular frame into the chair. 'It's not something I want to do. It's something I *have* to do, for Pamela. I can't explain exactly, but—well, she needs me and I can't let her down.'

'You're telling me your sister needs a nursemaid?' demanded Pierce uncomprehendingly, lighting his cigarette and inhaling the nicotine deep into his lungs. 'But I thought she was only two years younger than you are.'

'She is.' Laura sighed. 'Oh, that's not the only reason I'm staying. Don't ask me to explain, Pierce. It's a long story, and you wouldn't want to hear it.'

'Try me.'

Laura bent her head. 'Please. I can't go through all that now. If I say there's a man—a man I used to—work for, when I lived in Honolulu, will you try to understand? He ... well, he's offered to help Pamela, providing I'm prepared to ... to help him.'

'Work for, you mean?' Pierce stared at her blankly, and Laura was glad of the heat of the fire to disguise her burning cheeks.

'Yes,' she answered now, seizing the reprieve. 'I was his secretary for a time. The fact that I can speak several languages was an advantage to him.'

'Really?' Pierce regarded her suspiciously. 'Are you telling me there are no linguists in Hawaii? I can't believe it.'

'No, I'm not saying that.' Laura shifted uncomfortably. 'Pierce, Jason—Mr Montefiore, that is—has made my ... *employment* a condition of his helping Pamela.'

'How is he helping Pamela exactly?'

'I've told you.' Laura hesitated. 'He's allowing her to stay in the islands until she's had the baby. Then it's up to her.'

Pierce absorbed this silently for a few moments.

Then, he said quietly, 'So in what—nine months, maybe less, you'll be free to return to England?'

Laura frowned. 'I suppose so.' She blinked. That thought hadn't occurred to her. Once her sister had had her baby, Jason would have no further hold over her. Surely by then Pamela's mental condition would no longer be a cause for concern.

'Very well, then.' Pierce exhaled blue smoke into the air above their heads. 'If you insist on sacrificing yourself like this, I'll just have to find myself a *temporary* replacement.'

'Temporary?' Laura stared at him.

'Why not?' Pierce shrugged indifferently. 'Having just initiated you into my ways, I am not attracted by the notion of having to repeat the exercise. No. The new book must be completed, of course. That goes without saying. But once that is done, I am thinking of taking a break—somewhere like India, perhaps. Or the Far East. I've got an urge to see Singapore and Hong Kong. I was going to suggest that you came with me, to make notes, that sort of thing. But I suppose I can record my impressions on tape, for you to transcribe when you get back.'

'Oh, Pierce!' Laura was touched. 'I don't know what to say.'

'Say nothing, my dear. That's always the best way. Who knows, you may decide to stay with your Mr Montefiore, and I shouldn't like you to commit yourself without first considering all the facts.'

Laura pressed her lips together. 'I don't think that's likely.'

'Don't you?' Pierce's grey eyes were disturbingly shrewd. 'I wish I could be as confident. I'm afraid age, and experience, have made me wary.'

Nevertheless, it was a reassurance in the hectic days that followed, for Laura to know she was not severing all ties with England. She had to give up her flat, of course. She could not afford to pay the cost of renting and heating four rooms when she was not using them, but it had been a furnished flat, after all, and she could hopefully find another on her return. The belongings she would not be taking with her, Pierce agreed to store in the basement of his house in Eaton Terrace, and her mail was to be redirected there for his housekeeper to send on.

'You've been so kind,' Laura told him, the night before she was due to leave for San Francisco. For once, Pierce had invited her out for dinner, and they were seated at a table for two in the rather plush surroundings of his club. 'You've made everything so much easier. I almost feel I'm not making a break at all. Just taking a sort of . . . leave of absence.'

'That's what I want you to think,' declared Pierce firmly, pushing his horn-rimmed spectacles over the bridge of his nose. 'You know, Laura, I've never said this to any woman before, but if I ever thought of marrying, it would be someone like you.'

Laura smiled. The image of the fastidious and aristocratic Pierce Carver in the role of husband and father was not one she could easily summon. At forty-three years of age, he had always struck her as the quintessential bachelor, and she had never regarded him as anything more than a friend.

'You're very gallant,' she murmured now, pushing the fillet steak she had ordered round her plate, in an effort for it to appear that she was eating it. 'But I'm sure if you ever do decide to sacrifice your freedom, you'll find someone infinitely more suitable to share your life.'

'What you mean is—you don't see me as the man in your life,' Pierce amended drily. 'I know you weren't fishing for compliments, my dear, but I'll offer you one just the same. A man could do much worse than choose you for his wife, Laura. You're a beautiful woman—no!' this as she would have contradicted him; 'I mean it. Beauty isn't only a thing of the body, although I have to say, your appearance gives me much pleasure. It's also a thing of the soul, of the inner you, of the person you are inside. And you're a beautiful person, Laura. I've always thought so.'

'Oh, Pierce . . .'

Laura gazed at him helplessly, and he stretched out a

hand to touch her cheek. 'I know,' he said. 'I've waited too long to tell you. I realised that the minute you told me you were flying out to San Francisco because your sister had 'phoned you. I wanted to tell you then, but I couldn't, so I behaved quite abominably, I don't deny it.' He shrugged. 'Don't look so worried, my dear. I'm not about to threaten some dire consequence if you can't return my feelings. I fear I'm too selfish a person for that. But I shall miss you, remember that, and if you need me, I'll always be here.'

'Thank you.'

Laura was overwhelmed, and she was grateful for the advent of the waiter to lighten their mood. She had never dreamt Pierce might be harbouring any feelings for her, and she thought how ironic it was that Jason should have been proved right, at least in one respect.

The unwilling reminder of why she and Pierce were having this dinner together was not welcome. For the past days, she had been struggling to keep thoughts of Jason from intruding on her daytime hours, and although she had not entirely succeeded, only at night had she truly given way to her latent fears and apprehensions. She was sleeping badly, and her appetite was practically non-existent, and now the involuntary invasion of his image into this most-poignant of occasions was almost overwhelming. She was tempted to confide in Pierce; she was tempted to tell him what she was doing, and let him solve the problem for her, but she couldn't. She didn't love him, and it wouldn't be fair to put that burden on him. The fact that she didn't love Jason either, she dismissed. After all, she told herself defensively, if it hadn't been for Jason's brother-in-law, she wouldn't be in the position she was in now.

The meal was over and they were enjoying a liqueur with their coffee, when Laura became conscious of a sense of unease, of a disturbing awareness that she was being observed, and immediately she thought of Jason's private investigator. But he would not have engaged anyone to watch her during this short visit to London, she told herself firmly. With Pamela still in San Francisco, he could have no fears that she might not return.

Nevertheless, the feeling persisted, and lifting her head, she gazed dubiously about the room. Which of these rather distinguished-looking gentlemen was likely to be employed as a private investigator, she mused, fighting back the urge to ask Pierce if they could go. It was stupid, and she was probably imagining the whole thing, but she sensed a growing hostility, and she couldn't help associating it with her reluctant thoughts of Jason.

And as if thinking of him had conjured the man himself, it was at that moment she saw him, seated at the bar only thirty feet away. He was occupying one of the tall stools that flanked the curved counter, but he was half turned in his seat so that he could watch her, and she had no doubt now that he had been responsible for her sudden distress. In a wine-coloured velvet dinner jacket and tight-fitting black pants, he looked unusually sombre, the pleated front of his shirt contrasting sharply with the darkness of his skin. He was resting one elbow on the bar, beside the half-filled tumbler of what she assumed to be scotch that marked his place, and although one foot was hooked on the rail of the stool the other rested on the floor. His attitude tautened the flow of cloth across his thighs, drawing her attention to the muscled strength of his legs. His expression was not friendly; even when he met her shocked gaze there was no trace of recognition in his. On the contrary, she thought he was going to ignore her, and her mouth dried with the anticipation of wondering what he intended to do.

'Is something wrong?'

Pierce had noticed her unusual stillness, the sudden draining of colour from her face, and Laura struggled to recover her equilibrium. 'Not ... exactly,' she murmured, looking down at the coffee in her cup. 'I ... the man I'm going to work for in Hawaii has just come in. I didn't expect to see him, that all.'

'Montefiore? He's here!'

Pierce had noticed the direction of her gaze, and now he turned in his seat to stare frowningly across the room. Laura wanted to stop him, but she didn't know how she could, and when she ventured a fleeting glance towards the bar, she saw Jason sliding indolently from the stool to stroll towards them.

'That's him? That's Montefiore?' whispered Pierce, leaning towards her with some surprise, and Laura nodded. 'But I thought . . . I assumed he'd be older——' Pierce broke off in evident confusion. 'What is he doing here? Do you know?'

'I've no idea,' replied Laura in a low voice, just as Jason reached their table, and it was with a distinct effort she raised her eyes to his. 'Hello, Jason,' she greeted him stiffly. 'This is . . . unexpected.'

'Hello, Laura.' Jason had pushed his hands into two pockets that followed the waistband of his pants in front. The action pushed the sides of his jacket aside, exposing the width of his chest and the muscled contours of his thighs. It was a deliberate attitude he had adopted, she felt, his manner bordering on the insolent, and when she introduced Pierce, he shook the other man's hand with only perfunctory courtesy.

'You're in London on business, Mr Montefiore?' inquired Pierce politely, somewhat at a disadvantage when Jason waived his attempt to get to his feet.

'In a manner of speaking,' Jason responded smoothly, his expression giving nothing away. 'I understand you're a writer, Mr Carver.'

'I like to think so.' Pierce gave Laura a reassuring smile. 'Does your presence in London mean Miss Huyton will not be required to return to Hawaii immediately? If so . . .'

'I shall be returning to the west coast tomorrow,' Jason interrupted him swiftly, intercepting Laura's gaze and holding it with cold deliberation. 'I thought we might travel back together, Miss Huyton. That is, if you have no objection to that arrangement.'

'Of course not.' How could she have? Laura thought desperately, gazing up at him in pained resentment. Couldn't he at least have allowed her these last few days of freedom? Had he made the sixteen hour trip to London, just to ensure she didn't change her mind?

Pierce was watching their exchange with frowning speculation, and Laura guessed he was wondering exactly what it meant. However, good manners prevented him from voicing his feelings, and instead he invited Jason to join them for a drink.

'I'm afraid I can't.' Jason's refusal was tempered by a thin smile, and Laura expelled her breath on a trembling sigh, hardly aware until that moment she had been holding it. Let him go! she begged silently, all too conscious of his leg only inches away from her own. In spite of her hatred for him, she could not ignore him, and she was uncomfortably aware of the effect he was having on her.

Surreptitiously, she smoothed her damp palms on her linen napkin, keeping it well below the level of the table as she did so. But she could not slow the erratic thumping of her heart, or cool the burning temperature of her blood. It was incredibly difficult not to compare the two men, and against Pierce's bony angularity, Jason's decidedly sexual indolence was markedly pronounced. It was not a conscious thing with him; it was simply a matter of taste; but Laura could not deny the unholy attraction of a lithe, powerful body and features as arrogant as the devil's himself.

'As a matter of fact, I was wondering whether you would have any objections to my taking Miss Huyton home,' Jason continued now, stunning Laura by his audacity. 'I need to speak with her before tomorrow, and as we have had the good fortune to run into one another ...'

Pierce was taken aback. 'I—well—if you think ... Laura, what have you to say?' he faltered, evidently at a loss for words, and Jason turned to her with unconcealed impatience.

Laura didn't know what to say. She didn't believe Jason's remark about running into one another. It was too much of a coincidence. But on the other hand, how could she refuse him, without some reasonable excuse?

'Couldn't we talk here?' she asked, meeting Jason's pale eyes and shivering at the implacability she read there.

'I'd prefer to speak to you in private, Laura,' he essayed politely, and only she was aware of the inflexibility of his words.

'I—well, would you mind, Pierce?' she murmured unhappily, and he had little choice but to give his permission.

'If . . . if you have no objections, my dear,' he declared regretfully, and she wondered what he would say if she told him she had as little enthusiasm for the motion as he had.

It was hard saying goodbye with Jason looking on. 'Remember what I told you,' Pierce reminded her huskily, when he drew her close for moment and bestowed a warm kiss on her temple. 'I'll always be here, if you need me.'

'I'll remember,' said Laura tremulously. 'Take care.'

'And you,' added Pierce gruffly, and without looking at Jason again, Laura walked blindly away from both of them.

She was collecting her coat from the cloakroom when Jason joined her. 'Ready?' he inquired tautly, without really requiring a reply. Instead, he turned away to inform the doorman they were leaving, and by the time Laura had slipped her cape about her shoulders, a taxi was waiting for them. 'Shall I give your address or will you come back to my hotel?' he asked her carelessly as they descended the steps into Jermyn Street, and Laura thought how arrogant he was to assume that either alternative would please her.

'I'd prefer to go home,' she declared tightly, and it was only as he climbed into the back of the cab beside her that the significance of his having her address occurred to her. 'How did you know where I lived?' she exclaimed, as he flung himself on to the hard leather seat beside her, and he cast a shadowed glance in her direction.

'Think about it,' he advised drily, and she wondered

how she could have forgotten his humiliating surveillance.

'Wh—what did you want to talk to me about?' she demanded gathering the folds of her cloak about her.

'Later,' he responded without emotion, and her resentment grew at his deliberate insolence.

'It wasn't a coincidence, was it?' she exclaimed fiercely. 'Your being at Pierce's club. You're not a member of that club, are you? You came there looking for me!'

'For both of you,' offered Jason coolly. 'The stalwart British novelist and his oh-so-conscientious secretary!'

'What is that supposed to mean?'

'You weren't taking dictation this evening, Laura!'

'No.' She held up her head. 'We were having dinner together. What's wrong with that?'

Jasons eyes were turned on her, and although she couldn't see their expression, she could sense their hostility. 'Do you often have dinner with your—*employer*?'

'Not often, no . . .'

'I'll bet.' Jason's tone was contemptuous, and Laura gazed at him frustratedly.

'What are you implying?' she demanded. 'I told you. Pierce and I are friends . . .'

'And that, I suppose, is why he was holding your hand and stroking your cheek,' he remarked grimly, and Laura gasped.

'You were watching us!'

'Long enough,' he agreed, returning his attention to the lighted façade of a cinema they were passing.

'You—you bastard . . .'

'Don't call me names, Laura,' he advised her bleakly, keeping his eyes on the road. 'I may reciprocate in kind, and you wouldn't like it.'

Laura trembled. 'Do you know how much I hate you?'

'I can live with it.'

'You're going to have to!'

'Yes, I am, aren't I?' he countered mockingly, and

her chest heaved with the realisation that he meant every word he said.

When they reached the small square where Laura had her flat, she half hoped he would leave her there. He had achieved his objective, after all, she thought bitterly. He had taken her away from Pierce, he had already exerted his authority, and she didn't see what else he could have to say. But as she thrust open her door and scrambled out, she heard him asking the driver how much he wanted, and the cab drove away leaving Jason on the pavement.

'Number 47, isn't that right?' he inquired flatly, his hand gripping her upper arm compelling her into the building, and she expelled her breath wearily.

The bare tiled floor was much different from the carpeted corridors he was used to, she reflected, as they crossed the entrance hall and entered the lift. The metal cubicle was uninviting, too, with its scrawled graffiti and faint aroma of pine disinfectant.

Laura's flat was on the fourth level. The ground floor of the building counted as the first to simplify the numbering system, and it took little time to reach her floor. The lift doors slid back on a narrow corridor without warmth or character, and she hoped Jason was already regretting his decision to accompany her inside. Not that he seemed overly concerned. He followed her along the rubber tiled hallway to her door without any obvious sign of distaste, but she guessed he was an adept at hiding his true feelings.

The living room of the flat looked bare and uninviting, too. With her small collection of books and ornaments already packed and waiting for transportation to Eaton Terrace, the place looked as impersonal as an hotel room. Halting in the middle of the floor, she was struck once again by the ignominy of her position, and her shoulders sagged in an attitude of helpless defeat.

'How long have you lived here?' asked Jason quietly, as if perceiving her desperation, and she struggled to keep a sense of perspective.

'Al ... almost three years,' she got out unsteadily. 'When I—when I came back from—from Hawaii, a friend of Pamela's was just moving out. I was lucky enough to be offered it.'

'When you came back from Hawaii,' echoed Jason softly, and she wished she had not chosen that particular point of contact. 'It's been a long time, Laura,' he added, and although she had not been aware of his stepping towards her, his breath was now warm against her cheek.

'Not long enough,' she choked, and would have stepped away from him, but he grasped the epaulette of her cloak to keep her beside him.

'Don't fight me, Laura,' he advised her harshly, and she shivered again at the threatening note in his voice. 'I don't want to hurt you, but I should warn you, I'm finding it increasingly difficult to keep this conversation on a civil basis!'

'Is that what you think you're doing?' With desperation spilling over into reckless defiance, Laura whirled away from him, the cloak slipping from her shoulders as she did so. 'How could you be civil, Jason? You're not a civilised person! You're a savage! A barbarian! A man who doesn't hesitate to use other people's pain and misery to gain his own ends!'

'Be careful, Laura!' Jason was standing very still, the superfluous folds of her cloak still hanging uselessly from his hand, but she was beyond restraint.

'Be careful!' she mocked him. 'Why should I be careful? When has *being careful* helped me? I thought I was being careful when I came back to England. I thought leaving you was the *careful* thing to do. But I was wrong, wasn't I? You know, it has crossed my mind that perhaps you put Mike Kazantis up to having an affair with Pamela! How convenient that would have been for you, wouldn't it?'

In fact, until that moment, such a notion had not crossed Laura's mind, and as soon as the words were uttered, she thought how ludicrous they were. Even if Jason had welcomed Pamela's association with his sister's husband, which was unlikely, how could he have known Pamela would get pregnant? Or indeed that such a circumstance would force her into trying to take her own life!

But the words were said, and before she could take them back, Jason's patience snapped. Tossing the cloak aside, he crossed the thin expanse of carpet that separated them, and took her shoulders in a bruising grip. 'If you believe that, why should I disappoint you?' he said grimly, jerking her towards him. 'As you appear to regard me as the devil incarnate, I might as well take advantage of the fact. It isn't as if it hasn't been in my mind, ever since I saw you by the pool at the Kapulani.'

In spite of her hands crushed between them, his mouth ground down on hers without impediment, and she tasted her own blood on her tongue. He was so much stronger than she was, so much more powerful, and the violence of his action rendered any real resistance unviable. He was not wearing any overcoat and his unbuttoned jacket meant she was that much closer to him. Her knuckles dug into the muscled flatness of his stomach, and her knees bumped the unyielding hardness of his legs. She was enveloped in the heat and scent and feel of him, and although she fought against it, his sexuality was quite insidious.

'Jason, *for God's sake——*' she gasped chokingly, when he released her mouth to seek the exposed hollow of her shoulder, but her pleas were all in vain.

'Why appeal to that divine deity, when you believe I'm the seed of a lower order?' he taunted harshly, forcing the draped neckline of her simple black cocktail dress down off her shoulders and tearing the cloth in the process. 'You asked for this, Laura. I was prepared to be patient with you, but you changed the rules of the game.' His teeth skimmed her skin, and the nerves so near the surface palpitated wildly. 'Don't complain now, if your opponent stoops to cheating!'

'Jason, you can't do this!' she moaned, feeling the soft folds of the dress pooling around her ankles. She was vulnerable now, standing there before him in only a lacy waist slip and camisole, and although she made the protest, she had little hope of its being fulfilled.

'I can, and I must,' he told her thickly, his tawny eyes raking her slim figure with burning intensity. With one hand at her nape, holding her easily within his grasp, his free hand groped for his tie and the tiny concealed buttons beneath the pleating of his shirt. But his efforts were too slow and growing impatient with the task, he tore his shirt open, exposing the brown expanse of his chest.

Then, as if desperate to touch her, he dragged her close against him, and even through the satin camisole she could feel the taut abrasion of the hair that arrowed down to his navel and beyond.

'You have no idea how much I want you,' he muttered, his tongue making its own possession, and a dizzying feeling of weakness swept over her. His lips were gentler now, almost sensually persuasive, and when his fingers slipped beneath the hem of the camisole and spread against the fragile hollow of her spine, she felt an involuntary shudder of desire.

With his mouth still on hers, he pressed the straps of her camisole down off her shoulders, and her breasts emerged to thrust against his bared chest. Just for a moment, he held her against him again, his hands on her hips hard through the thinness of her slip and panties. But the swollen ridge of muscle riding up between them demanded release, and with a muffled oath, he shrugged off his jacket and shirt and swung her up into his arms.

He seemed to know instinctively which door led to her bedroom, and although he put no lights on, the illumination spilling from the living room behind them showed him the narrow outline of her single bed. With infinite indulgence, he laid her on the bed, and even though in some distant corner of her mind a small voice was screaming at her to escape now, when she had the chance, she lay open-mouthed watching Jason strip the rest of his clothes from his body.

It was only when the pulsating proof of his maleness was exposed that she knew a momentary sense of panic. But before the realisation that neither of them was taking any precautions could evoke any positive action from her, he was beside her on the bed, and the hungry pressure of his mouth made any resistance impossible.

'Don't fight me,' he breathed against her lips, his fingers disposing of the flimsy shreds of fabric that still separated them, and Laura trembled beneath the probing intimacy of his hands. No man had touched her since her reckless flight from the man who was touching her now, and in spite of their previous relationship, she felt as tense and sensitive as if she had not once known Jason's body as well as her own. 'You're so beautiful,' he groaned, lowering his head to her taut nipples and suckling from each of them in turn, and Laura's breathing felt suspended as she watched his dark head moving against her breast. Almost without volition, her hands came up to tangle in the silky smoothness of his hair, and he shifted sensuously against her, letting her feel his throbbing need.

'Relax,' he whispered, moving over her, and her legs fell apart so that his hardness nudged her with sensual arousal.

It was almost like the first time he had made love to her, except that this time she knew what to expect. The temporary discomfort of his entry was quickly dispelled by the liquid response of her senses to his undeniable attraction. And Jason's murmured, 'So there has been no one else!' was only a momentary irritation as her tender muscles opened to his urgent penetration. The seductive caress of his tongue was making rational thought an effort, and in spite of her mental opposition to his arrogant appropriation of her life, her body seemed to have a will of its own. Her limbs wrapped themselves about him eagerly, as if welcoming his invasion, and when he moved against her, she couldn't prevent her involuntary response.

He possessed her passionately, his muscles thrusting urgently into her, his quickening breath only matching her own for fervency. She couldn't see his face, but she could feel the sweat on his forehead when he buried his face in her neck, moistening the strands of hair that had broken loose from her braid, cooling on her flesh as he lifted himself above her.

It was all over quite quickly. Although Jason would evidently have liked to prolong his pleasure, his need was too great, and Laura felt the quivering delight released within her only seconds before Jason flooded her with his warmth. He slumped against her, shuddering in the aftermath of his emotion, and although she knew she ought to push him away, she was too languorously content to do it . . .

CHAPTER FIVE

LAURA had been working in the Honolulu office less than two weeks when she first met Jason Montefiore.

As a newcomer, her initial duties had kept her employed within the agency itself, and the novelty of living and working in such exotic surroundings was such, she had not yet started envying the other girls when they were sent out on assignments to clients on Oahu, and to other islands in the group. Sharing a flat with two other employees of the agency near the Moanalua golf course, she was quite content to spend her days answering the 'phone and attending to client's queries, when in the evenings and at weekends she could swim and sunbathe and enjoy all the other delights that the island had to offer.

She soon made friends with her colleagues, and the one thing she did envy was their natural resistance to the sun's rays. Her own skin was so fair, she had to avoid over-exposure, and she despaired of ever achieving the gold tan her friends took for granted. She was totally unaware of how outstanding her colouring was, or that its very individuality was extremely attractive. Instead, she persevered in her efforts to achieve her objective, suffering the pain of sun-burn with a fortitude she had not known she possessed.

By the time Lucas Kamala walked into the agency, looking for a temporary secretary for his employer, her skin had acquired the glow of pale honey; and with her silvery hair drawn back loosely from a central parting and secured at her nape with a barrette, he had been instantly intrigued by her air of cool detachment.

Paula Sylva, who ran the agency in Honolulu, had not been enthusiastic about assigning Laura to this particular client. Jason Montefiore's name was not unknown in the islands, and she would have preferred to send one of her more experienced secretaries. It was the first time he had contacted the agency, and she was loath to assign someone whose experience was still confined to English ways. But, there was no one else available at that time, and Lucas Kamala was evidently prepared to employ the English girl.

For her part, Laura was delighted to be given the chance to prove herself. Paula's warning that as a representative of the agency any future employment rested in *her* hands, seemed over-dramatic, until she walked into the opulent surroundings of the Blue Orchid Club. Only then did she realise that this was no ordinary assignment, and that Jason Montefiore was probably the most influential client she was ever likely to meet.

The club itself was situated on Kapiolani Boulevard, and occupied the basement and lower floors of a skyscraper block, also owned by the Montefiore corporation. Although Laura got her first glimpse of the Blue Orchid as she accompanied Lucas Kamala through the marbled lobby of the building, Jason's office, and his apartment, were on the penthouse floor.

She remembered clearly her first interview with the owner of the Blue Orchid. When she had been shown into the office where she was to work, Jason had not been around, and Lucas Kamala had spent some time explaining where everything was, and what she was required to do.

'Mr Montefiore's secretary has broken her wrist, windsurfing,' he replied, in answer to her instinctive query. His eyes filled with reluctant amusement. 'You don't windsurf, do you, Miss Huyton? Or if you do, can I ask you to refrain from doing so until Marsha's back on her feet?'

'I don't,' confessed Laura ruefully, examining the sophisticated word-processor with some misgivings. 'And I have to tell you—I've never used one of these before either. Perhaps Paula was right. Perhaps she should have assigned one of the other girls, after all.'

'I wouldn't say that.'

The faintly mocking comment had come from somewhere behind her, and Laura had swung round to find a man leaning against the frame of the door which led to the inner office. In a navy blue knitted shirt, with short sleeves and opened at the neck to expose the brown column of his throat, and matching shorts which came mid-way down his thigh, he exuded an air of careless sexuality, that was no less potent in its casual form. That he had been exercising, or involved in some other physical activity, was evident in the sweat gleaming in the hollow of his throat and moistening the dark hairs that liberally covered his arms and legs. His hair, too, was damp across his forehead and clung wetly to the nape of his neck, and Laura, who had never found anything attractive in sweating bodies in the past, was instantly aware that there were exceptions to every rule. As he stood there, propped lazily against the frame, the heated scent of his body came to them, but Laura found nothing to repulse her in that distinctly masculine smell.

Even so, she had never suspected that this might be her employer. Some relative of his perhaps, she had surmised, acknowledging the fact that he had evidently entered the suite of offices through Jason Montefiore's room. But not Montefiore himself, not the rich and powerful proprietor of the Blue Orchid Club, not the owner of the building in which they were standing. It was for this reason that she had not looked away from those lazy golden eyes or been intimidated by his decidedly insolent appraisal. She had met his gaze fearlessly, slim and golden herself, in a simple primrose-coloured island cotton, with narrow straps and an elasticated waist.

'Jase!' It was Lucas Kamala who alerted her to the man's identity, and as her eyes widened in disbelief, Jason Montefiore straightened away from the door and came indolently into his secretary's office.

'I see you found a replacement for Marsha,' he remarked, addressing his comments to Lucas, but keeping his eyes on Laura's discomfited countenance. 'Did I detect an English accent? She certainly doesn't look as if she was born in the islands.'

Resenting the fact that he was speaking of her as if

she was either deaf, dumb, or both, Laura leapt to her own defence. 'I am English,' she admitted quickly. 'But the agency likes to give its employees experience in other agencies around the world, and I'm working in Honolulu for six months while someone else does my job in London.'

Jason halted in front of her, disconcerting her by his height and darkness, and by the lean muscularity of his body that much closer to her own. 'Your opposite number here, I guess,' he remarked, addressing her for the first time, and she tilted her chin determinedly, not wanting to reveal how aware of him she was.

'No,' she replied, swallowing. 'I—I believe the girl who used to work here is working in the New York office at the moment.' She flushed in spite of herself. 'It isn't as complicated as it sounds.'

'No?' Jason regarded her intently. 'So—what's your name?'

'Huyton. Laura Huyton,' said Laura hurriedly. 'But I may not be the replacement you're looking for.'

'Why not?'

'Because—I'm not used to such sophisticated machinery,' murmured Laura awkwardly, glancing round the room. 'I think perhaps you ought to contact Mrs Sylva again. She may be able to supply you with a more experienced operator.'

Jason exchanged a look with Lucas Kamala and then lifted his shoulders in a dismissing movement. 'No sweat,' he declared. 'Luke can give you any instruction that's necessary. You do type, don't you? You can use an audio machine?'

'Of course.' Laura moistened her lips.

'Okay.' Jason turned abruptly away, and strolled back towards his office. 'I need a shower. See you in fifteen minutes, Luke,' and before Laura could make any objection, the door slammed behind him.

He summoned her into his office some twenty minutes later. Sleek and darkly attractive now, in a pale grey silk suit that fitted him with the glove-like elegance of expert tailoring, he proceeded to prove why he was already a millionaire at the age of thirty-three. By the end of that day, Laura felt as limp and exhausted as a runner at the end of a marathon, whereas her employer revealed no visible strains whatsoever. On the contrary, she knew from telephone calls he had made and received in her presence that he would be spending at least part of his evening in the club downstairs, and the letters and contracts she had typed were aside from the everyday problems of the Blue Orchid.

In the days that followed, Laura learned to cope far more quickly than she had anticipated. Lucas Kamala helped her a lot, and Jason himself was generally tolerant of her initial errors. Their relationship never quite achieved the same informality that it had on that first occasion, but he was always polite and considerate, and willing to give her time to find her feet. It was tiring work, and she seldom had time to sit back and put her feet up as she had been used to doing in the London office. But because of this, the time passed swiftly, and she looked forward to each day with growing anticipation.

Sylvie Lomax, one of the girls she shared the flat with, was the first to express any opinion about her employer. 'Better you than me, sweetie,' she remarked rather maliciously, after learning who Laura was working for. 'The man's got quite a reputation, and I don't just mean as a stud! Don't get in his way, will you? I hear he's pretty ruthless when he's crossed!'

'Isn't everybody?' Rose Cheong, the other occupant of the flat, demanded impatiently. She turned to Laura, her narrow features alight with sympathy. 'Take no notice of Sylvie. She's only jealous.'

'Jealous!' Sylvie snorted, but her expression softened when she met Laura's anxious eyes. 'Well, perhaps I am . . . a little,' she confessed drily. 'Though there are rumours about how he made his money, which aren't exactly savoury.'

In the weeks to come, Laura had reason to remember what Sylvie had said, at least so far as Jason's private life was concerned. She got tired of intercepting 'phone calls from females angry because he hadn't contacted them, and accepting their abuse when they refused to believe she had passed on their messages.

'It's not his fault,' Lucas assured her gently, when she expressed her frustration to him. 'Honestly, Laura . . .' they had soon progressed to first name terms '. . . in his position, it's an occupational hazard! Be thankful Regina's away in Europe at the moment. She, you might not find so easy to handle!'

That was the first Laura had heard of Jason's ex-wife, but eventually she learned all about the sultry Italian model he had married when he was scarcely out of his teens and who had divorced him less than three years later. Despite the alimony he paid, Regina's demands on her ex-husband, particularly financial ones were considerable, and the fact their daughter, Lucia, lived with her mother, seemed to make Jason more tolerant than he might otherwise have been.

Laura gradually made the acquaintance of the other members of Jason's staff. Lucas took her downstairs one afternoon, and showed her round the luxurious nightclub, with its bars and gaming facilities, and the theatre-restaurant, where diners were entertained by some of the most highly-paid performers in the world. Anyone who was anyone eventually appeared in the Pagoda Room at the Blue Orchid, and Laura got used to seeing people whose names were household words passing through her office on their way to Jason's inner sanctum.

One evening, about three weeks after she had started working for the Montefiore corporation, Jason invited her into his sitting room for a drink. She had been working later than usual, so that Jason could finish dictating the details of a plan for some real estate he had tendered for. It was not the sort of thing he could consign to a tape and he had paused every now and then to explain certain complications to her. In consequence, it was after seven o'clock when they finally completed the job, and Laura was not altogether surprised by his cursory invitation.

'It's not necessary, Mr Montefiore,' she assured him firmly, getting up from her chair, and flexing her aching back muscles, and he looked up at her broodingly, his pale eyes guarded behind the fringe of his lashes.

'I know it's not,' he essayed after a moment, pushing back his own chair and standing. 'But I want to talk to you. Okay?'

Laura could think of no reason to refuse, even though her skin prickled at the thought of being alone with him in the privacy of his apartment. It was one thing to face him across the width of a desk, with the whole gamut of office protocol between them, and quite another to join him in a purely social capacity, knowing as she did how vulnerable she had felt on that other occasion.

It was her first glimpse of Jason's apartment, and she was suitably impressed. Luxuriously furnished, with wide balconies facing the ocean, it overlooked the whole curve of Waikiki, the sounds from below muted by its soaring exclusivity. Pausing by the open balcony doors, Laura could see there were still surfers lying offshore, their heads bobbing about in the water, waiting for the breakers to sweep them inward. But after dark, she guessed the view would be even more spectacular, with the colourful lights of Kalakaua Avenue gleaming like the jewels in a necklace.

'What would you like to drink?' Jason inquired behind her, and turning, Laura saw he had stepped behind a small bar, set in one corner, and generously equipped with every kind of alcohol she could think of.

'Oh—anything will do,' she murmured, not liking to ask for the cocktail she had tried on several occasions with her friends, and Jason shrugged.

'How about a pina colada?' he suggested carelessly. 'My daughter likes them a lot. It's like a Chi Chi, with rum instead of vodka.'

Laura gazed at him. 'Your daughter's only twelve, isn't she?' she asked aghast, and his lazy grin sent a quiver of unwilling excitement down her spine.

'Haven't you heard of virgin cocktails?' he asked, mixing the ingredients in a blender.

Laura shook her head. 'No.'

'Well, you have now,' he conceded lightly. 'No alcohol!'

Laura moistened her lips. 'I've never met your daughter,' she murmured, as much for something to say as anything. 'Is she like you, or—or your wife?'

'My *ex*-wife,' amended Jason evenly, the crushed ice chinking deliciously as he poured her cocktail into a tall glass. He paused to add a slice of pineapple to the side of the glass before handing it to her. 'She's one of the reasons why I wanted to speak to you.'

Laura took the glass and their fingers touched, and it was as if his skin had burned hers. His hands were cool, but she could feel the brush of his flesh long after he had returned to the bar to pour himself a more-prosaic scotch on the rocks. She sipped the cocktail urgently, glad of the alcohol to strengthen her determination not to be disconcerted by his nearness, but his lean indolence was very appealing, particularly when he pulled off his tie and loosened the top three buttons of his shirt.

'So,' he said, watching her reactions over the rim of his glass, 'shall we sit down?'

Laura subsided on to a low cushioned sofa and tensed anew when he came down beside her, his long legs splayed carelessly across the Chinese carpet. She had never been this close to him before, and the awareness was disturbing. She wanted to remain composed, but it wasn't easy in this position.

'My wife—Regina—has been in Europe for the past six weeks,' he began, suspending his glass between his knees and smoothing its frosted surface with his fingers. 'She's due back day after tomorrow.'

'Yes?' The sound was barely audible, but evidently he heard it and continued:

'Lucia's been with her.'

'Your—daughter.'

'That's right.' He turned his head to look at her, his eyes narrowing. 'Do you like kids, Laura? I guess you do. You're not much more than one yourself, are you?'

'I'm almost twenty-two,' Laura exclaimed defensively,

not altogether pleased that he should be thinking of her as a juvenile, however much of a relief it might be in other ways.

'A great age,' he remarked drily. 'Do you realise, I was about your age when Lucia was born.'

'So?' A trace of colour entered Laura's cheeks at the implied impertinence. 'Why do you want to know?'

Jason hesitated. 'Because I have to go to the Big Island at the weekend, and Regina expects me to have charge of Lucia for the next couple of weeks.'

Laura swallowed. 'I still don't——'

'I want you to come to Hawaii with us,' said Jason evenly. 'I need you anyway—in your professional capacity,' he added. 'And I hoped you and Lucia might be company for one another when I'm tied up.'

Laura stared at him helplessly. 'But, I—I——'

'I thought we'd use the yacht,' he went on levelly. 'Kona—that's where we'd be making for—is about a day's sailing from here. It's across the island from Hilo, the capital, but I think you'll enjoy the trip around the coast. We could sail on Friday, spend Saturday on the island, and sail back Sunday. What do you say?'

Laura shook her head. 'I—I've never sailed before.'

'I'm not asking you to take the helm,' he responded wryly. 'I have a crew for that.'

'I might be sea-sick!'

'You might,' he conceded quietly. 'But I don't think you will.'

Laura took another sip of her pina colada. 'Won't your daughter think it odd that I—that I should be coming with you?'

Jason finished his drink and then regarded her sombrely. 'You don't want to come,' he said flatly. 'Why don't you just say so?'

'It's not that,' she burst out quickly, almost before she had considered her words. 'I . . . I . . . need time to think.'

'Okay.' Jason got to his feet, a dark shadow over her. 'How much time do you need?'

'I'm not sure.' Laura's shoulders were stiff from the amount of dictation she had taken that day, and almost unconsciously she lifted a hand to massage her aching neck muscles. 'I should have to ask Mrs Sylva.'

'Leave Mrs Sylva to me,' declared Jason crisply, dropping his glass on to an exotically carved map table. 'Here,' he added. 'Let me!' And to her utter distraction, he came round the couch behind her, and pushed her hand away. With expert fingers, he kneaded the throbbing muscles in her shoulders, and then moved to her neck and the slender cords that vibrated beneath his probing touch. 'Better?' he inquired, bending his head to look at her, and it was all she could do not to give in to the almost irresistible urge to rest her head back against his thighs.

'M ... much better, thank you,' she murmured, moving forward out of temptation's way, and with a half smile, he walked across to the bar to pour himself another scotch.

In his absence, Laura finished her drink and got hastily to her feet. She was aware that the upper part of her body was now suffused with colour, and she hated the idea that he might get the wrong impression. But was it the wrong impression? she asked herself impatiently. When Jason had touched her, hadn't she felt as weak and vulnerable as any one of those females who hung on his 'phone at all hours of the day and night? And he probably knew it, she reflected glumly; and was amused by it!

Of course, Laura fell in with his wishes—although it was not entirely due to Jason's persuasion.

Regina Montefiore—she still retained her married name—and her daughter, swept into the office the following morning, having returned from Italy earlier than expected, and both of them stopped short at the sight of Jason's new secretary.

'Where is Marsha?' demanded Regina imperiously, looking round the office as if she suspected the other girl might be hiding from her. 'Who are you? What are you doing here?'

'My name is Laura Huyton and I'm Marsha's temporary replacement,' replied Laura politely, glad

Jason had prepared her for this invasion. 'You must be
... Mrs Montefiore, and ... and Lucia. How do you
do? Can I be of some assistance?'

Regina's dark eyes flashed with impatience. It was
obvious that, whatever her relationship with her ex-
husband, she still resented any change in his staff
without her notice. Her colour heightened, and her lips
twitched in irritation, and she flicked back her black
hair with heavily lacquered nails on fingers fairly
dripping with diamonds.

She was certainly very sure of herself, Laura
acknowledged tensely, and why not? With voluptuous
features, and a body as generously rounded as a
Botticelli Venus, she could afford to feel self-confident,
and the clothes she wore accentuated her sensual
appeal.

Lucia, on the other hand, was more like Jason than
Laura had expected. She was dark, but then, so were
both her parents, and while Laura could see traces of
her mother in the faintly insolent gaze she cast upon the
English girl, her height and build were more in keeping
with her father's lean frame.

'You can tell Jason I am here,' Regina declared now,
tapping impatient fingers on Laura's desk. 'He is here, I
suppose. He hasn't disappeared in my absence!'

'He is here, Mrs Montefiore, but he's in a meeting at
the moment,' Laura replied carefully. 'He shouldn't be
too long. Can I get you and your daughter a cup of
coffee while you wait?'

Regina's smile was malicious. 'Just tell him I'm here,'
she repeated arrogantly. 'Jason will see me. You'll see.'

Laura's nostrils flared. 'I have orders not to interrupt
him, Mrs Montefiore,' she said, controlling her tone
with an effort. 'If you and Lucia would like to sit
down——'

'Oh, don't be so stupid!' Losing her temper, Regina
leant across the desk and pressed down the call button
on the intercom. 'Jason!' she said imperiously. 'Will you
come and tell this creature who I am!'

There was silence from the other end of the line, but
seconds later Jason's door opened and he came out,

closing it sharply behind him. Laura dared not look at
his face, but Lucia relieved the situation by darting
forward and throwing herself against him.

'Daddy!' she exclaimed, wrapping her arms around
him. 'Oh, Daddy, I've missed you!'

'Have you, sweetheart?'

Jason's response was more controlled than Laura
would have expected, and glancing at Regina she saw
the look of satisfaction on her face. If Jason's wife had
engineered the whole scene, she could not have chosen a
more apt way of defusing the situation, and Laura
found herself wondering, rather cynically for her,
whether Lucia was used to playing this role.

'I told *her*,' declared Regina contemptuously, flicking
a thumb in Laura's direction, 'I told her you would not
expect us to wait, Jason, but she would not listen.'

'Miss Huyton has her job to consider,' he responded
evenly, releasing himself from Lucia's clinging fingers.
'And you were not supposed to be flying home until
tomorrow.'

'So—I got bored!' retorted Regina, the faint accent
Laura had noticed deepening as she addressed her ex-
husband. 'You are not pleased to see us?' She cast
another scornful look in Laura's direction. 'I cannot
believe it.'

Jason, too, looked at Laura then, over his daughter's
head, and she wondered later if she had only imagined
the trace of sympathy that entered his eyes during that
brief exchange. 'I'm pleased you arrived back safely, of
course,' he replied, transferring his attention back to his
ex-wife and leaving Laura with a curiously breathless
feeling. 'But I really can't talk to you now. I suggest we
have lunch together. Say one o'clock at Bagwells? I'll
try not to be late.'

Regina's lips pursed. 'Oh very well. But I came to
warn you—I shall be leaving for New York in the
morning. And naturally, I shall expect you to look after
Lucy while I'm gone.'

Jason looked down at his daughter. 'Naturally,' he
said, a faint smile touching his lips as he met his
daughter's somewhat anxious gaze. 'I've already made

plans.' He addressed himself to Lucia. 'How does the idea of spending the weekend on the yacht grab you?'

'Oh, Daddy!'

Lucia was evidently excited at the prospect, but Regina's mouth tightened. 'I trust you do not intend to introduce our daughter to your latest mistress, Jason!' she remarked angrily, causing Laura's lips to part in shocked anticipation. 'Or do you really expect me to believe you intend to spend the weekend without female companionship?'

Jason's lean face hardened. 'You can believe what you like, Regina,' he responded dispassionately, and Laura was not the only one to sense the threat inherent in his words.

Regina wavered. 'I just meant—well, I would not have expected you to take Lucy on the yacht without another female in attendance. What if something happens? What if she is sick?'

'Don't worry, Mrs Montefiore.' To her astonishment, Laura realised it was she who had spoken. Getting to her feet, she cast an appealing look at Jason, and then went on, 'I'm going with them, you see. It's partly a business trip.' She paused, aware that Lucia was looking distinctly resentful now. 'I'll look after your daughter, Mrs Montefiore. She'll be quite safe with us.'

CHAPTER SIX

AFTERWARDS, Laura was to feel amazed that she had had the nerve to speak out as she did, but at the time it had seemed the only thing to do. Besides, it did give her a totally unforgivable feeling of satisfaction to beat Regina at her own game, even if Lucia's response was less than enthusiastic.

Still, the die was cast, and on Friday morning Laura was ready when Jason's chauffeur came to pick her up at six o'clock. 'You must be mad!' Sylvie groaned, hearing the other girl moving quietly about the flat before she left, and coming out of her room to speak to her. 'I can't believe you've agreed to spend the weekend on this boat of his. I thought you were the quiet type!'

'Oh, Sylvie! I'm not planning on sleeping with him,' Laura responded hotly. 'His daughter's going with us, you know she is. And he's not interested in me. He's never even made a pass at me.'

'That's what worries me,' retorted Sylvie drily. 'He's played it very cool, I'll give you that. But I hope you're prepared, just in case.'

'Just in case of what?' Laura flushed. 'Oh, Sylvie! Not that again!'

'Why not? D'you want to get pregnant?'

Laura suspected she might need prior notice of that question. The idea of Jason making her pregnant was not one she could consider with equanimity. It was crazy, she knew, and Sylvie would despise her even more if she suspected, but Laura could not avoid the unpalatable fact that emotionally he disturbed her more than any man she had ever known. And the thought of making love with him was something she could not discuss, with anyone.

'Don't be silly,' she said now, stuffing her bikini into her canvas holdall. 'I shall more likely throw up as soon as we get out into the open sea.'

The car came soon after, and Laura drove away feeling far less confident than she appeared. What if Sylvie was right? she fretted. What if Jason did try to make love to her? Her own inexperience had never been a problem before now, but remembering how experienced most of the girls of her acquaintance were, she couldn't help wondering how Jason would react to a twenty-one-year-old virgin!

The sight of the schooner drove all other thoughts from her head—at least temporarily. She had never been aboard such a vessel before, and her absorption in her surroundings helped to ease the situation. It was not easy to treat Jason casually after what Sylvie had said, and in a sleeveless black vest and another pair of the shorts that fit his legs closely to mid-thigh, he was a disturbing presence. Even Lucia's scowling face could not dispel Laura's awareness of him, and she was glad when the anchor was raised and they sailed out of the marina.

Only once in those first few minutes did she forget to be on her guard with him, and that was when she discovered the name of the yacht was the *Laura M.* 'Laura!' she exclaimed, gazing at him with arched brows. 'How did you——'

'It's my mother's name,' he responded softly, his eyes running with disturbing thoroughness over the honey-gold skin of her throat, exposed above the neckline of her sleeveless blouse, and she flushed. 'It was what I wanted to call Lucia, but Regina wouldn't have it. So we compromised. But I still prefer the original.'

Laura looked away from him then, aware of his daughter's sharp eyes watching them. But she couldn't dismiss what he had said as quickly, and her throat dried unpleasantly as she curled her fingers over the rail.

It was a glorious day, albeit a little choppy, once they left the harbour. However, Laura found the pitching motion of the vessel didn't trouble her at all, and seating herself on one of the cushioned loungers, set in the lee of the bulkhead, she turned her face up to the sun.

Lucia was being very unsociable. She had not responded to any of Laura's attempts to make friends with her, and now she was below decks somewhere, taking out her anger on the crew. Laura could hear her complaining voice as she closed her eyes against the glare, and she wondered if the younger girl was really as much like Regina as she seemed.

'Wouldn't you be cooler in something less cumbersome?' suggested Jason quietly, lowering his length on to the chair beside her.

Laura had not heard his approach, and her eyes opened to find her employer regarding her with lazy inquiry. 'I . . . I burn easily,' she stammered, drawing up her legs and wrapping her arms around her knees. The cotton pants she was wearing were all-enveloping, but the idea of exposing herself before Jason in a bikini was daunting.

'Don't you have any oil?' he asked pointedly, and aware that he could see the bottle of coconut lotion protruding from the bag beside her, she coloured anew.

'Well, yes . . .'

'Put your swimsuit on,' he recommended flatly. 'I'll see you don't get burned.'

She could have argued, but it seemed pointless. She could hardly spend the whole weekend behaving like an outraged virgin every time he looked at her. Scrambling to her feet, she went down to her cabin and pulled out the skimpy blue bikini.

Back on deck, she discovered Jason had removed his T-shirt and was lying flat out on the cushioned lounger, his closed eyes enabling Laura to reach her own seat without observation. She guessed he would have no problem with over-exposure to the sun. His body was brown and muscular, and already gleaming with moisture, and unable to prevent herself, she allowed her eyes to linger on the arrowing whorls of fine dark hair that disappeared below the waistband of his shorts.

His eyes opened as the chair moved with her weight, and she suffered his appraisal as he reached for the bottle of oil. 'Okay,' he said, sitting up. 'I'll do your back first. Turn over.'

Laura hesitated. 'I can do it . . .'

'How?' His eyes challenged hers, and she faltered. 'Go on,' he added. 'Lie down. Even I draw the line at performing before an audience.'

Laura rolled on to her stomach. 'I don't know what you mean.'

'I think you do.' He was dispassionate. 'That's what this parade of feminine modesty is all about, isn't it? Someone's told you something about me. Someone's warned you I'm not to be trusted.'

'No!'

'Yes,' he said inflexibly, causing her to gasp in protest when he poured a pool of chilling liquid into the warm hollow of her spine. 'Who was it? Regina? I didn't think you got to know her that well.'

'I didn't.' Laura rested her cheek against her folded arms. 'I hardly spoke to her. You know that.'

'Okay.' He swept the silky curtain of her hair to one side and dipped his fingers into the oil. 'Who then? Luke? Phil Logan?'

'No one,' she persisted, as he began to massage her shoulders. His hands were a forbidden delight, and she couldn't prevent the involuntary surge of pleasure she felt as they moved against her skin. 'Hmm. That feels good.'

'Does it?' With experienced fingers, he released the clip of the bikini bra and stroked the whole sensitive length of her spine to the spot where the band of her briefs rested. 'I'm surprised you let me touch you at all.'

'Mr Montefiore, *please!*' Laura was having difficulty in holding on to her composure. 'I . . . please, fasten that clip again, will you? I can finish the rest myself.'

Jason ignored her, smoothing ribbons of oil from the curve of her buttocks down over her thighs, and into the sensitive hollow behind her knees. While Laura struggled to attach the two sides of her bikini without lifting her body from the pad, Jason completed his task with evident satisfaction, his fingers probing even the soles of her feet.

When Laura at last scrambled on to her knees, there was a curiously sensuous smile playing around Jason's

lips, and she had to force herself to face him without
flinching. 'Thank you,' she said, though it was hardly a
term of gratitude. 'Can I have the oil now?'

Lucia appeared as Laura finished oiling her midriff,
and she looked up at the girl cautiously, prepared to
face antagonism of another sort. But to her surprise,
Lucia was looking decidedly unhappy, and her pale
cheeks and sweating skin told another story.

'Daddy, I don't feel well,' she protested, pressing her
hand to her bare stomach. Like her father, Lucia was
wearing shorts, with a simple halter top that tied at the
back.

Jason came to his feet in a lithe easy movement.
'Don't you, sweetheart?' he murmured, the disturbing
gentleness of his smile almost taking Laura's breath
away. 'Did you eat anything this morning before we
left?'

Lucia shook her head. 'I couldn't. I was too excited,'
she mumbled, though Laura had her doubts about that.
'Oh, Daddy! I think I'm going to be sick! Isn't there
anything you can do?'

Jason pushed a helpless hand through his hair, and
when his eyes encountered Laura's, she put the oil aside
and stood up. 'Let me look after her,' she murmured,
stepping to Lucia's side and putting a sympathetic arm
around the other girl's waist. 'Come on, Lucy. Let's go
below.'

Even though Lucia might have preferred to stay
with her father, she offered no objections when Laura
took her down to her cabin. She was obviously too
distressed to put up any real protest, and besides,
Laura guessed she was not keen on making a fool of
herself in front of Jason. After all, theirs was hardly a
normal father-daughter relationship, and Lucia was
fast approaching the age when appearances became so
important.

In fact, she wasn't sick. After making her comfortable
on the bed in her cabin, Laura sped into the forward
saloon and purloined a bottle of brandy from the bar.
Then, mixing it with a little water, she encouraged the
prostrate girl to sip the fiery liquid, hoping that the

remedy she had once used on the Channel Islands ferry still held good.

It did. The combination of being flat on her back and the warming glow of the alcohol eventually calmed Lucia's heaving stomach, and a little of the colour returned to her cheeks as she felt the sickness fading.

'Thanks,' she murmured offhandedly, still not prepared to accept Laura unreservedly, and the older girl smiled.

'I should try and sleep, if I were you,' she responded gently, making for the door. 'If you need me, I'll be in my cabin. As it's almost lunchtime, I might as well put my clothes on again.'

'Sorry I spoiled your morning,' Lucia mumbled, turning on to her side away from her, and Laura grimaced.

'No problem,' she said, letting herself out of the door, and Lucia's only response was a sleepy grunt.

She was drying herself after her shower, when she heard someone moving about in her cabin. As she had left her clothes on the bed, she was forced to emerge with only a towel wrapped sarong-wise around her slim body, and she gazed rather apprehensively at her uninvited visitor. Jason was standing gazing broodingly out of the narrow windows that gave the sleeping compartment privacy, his feet slightly apart, his arms folded across the muscled expanse of his chest.

He turned at her appearance, his eyes moving down over her makeshift toga. Then, allowing his arms to fall to his sides, he said quietly, 'I thought for a minute you were sick, too.'

'No. No, I'm fine.' Laura spoke quickly, her nervousness showing. 'Have you seen Lucia? I think she's going to be all right.'

'She's asleep,' said Jason nodding. 'I'm grateful. She and I don't see one another often enough to build a proper relationship.'

Laura hesitated. 'Is that her mother's fault, or yours?'

Jason lifted one dark eyebrow. 'Mine, I guess,' he admitted, although Laura had the suspicion that this wasn't exactly true. Regina might find Lucia an

encumbrance sometimes, but she was far too valuable
an ally when it came to gaining Jason's attention to be
allowed free access to her father.

'Oh, well,' she said now, making a display of securing
the towel more closely about her. 'I expect when she's
older, she'll be able to choose where she wants to stay.'

Jason did not take her remark the way she had
intended. 'What am I to glean from that?' he inquired,
tautly. 'That you think Lucia might choose to spend
more time with me? You heard what Regina said, my
daughter's opinion of her father is not exactly
unprejudiced.'

'Even so . . .'

'Even so, what?'

Laura bent her head. 'It's not really anything to do
with me.'

'No, it's not. But I'm interested anyway.' Jason took
a step nearer. 'I gather you didn't like Regina.'

'Oh, Mr Montefiore . . .'

'My name is Jason,' he said flatly. 'Use it. I know all
about your English reserve, but in a situation like this,
don't you think it's pretty foolish to keep treating me
like a stranger.'

'I'm not treating you like a stranger, Mr Montefiore.'
Laura licked her dry lips. 'Just as my employer.'

'Your employer, hmm?' Jason's mouth thinned.
'Well, as your employer, I'm asking you to give me
your opinion of my ex-wife. Don't you have one?'

Laura sighed. 'Oh, please . . .'

'Please what?' he snapped, his patience threading.
'For God's sake, Laura, there are times when you make
me so angry! What the hell do you expect me to do to
you anyway? You've acted like I was going to jump on
you ever since you came aboard! Hell, I'm not into
forcing myself on anyone—least of all a timid virgin,
who doesn't even know what it's all about!'

Laura's face mirrored the pain his cruel words had
deliberately evoked, and she automatically fell back a
step, her hand pressed to her throat. Sylvie had been *so*
wrong, she thought unsteadily, wishing she had not
listened to the other girl. She had turned an awkward

situation into something worse, and Jason probably assumed she was one of those awful females who thought every man they met couldn't wait to get his hands on them.

'I'm sorry,' he grated now, raking back his hair with obvious frustration, and Laura quickly shook her head. 'It doesn't matter . . .'

'It does matter,' he retorted harshly, overriding her. 'I didn't mean to say what I did, and I certainly didn't mean it. For Christ's sake, Laura, why do you think I brought you on this trip?'

Laura swallowed a little convulsively. 'You told me.'

'No, I didn't.' Jason turned away from her with an impatient gesture. 'At least, not all of it. I invited you along because I wanted to spend some time with you, away from the office. I like you. You're a nice kid. I guess I never thought it through, that's all.'

Laura absorbed what he was saying with a growing sense of disbelief. 'You mean . . .'

'I mean I am attracted to you,' he interrupted her flatly. 'And for once in my life, I'm finding it hard to make the running.'

Laura quivered, but she had to say it: 'I—I may be a timid virgin, but I'm not a kid, Jason.'

He half turned to look at her. 'What's that supposed to mean?'

Her courage deserted her. 'I . . . why . . . nothing . . .'

'Laura?' He was in front of her now, his hands descending on her shoulders, his thumbs moving with disturbing sensuality against her flesh. 'Oh hell—look at me!'

She lifted her head reluctantly, half afraid of what he might see in her face, but the smouldering warmth of his irises drove all other considerations out of her head. With a feeling of inevitability, she saw his face descending towards hers, and then his image blurred as his lips found her trembling mouth.

She realised in those first few seconds how often she had wondered what it would be like if Jason kissed her. She had frequently studied his dark face while he was intent on dictation, mentally tracing the taut planes of his features, stroking the silky fringe of his lashes. But she had never expected to find out for herself, or to feel that lean mouth pleasuring hers with so much urgency. The moist flick of his tongue was an added stimulation, and her lips opened wider to allow his hungry invasion.

She gulped for air when he at last released her to bury his face in the silken skein of her hair, and his voice was unsteady as he groped for speech. 'I didn't intend this to happen,' he muttered, one hand beneath her hair caressing the delicate column of her neck. 'At least, not yet anyway,' he added honestly, lifting his head to look down at her. 'Do you mind?'

Laura lifted her hand to touch his cheek, still too bemused by what had happened to be able to think coherently, and with a groan, Jason sought her mouth again. An uncontrollable surge of pleasure enveloped her when his hands brought her body closer to his, and when next he lifted his head, she murmured in protest.

'You don't know what you're doing,' he said roughly, propelling her gently but firmly away from him. 'Look—I'd better go. Get dressed. We'll have lunch on deck, hmm?'

'Why?' she breathed, still rapt in the emotions he had aroused in her, and with a muffled oath he walked towards the door.

'Because if I don't go now, I won't be able to,' he told her frankly, and her face flamed with colour at the flagrant acknowledgement in his words.

Lucia was able to join them for lunch, and although she ate little of the fresh salmon the chef had prepared, she did enjoy the fruit salad that followed it. If she was aware of any tension between her father and his secretary, she didn't show it, and she even spoke to Laura once or twice, albeit in that same offhand manner she had adopted in her cabin.

For Laura, the meal was something of a trial. She could hardly bear to look at Jason, remembering the abandoned way she had behaved earlier, and she suffered his silent censure of her attire without giving him an opportunity to voice it. But she could not have emerged in a swimsuit again; not after what had happened between them, and although she was overdressed for the occasion, she refused to consider the alternatives.

During the afternoon Jason disappeared into his cabin, apparently to work, and Laura decided to rest. She had hardly slept the night before, and she had been up at five to be ready when Jason's chauffeur appeared. To her surprise, she slept almost immediately, and by the time she woke up, the sun was sinking fast.

Dinner was served in the main saloon. The captain, Alec Cowray, joined them, and Laura was glad she had brought at least one suitable dress. Made of dark blue silk, with a pleated bodice below narrow bootlace straps, the skirt swung flatteringly about her slender legs, and the colour accentuated her extreme fairness and deepened the colour of her eyes.

She was ridiculously pleased when Jason complimented her appearance, and although his comment had been casually made in the presence of his daughter and Alec Cowray, the disruptive quality of his regard over the dinner table could not be ignored.

'Do we have much further to go, Daddy?' Lucia asked, hopefully distracting her father's attention while the waiter re-filled her wine glass, and Jason frowned.

'We'll be lying off the Kona coast by the time you wake in the morning, pretty lady,' Alec Cowray answered gallantly. 'And if you're up at seven you can join me for my early morning dip.'

'I might just do that,' declared Lucia, scowling as her father covered her glass with his hand. 'Will you come, too, Daddy? You don't have any objections to me swallowing too much water, do you?'

'None whatsoever,' responded Jason pleasantly, dark and disturbing in a black shirt and matching pants. Although both men wore ties, jackets had been dispensed with, and Laura didn't blame them. In spite of the trade winds, it was still very warm. 'But I suggest you turn in shortly, if you're planning on matching Alec.'

'And you? Will you come?' Lucia was persistent, and

her eyes flickered reluctantly to the other girl. 'And—Laura, too,' she added. 'If she wants.'

'I'd like that,' responded Laura eagerly, glad that Lucia was at least making an effort to be sociable. 'We'll see you at seven, Mr Cowray. All of us.'

'Not me,' said Jason smoothly, putting his napkin aside and getting to his feet. 'Count me out, Alec. Tomorrow's going to be too long a day as it is.'

Laura looked up at him doubtfully, not altogether understanding his explanation, but she averted her eyes when he caught her watching him, and Alec Cowray's departure prevented any further discussion.

Lucia left soon afterwards, the wine she had consumed before her father's embargo causing her eyelids to droop. 'Night, Daddy,' she said, giving him a prolonged hug and a kiss on his cheek, and Jason smiled affectionately as she disappeared out the door.

Left alone with her employer, Laura was tempted to say her good nights too, but Jason forestalled her. 'Let's go up on deck while they clear the cabin,' he suggested quietly, and Laura could think of no reason to refuse.

It was a marvellous night. The sky was inky dark yet, shot with stars, it evoked the image of diamonds on velvet. The powerful schooner seemed to be skimming over the water, its canvas taut against the wind. Laura thought there could be few things more beautiful than a ship under sail, and she shivered with the awareness that she was a part of it.

'You're cold?'

Jason had noticed the involuntary movement, but Laura shook her head. 'Just ... exhilarated, that's all,' she murmured, shaking her head in wonder. 'You're very lucky, Jason. This is a beautiful craft.'

'I think so.' Jason relaxed on the rail beside her, his face shadowed in spite of the light from the staterooms. 'I'm glad you feel the same.'

Laura lifted her shoulders. 'Thank you for bringing me.'

Jason hesitated. 'Do you mean that?'

Laura quivered. 'Of course.'

'Even after what happened.'

Laura bent her head. 'Nothing happened.'

'No.' He conceded the point, concentrating on the distant horizon. 'I haven't sunk that low yet.'

'What do you mean?'

'I mean—seducing virgins,' retorted Jason succinctly. 'Shall we talk about something else?'

'Didn't you expect me to be?' asked Laura softly. 'After what you said, I——'

'I hoped you weren't,' replied Jason, turning to face the deck. 'Come on. Let's go and get a drink. I could surely use . . .'

'Wait!' Laura could not let him go like that. 'Don't you—I mean—is it a crime? Not having had sex, I mean.'

'Don't be foolish!' Jason was impatient.

'Then what is it?' Laura forced him to look at her. 'Am I . . . am I less desirable because I haven't been with a man before?'

Jason stared at her. 'Do you realise what you're saying?'

Laura flushed. 'Do you?'

Jason made a negative gesture. 'I think the wine has gone to your head.'

'But not to yours.'

'I'm more used to it.' He looked down at her intently for a moment, and then he swore. 'Laura, don't play with fire!'

Laura couldn't help herself. The night; and the yacht; and Jason's disturbing presence—not to mention the wine she had drunk at dinner—were all combining to give her a confidence she had never had before, and it was a tantalising thing, this verbal love-play.

'Why am I playing with fire?' she asked huskily. 'I asked a perfectly reasonable question.'

'All right, all right.' With a smothered oath, Jason turned and imprisoned her against the rail between his hands. 'I'll give you an answer,' he said harshly. '*Yes!* Yes, you would be more attractive to me if you'd already slept with another man! Does that satisfy you?'

Laura's bubble burst. 'Thank you,' she mumbled, barely audibly.

'Don't mention it!' He straightened, releasing her. 'Now shall we go and have that drink?'

'I—I don't think I want one,' said Laura tightly. 'If . . . if you'll excuse me.'

The door to her cabin had no lock, but in any case, she didn't need one. Nevertheless, when she lifted her head from the coverlet some time later to the sound of someone knocking at her door, she could have wished for the privacy to shed her tears without interruption. Had Lucia heard her crying? she wondered, scrubbing her knuckles across her face. The younger girl's cabin was just next door. Had her distress been audible even through the wall?

'Wh . . . who is it?' she asked in a low voice, hoping that whoever it was might not hear her and go away, but there was no reply. Instead, to her horror, the door was propelled inward, and in the glow from the wall-lights suspended above the bed, she met Jason's tormented gaze.

'*Christ!*' he muttered, taking in the situation with one encompassing look, and leaving the door ajar, he came across to the bed.

He was wearing a dark red kimono-style robe, embroidered around the hem and cuffs, and she guessed from his bare legs below its folds that it was all he was wearing. His hair was damp, as if he had just taken a shower, and she could smell the tangy fragrance of some lotion he had been using.

'I thought it must be you,' he said, looking down at her with brooding eyes, and then, startling her by his strength, he bent down and lifted her up into his arms. 'We can't talk here,' he added, when she gave him a tearful glance, and without giving her time to protest, he strode back to the door.

Jason's suite was infinitely more masculine in design, his bed, where he eventually deposited her, strewn with dark brown silk sheets, and a figured brown and gold bedspread. He had evidently been reading– there was a file tossed carelessly on to the table beside the bed and the distinctive aroma of brandy indicated he had been having a nightcap.

Leaving her for a moment, he went into his sitting room to fetch her a glass, and presently he pressed a goblet of the same remedy she had given Lucia earlier in the day into her hand. 'Drink it,' he said, sitting down beside her in a partly cross-legged position. 'It won't make you drunk, but it might make you sleep.'

Laura sniffed. 'I'm sorry.'

'Why are you sorry?'

'For ... for making a fool of myself. I don't ... usually.'

Jason's mouth took on a sardonic slant. 'I should hope not.'

'No. I mean it.' Laura took a sip of the brandy and grimaced. 'What must you think of me?'

Jason regarded her with some irony. 'I think you know.'

'No, I don't.' She sniffed again, and he handed her a box of tissues. 'Oh, this is so embarrassing!'

Jason waited until she had composed herself, and then he said softly, 'Do you want to stay?'

Laura's lips parted. 'You mean—here?'

Jason took the glass that was in danger of spilling itself all over the sheets out of her hand. 'Where else?'

Laura gazed at him. 'You mean—sleep with you?'

'I mean—sleep with me,' he conceded. 'God knows, it's what I want!'

'But ... you said ...'

'I lied,' he admitted huskily, taking her wrist to his lips and caressing the sensitive inner curve with his tongue. 'Laura, I'm about ten years older than you are. And I know there are plenty of people more than willing to tell you the kind of guy they think I am. We both know what I *should* do, and that's why I said what I did.'

'Jason——'

'No, listen!' He bent his head and silenced her with his mouth. 'If you stay, you know what will happen. I'm a man, not a saint. I don't admire myself for this, but I know what I'm doing. Just be sure you do, too.'

It was not until she was in Honolulu that Laura really

considered what Jason had said, and by then it was much too late to have second thoughts. Still, she did take Sylvie's advice about birth control. She had no wish to present Jason with the news that he had fathered another child, and although the idea of having his baby was one she cherished, she was practical enough to realise that that was not her role.

Fathoms deep in love with him, though she was, she knew he had never once said he loved her. He wanted her; she had no doubt about that. Indeed, within two weeks of their becoming lovers, he had asked her to move into his apartment with him, and although Laura had hung out for a further four weeks, eventually she had succumbed to his expert persuasion.

Besides, she had wanted to be with him equally as much as he wanted to be with her. Getting up and dressing, and allowing him to drive her back to the lonely isolation of her own bed in the early hours of the morning soon lost its appeal, and it was a tantalising delight to wake in the mornings and find him beside her. To feel his lean, muscular frame wrapped possessively about her was a very satisfying experience, and she also came to appreciate the other advantages that came from being there when he woke.

Nevertheless, she had no illusions that one day Jason would find someone else. He was not the kind of man to be content with the same woman for too long, and Regina was always about to maliciously remind Laura—as if she could ever forget—that she was only the latest in a long line of females.

'It isn't as if you're anything special,' she remarked, on one occasion, her lips tilting scornfully. 'I mean, I understood Jason's desire to wipe that smug touch-me-not expression off your face, but even I couldn't hold him after Lucy was born. And you have to admit, I have a little more to do it with than you have!'

Laura had weathered these comments manfully, and their association continued even after his secretary, Marsha, returned to her desk. Indeed, Jason took advantage of the fact, encouraging Laura to give in her notice at the agency so that he could take her with him on his frequent trips to the mainland. He even introduced her to his sister and his mother, though his relations with his father were rather less cordial. Laura knew it had something to do with Marco Montefiore's business dealings, but she didn't probe. If Jason wanted her to know, he would tell her. She believed they had few secrets from one another.

Two years into their relationship, she was actually beginning to feel her position was secure, and that was why, when the bombshell exploded, she was so unprepared to deal with it. Discovering Jason had been deceiving her was bad enough; discovering he was also responsible for another man's death was intolerable.

She had tried to discuss it with him. She had tried to tell him how she felt, and how he had hurt her, but he wouldn't listen. In one terrible afternoon, her whole world had been shattered, and she had never thought she would pick up the pieces again . . .

CHAPTER SEVEN

THE warm waters of the Pacific were distinctly clearer now as the Learjet began its descent towards the island. For hours they had been flying west and south over a blue expanse of ocean that was totally indistinguishable from more than thirty thousand feet. But now, having glimpsed landfall over Molokai, they were rapidly losing height in their approach to Kaulanai, and in spite of her misgivings, Laura could not deny a certain sense of anticipation.

It was perfectly natural, she told herself firmly, when an inner voice chided her weakness. Whether she liked it or not, the island was to be her home until Pamela had had the baby, and she could hardly be blamed if she was curious to see the house Jason had built.

The fact that Pamela was already there had come as something of a shock. When Laura had left San Francisco, the arrangement had been that she should return there after settling her own affairs in London, thus giving her sister time to dispose of the apartment she had been leasing, and pack her belongings ready for the transfer to Kaulanai. But instead, Jason had gone to see Pamela in her absence, and offered the services of his lawyer to facilitate matters for her. And her sister, much to Laura's astonishment, had accepted his offer, and in consequence Pamela had been living in Jason's house for the past three days, enjoying the freedom of a total lack of responsibility. That was why he had flown to London, Jason had explained, in the drowsy aftermath of his lovemaking. Not to spy on her, but to inform her of the change in arrangements, which meant she had no reason to land on the mainland, after all.

To say that Laura had been taken aback by this new development was an understatement. She had believed

Pamela's acceptance of Jason's suggestion had been
apathetic at best, and she had been half prepared to
face an argument on her return. In spite of the obvious
advantages of his offer, she had been surprised that her
sister had apparently given up her search for Mike
Kazantis. For although Laura had made some vague
reference to the fact that Jason had promised to inquire
into his whereabouts, she had told Pamela nothing of
his relationship with Jason. She had not even told her
he was married, which she could have done quite easily.
To say that Jason knew of him and not to elaborate on
it, had made her feel quite a fraud. But until Pamela
had been satisfactorily installed on Kaulanai, she had
not wanted to say anything to upset her, and it had
been somewhat troubling to discover that Pamela's
state of mind had not been as emotionally fragile as she
had thought.

'Are you tired?'

Jason's controlled inquiry above her brought her
head up with a start, and she was annoyed to feel the
blood surging into her face. If he could be so objective
about it, why couldn't she? she asked herself fiercely,
despising her reactions to his hard muscled body. It was
incredibly difficult for her to put what had happened
the night before out of her mind, but although he had
been left in no doubt as to her contempt for his
behaviour, he showed a cool indifference to her feelings.
The heated accusations she had flung at him in the
sobering light of morning had left him cold, and getting
up he had put on his clothes and left her, without so
much as a word of apology. He had evidently no regrets
for what had happened, and she loathed herself utterly
for making it so easy for him. By making love to her, he
had successfully re-established his claim to her body,
and no matter what happened subsequently, he had
proved his superiority over her.

'A little,' she mumbled now, in answer to his
question, conscious that the young stewardess, Julie,
was close enough to overhear their conversation. It had
been a long journey, and although the afternoon sun
was still shining on the islands, her metabolism was

telling her it was already the early hours of the next
morning.

'Did you sleep?' Jason persisted, and she was forced
to look up at him once again. In black Levis and a
matching cotton shirt, the sleeves rolled back to his
elbows, exposing the fine hairs covering his forearms,
he looked disruptively handsome, and Laura ducked
her head swiftly to evade his probing appraisal. It was
unfair, she thought, that even the slight pouches
beneath his eyes, evidence of the exhausting night he
had spent, only added to his dark magnetism. His raw
masculinity was as natural to him as the sexuality he
exuded without effort. He was aware of it, she was sure
of that, and he would use it if he had to, but she was
determined he would never know the effect it had on
her.

'A little,' she murmured, linking her fingers together
in her lap. 'Did you?'

It was a perfunctory inquiry, made for Julie's benefit,
but he chose to answer it, squatting down beside her
with lazy indolence. 'For a while,' he conceded softly,
running long fingers over the arm of her chair, so that
she had to press her arm to her side to avoid his touch.
'I rested on the bed for a while,' he added, and the
emotion in his voice was unmistakable now. 'I thought
you might have joined me . . .'

Laura quivered. 'You didn't think any such thing!'

'Why not?' His voice was still deceptively soft, but
there was a faint edge which had not been there before.
'There's nothing new about us sharing a bed——'

'*Stop it!*' Laura cast an imploring glance in Julie's
direction, but the stewardess had disappeared into the
forward cabin to speak to the pilot and they were
completely alone. 'Why must you torment me? Do you
get some perverted kind of enjoyment out of it?'

'Was I tormenting you?' Abruptly, he straightened.
'How am I supposed to take that? You didn't exactly
claw my eyes out last night, did you? Although, I have
to say, I have several weals in other places, which seems
to prove something.'

'Jason, *please!*'

'I disgust you, I know. You said this morning.' His lips twisted. 'Unfortunately, that's something *you're* going to have to live with.'

He left her then, crossing the cabin of the plane to fling himself into an armchair at the opposite side, and Laura fumbled awkwardly for her seat belt as the powerful little jet came down low over the ocean. The island was just ahead of them now, the creaming swirl of water marking the reef giving way to turquoise shallows lapping on sand bleached almost white by the sun. It was breathtakingly lovely, truly an island paradise, accorded Laura reluctantly, and she would not have been human if she had not felt a surge of wonder at its beauty.

The thin blade of the runway appeared beyond a belt of tall pandanus palms, whose roots were bedded in a thicket of shrubs and flowering plants. The ribbon of tarmac shimmered in a haze of heat, looking scarcely long enough to accommodate the plane. But the Learjet landed smoothly, the screaming reverse-thrust of its engines bringing it quickly to a halt. As it did so, a fluttering flock of doves rose protestingly from the bushes, scattering scarlet petals in the headlong panic of their flight.

As soon as the plane had landed, Jason flicked open his safety belt and got to his feet, gathering together the few belongings he had brought with him on the flight The black suede jacket he had needed at Heathrow, he now slung carelessly over one shoulder, and the briefcase, whose contents he had studied during the early part of the trip, was closed and locked securely before it was suspended from his hand.

Realising he was waiting for her to make a move, Laura unfastened her own seat belt and stood up as Frank Danielli came through from the forward cabin. 'Good flight, Frank,' said Jason evenly, never forgetting to treat his employees with respect, and the older man smiled.

'Just a little turbulence over northern Canada,' he admitted ruefully, flexing his shoulder muscles with weary satisfaction. 'I don't mind telling you, Jase, I'm looking forward to a hot soak and a cold beer! Just don't ask me to fly back to London again in the foreseeable future! That's some trip, and Clark and I have made it four times in the last seven days!'

'Request granted,' said Jason, with an easy grin, and Laura's stomach tightened at his casual charm. Despite his attraction for the opposite sex, he was equally relaxed in male company, and she didn't need to see Frank Danielli's responding grin or hear Clark Sinclair's chuckle of laughter to know that here were two more people who regarded him with affection.

The door of the jet was unlocked, and thrusting it outwards, Clark uncoiled the flight of steps concealed in its structure. 'Home sweet home,' he remarked, stepping back to allow Jason to precede him down on to the tarmac, and Laura realised there was no element of censure in the friendly glance he cast in her direction.

Following Jason down the steps, she was glad now she had not succumbed to the urge to wear the jersey suit she had first put on that morning. In the chill of Jason's departure, she had felt the need for something warmer than the cotton shirt and pants she had planned to wear. But sanity had prevailed, and now, stepping out into the heat of an Hawaiian afternoon, she applauded her choice.

After bidding goodbye to the crew, Jason nodded towards a cream convertible parked at the edge of the runway. 'Let's go,' he said, his tone cooling perceptibly when he spoke to her, and Laura cast a doubtful glance over her shoulder.

'My cases,' she murmured, wondering if he had forgotten, but Jason merely gestured her onward.

'Frank will see they're sent on,' he declared, nodding a greeting to an olive-skinned Chinese boy, dressed in beige overalls, who was already sprinting towards the plane. 'Don't worry. You won't have to sleep in the raw—not unless you want to, of course.'

Laura pressed her lips tightly together. 'Must you keep making remarks like that?' she asked, curiously near to tears, and his expression softened slightly.

'Must you keep pretending you didn't want me just

as much as I wanted you?' he countered harshly, and she turned her head away.

'You forced me . . .'

'Only up to a point,' retorted Jason curtly. 'I've never raped a woman in my life!'

'I never said you raped me——'

'You damn near implied it,' he returned, reaching the car and tossing his briefcase carelessly into the back. Then, recovering his expression, he turned to give the young man leaning on the car a friendly smile. 'Hi, Jonah,' he greeted him cheerfully, giving Laura another demonstration of his rare ability to adapt himself to any situation. 'How's your mother? Did she take those tablets Luke sent her?'

'Yes, sir, Mr Montefiore,' exclaimed Jonah self-importantly, swinging open the passenger door for Laura to get inside, and as she did so, the name Jason had used made her briefly forget their antagonism.

'Luke, Jason?' she probed, as he fitted his length behind the driving wheel. 'Do you mean Lucas Kamala?'

'So you do remember some things,' remarked Jason drily, and Laura guessed she deserved his cynicism.

'I remember Luke,' she declared defensively, as Jonah vaulted into the back of the vehicle. How could she forget the charming Hawaiian who had first made her welcome at the club? He had always been so kind to her, and she had missed his gentle humour more than she realised. 'Where is he now?'

'Where he always was,' replied Jason, casting a reflective glance in her direction before flicking the ignition. 'At the Blue Orchid. He's in charge there now.' He paused. 'You should have asked for him. He might not have told me of your call.'

Laura frowned. 'What do you mean?'

'Luke cares about me,' responded Jason obliquely, setting the car in motion, and before she could ask him what he meant, he started to speak to Jonah again.

But his words gave her something to think about as the road from the airstrip wound upwards, through a glade of pine and eucalyptus trees, to emerge on a

gravelled track some distance above the shoreline.
From above, it was possible to see the shape of the
beach as it wound around a jutting headland. It was
also possible to see cultivated fields stretching away
from the coast, fields planted with banana and
pineapple, and the waving stalks of sugar cane. Laura
gazed about her in wonder, realising as she did so that
the island she had assumed accommodated only Jason's
house and its surroundings was really a thriving
community.

The village, when they reached it, proved her theory,
with a cluster of cottages set about a square, with a
general stores and petrol pumps to service its
inhabitants. A stream ran through the middle of the
village, and there was a shaky wooden structure
spanning it, which scarcely looked strong enough to
support the powerful car. But Jason negotiated it easily,
waving to the group of children who ran to shout a
greeting. The mix of Chinese and Polynesian blood was
reflected in their faces, and Laura was forcibly
reminded of the beauty in these islands. The older girls
regarded Jason with open admiration, and looking at
their sweep of ebony hair and the dusky symmetry of
their features, she couldn't help wondering what he
could see in her unremarkable appearance. Compared
to their vivid warmth and colour, she felt pale and
uninteresting. She could only believe that what he had
said just two weeks ago was true. He did resent her
defiance in walking out on him, and he was determined
to make her pay for it, one way or the other.

'Is Miss Pamela all right?' Jason asked Jonah
suddenly, and Laura put her own anxieties aside to turn
and look at the young man behind them. Apart from
Jason's casual explanation, in the somnolent afterglow
of his lovemaking, they had not discussed her sister's
condition at all, and the bitter acrimony of his leave-
taking had created a barrier between them that had
made further communication impossible. But now, he
had made a direct reference to Pamela's presence in his
house, and Laura waited in anticipation for Jonah's
reply.

'She's fine,' he responded swiftly. 'Leah's looking after her real well.'

'Leah!' echoed Laura disbelievingly, and Jason pulled a wry face.

'Another blast from the past?' he inquired mockingly. 'You didn't think I'd lose a good housekeeper like Leah, did you? She's been with me for too many years to leave now.'

Laura shook her head. 'I never thought she'd leave Oahu.'

'I didn't either,' admitted Jason, with a shrug. 'But I guess I mean more to her than we thought. Strange, isn't it? I'd have gambled my soul she was more likely to walk out on me than . . . anyone else.'

Laura rested her elbow on the door, her fingers plucking nervously at the glossy paintwork. 'But, you did, didn't you?' she murmured huskily. 'Gamble your soul, I mean. There's more than one way to risk immortality.'

'Now, who's making nasty remarks?' he demanded in an undertone, using the accelerator to mask his words, and she expelled the air in her lungs on an unsteady breath.

Forcing herself to concentrate on her surroundings instead of on the disturbing presence of the man beside her, Laura shaded her eyes against the glare of the lowering sun. The narrow road had descended almost to sea level again, and the brilliance of the sun-streaked water was blinding. But she couldn't be absolutely sure the moistness of her eyes was only the result of physical causes. There was a tightness in her chest that had nothing to do with the beauty of the island, and she wondered how Jason could hurt her so easily when she hated him so much.

Minutes later, the perplexities of her emotions were forgotten as they turned between the white gateposts which marked the boundary of Jason's house. A narrow paved drive curved around a bank of flowering hibiscus, and then mounted a gentle incline to where flame trees framed a sprawling plantation-style house. White painted with louvred green shutters folded back beside all the windows, it had a wide terrace flanked with tall columns, that supported the iron-railed balcony above. Shallow steps flowed along the front façade, blending into stone urns, overflowing with creamy camellias and scarlet poinsettias. The terrace curved gracefully round the sides of the house, where clipped green lawns sloped towards a cluster of papayas. The back evidently faced the ocean. Laura could hear its muted thunder as she got herself out of the car. The house had evidently been built to take advantage of the trades, and she guessed they would keep it deliciously cool, even on the hottest day.

'It's ... beautiful,' she murmured, her hand lingering on the car door as she looked up at its simple elegance, and Jason gave her a considering look.

'Then you won't find living here such a hardship, will you?' he observed, sliding out of the car to stand beside her.

Her breath caught in her throat before she asked quickly: 'Where's Pam?'

The emergence of an enormously fat Polynesian woman from the house prevented his reply, and Laura waited a little nervously when Jason went to meet her. After the way Phil Logan had behaved, and Jason's own reactions to her return, she was not at all convinced that his housekeeper would make her welcome, and although she told herself it hardly mattered, she was apprehensive just the same.

'Have you really been to London and back again, Jason?' the woman exclaimed, enfolding him in her ample embrace. Her dark eyes closed briefly, as if to say a prayer of thanks for his safe return, and then opened to encompass Laura's anxious face. 'You're looking tired,' she added, drawing back to study his lean features. 'You had any sleep at all since you left?'

'Enough.' Jason's tone was tolerant, but he turned to include Laura in their exchange. 'You see, Leah,' he said, 'I brought her back, like I promised. You'd better tell her you're pleased to see her. I think she's afraid you're going to break her legs.'

'I am not.' Laura's lips tightened, and her blue eyes

flashed her indignation in the moments before Leah
came between them. 'It's good to see you again, Leah. I
hope you don't object to this invasion.'

'It's Jason's house. I'm only his housekeeper, missy,'
Leah declared, giving the girl the same comprehensive
appraisal she had given her employer. 'It's been a long
time. You fixing on staying this time?'

Laura hesitated. 'If you'll have me,' she murmured,
her eyes meeting Leah's dark ones with steady
determination, and the housekeeper glanced at Jason
over her shoulder.

'She's grown up,' she remarked, returning her gaze to
Laura and revealing a reluctant admiration. And
although Laura didn't care for their deliberate
provocation, she controlled the impulse to voice it, and
won Leah's tacit approval.

'Where's Pamela?' she asked again, feeling that was
safer ground, and Leah arched her dark brows.

'She'll be over later, I guess,' she replied, somewhat
obscurely, and Laura lifted her eyes to Jason's dark
face.

'Over?' she echoed, the one word epitomizing her
lack of comprehension, and with an impatient look at
the housekeeper, he said:

'She's here. Don't worry. I guess she's resting right
now. Yes?' This, as Leah's chins wobbled her assent.
'Okay. I suggest you go and freshen up. Leah will show
you your room. Then, later on, we'll all have a drink
together.'

Laura wanted to ask exactly where Pamela was, and
why she couldn't simply go to *her* room instead, but she
did feel hot and sticky, and the idea of freshening up
was appealing.

'All right,' she said, unable to penetrate the cool
mask of his expression, and with a helpless shrug of her
shoulders, she followed Leah into the house.

Half an hour later, she stepped through french doors on
to the balcony opening off the bedroom behind her.
From the moment Leah had shown her into these
apartments, she had been conscious of the fantastic

view, and although washing her face and hands, and
sluicing the moist area beneath her breasts had taken
more time than she had anticipated, she could not resist
this fleeting glimpse of what lay beyond the windows.

As she had thought, the back of the house faced the
ocean just far enough away to allow for a stone-tiled
patio and the sickle curve of a swimming pool. Beyond
the thatched cabanas, used for changing, soft dunes
sloped down to a beach washed clean by the incoming
tide. Between nubby-trunked palms, the Pacific creamed
on damp sand, unmarred by any human footprint—
blue-green waters shedding skeins of foam over grains
of coral. It was a scene out of a city-dweller's
imagination; a desert island, complete with tropic seas
and waving palms.

But then, the house too, had all the attributes of a
dream home. From the moment Laura had stepped on
to the cool marquetry of the terracotta-tiled floor, she
had been aware of its style and elegance, an impression
reinforced as Leah took her up the fan-shaped
staircase with its ivory banister rail.

There were paintings everywhere, large and small,
grouped and singly hung, upon walls colour-washed for
coolness. A sunburst of a chandelier was suspended
from the arching roof of the atrium-styled entrance hall,
which in its turn created a natural gallery, around
which all the upper rooms were spaced.

Laura had no doubt that the rooms into which she
was shown comprised the master suite. A generous
sitting room, furnished in shades of cream and gold,
possessed a buttoned sofa and a matching armchair in
rich ivory velvet. There were polished oriental cabinets,
and a screen of evidently Japanese origin, all set on a
dusty-gold carpet, whose design was cleverly muted.

The bedroom opening from it was equally as large,
though the bed that occupied less than half the space
was what imprisoned Laura's gaze. Like the room itself,
it was huge, and although the headboard was
conservatively carved the coverlet thrown upon it was a
vivid splash of jade.

'I'll leave you to wash and freshen up,' said Leah,

after assuring herself that the girl was suitably impressed, and Laura was left to explore the imposing bathroom away from the housekeeper's watchful gaze. Nevertheless, she had still been somewhat daunted by the two circular step-in tubs, with their added sophistication of jacuzzi attachments. Smoked glass threw back her reflection from a dozen different angles, and she suspected one would have to have a fine conceit not to find something of dissatisfaction in so many refractions of one's personality.

Now, as she rested her hands on the cool wrought-iron that fenced the balcony, she found herself wondering how many of Jason's women had used that bathroom with him, and her stomach contracted. It was all very well for Leah to treat her with a mixture of disapproval and speculation, but how had she reacted to the women who had taken Laura's place?

Her thoughts were so distasteful to her, the view no longer had the power to hold her interest, and abandoning both she found her way out of the apartments. The house was quiet as she descended the stairs, and she paused for a moment in the impressive entrance hall, trying to get her bearings. To her right, a scalloped row of arches gave on to elegant withdrawing rooms and Laura was briefly struck by the contrast evoked by dark green alcoves set in stark white walls. But although she was tempted to explore these rooms, which might reveal yet another facet of Jason's character, she turned in the direction she hoped would lead to the back of the house. A sun-lit corridor promised success, and after a few moments she emerged into the sun-baked heat of the patio.

To her surprise, there was no one about, though the striped cushioned loungers by the pool looked inviting. The blue-tiled pool looked inviting, too, but she was too exhausted at present to contemplate its pleasures. Maybe tomorrow, she thought, her pulse quickening at the unwilling realisation that she was actually here, in Jason's house; that she was *committed*. It was an unreal sensation, made the more so by the distinct feeling of jet-lag that was gripping her. It didn't seem possible that less than twenty-four hours ago she had been in London, and despite the proof in front of her, the whole situation was acquiring the vague insubstantiality of a dream.

She swayed a little, putting a hand to her head, and started when a hard masculine arm came around her. 'You're worn out,' Jason murmured softly, his tone almost gentle, but she pulled herself away to face him.

'What you mean is—I look a hag!' she exclaimed, tears not far from the surface. 'Wh . . . where is Pam?'

'Here she is now,' he responded flatly, and leaving her he went to meet the tawny-haired young woman who was just crossing the lawns towards them. Cool and dismissive, he ignored her look of surprise, and Laura expelled a shaky, confused breath before going after him.

'You're back!' Pamela's greeting was relaxed and welcoming, and Laura had to squash the unworthy thought that for someone who was just getting over an attempted suicide, her sister looked healthier than she had ever seen her. She accepted Laura's kiss and smiled. 'Isn't this a heavenly place?'

'Heavenly,' agreed Laura, hoping her sister would not notice the edge in her voice. 'How are you, Pam? Where were you?'

'Oh, didn't Jason tell you?' Pamela turned easily to the man beside her. 'I'm staying in the bungalow— over there.' She waved her hand carelessly towards the trees. 'Jason thought it would be easier for me than staying in the main house. I've got my own maid and my own kitchen, and I can be quite self-sufficient if I choose to be.' She touched Jason's arm with evident affection. 'Of course, I haven't up till now. Before he went away, Jason and I ate together, didn't we?'

'We did.'

Jason returned her smile, and Laura felt her stomach clench with painful emotion. 'How nice,' she murmured, unable to avoid the fact of their easy cordiality, and although she knew she was tense and over-tired, it suddenly seemed the last straw.

'Well,' she said, as they walked back to the patio together, 'I don't suppose you'd mind if I left you to yourselves this evening.' She ignored Jason's sudden intake of breath, and continued raggedly, 'I am very tired. I suppose the journey—so many miles . . . the time change——' She broke off unsteadily, and forced a faint smile. 'I'm sorry, Pam, but I don't think I can keep my eyes open any longer.'

A maid was unpacking her suitcases in the bedroom when Laura reached the sitting room of the suite, but she hardly registered the fact of their arrival.

'Please,' she said, realising she was going to cry and unable to do anything about it, 'I can finish these. Just—just leave them, won't you? I don't need any further assistance.'

The young maid, who had been hanging her clothes away in the closets of the dressing room that lay between the bedroom and the bathroom, looked doubtful. 'But Leah said——'

'I'll speak to Leah,' cut in Jason's harsh tones, and the girl flushed. 'You can finish in the morning,' he added, pointedly holding the door open, and with a little bob of her head, the maid left them.

Alone with him, Laura took a deep breath. Coping with the maid had strained her resources to their limit, but coping with Jason was something else entirely. Without waiting for the censure, which she was sure was why he had followed her, she dived into the bathroom, only to gaze about her in dismay when she discovered there was no lock on the door. Her paltry weight was easily propelled away by Jason's forced entry, and he stood looking at her distractedly as she wrapped her arms about her.

'What in hell do you think you're doing?' he demanded. He shook his head. 'I thought you were all-fire keen to see your sister.'

'I was. I—I am.' Laura shivered. 'I'm sorry.'

'Like hell!' Jason raked back his hair with an impatient hand. And then, as if acknowledging her complete exhaustion, he swore rather more colourfully. 'Okay, okay,' he said tersely. 'You win. Get undressed and get into bed. This is going to look a whole lot different in the morning.'

'Do you think so?' Laura's throat ached with the effort of keeping her tears at bay, and as if sensing the extent of her imbalance, Jason hauled her not ungently towards him.

'Believe it!' he told her harshly, running his hands along the curve of her neck. 'Do you want me to undress you?'

Laura jerked back as if he had struck her. 'As you did last night?' she choked, and with a twisted snarl, Jason turned away.

'You have to be kidding!' he grated brutally, his eyes raking her with unconcealed contempt. 'You're right,' he added. 'You do look a hag! And I don't happen to be that desperate!'

CHAPTER EIGHT

LAURA awakened to the scent of roses and verbena, the distinctive perfumes of a dozen different blossoms mingling with the salty tang of the sea, and drifting irresistibly in through the open shutters.

Turning her head on the fine linen pillowcase, she saw the open balcony doors and frowned. She could have sworn she had closed them before going to bed, but her memory of the night before was so hazy, she could have been mistaken. She blinked, stretching luxuriously beneath the thin sheet, which was all that covered her, and then gathered her knees up tight against her chest as a spasm of apprehension swept over her. Where was Jason? Twisting her head still further, she waited for her eyes to alight on the other occupant of the bed, but to her surprise—and relief—she was alone.

Turning over fully, she realised the place beside her had not even been slept in, and her brows, several shades darker than her hair, drew together in unwilling comprehension. Jason had not shared her bed. Wherever he had slept, it had not been beneath the sheets of this colonial-styled four poster, and re-membering her opinion that these were the principal apartments of the house, she wondered rather anxiously where he had laid his head.

Propping herself up on one elbow, she ran a thoughtful hand over her untidy braid of hair. Dipping down to her breasts, it drew attention to the fact that the strap of her nightgown had slipped off one shoulder, and she pulled it up absently as she gazed across the room with troubled eyes.

What time was it? she wondered, twisting her watch round on her wrist so that she could see its face. Five o'clock, she read, without enthusiasm. The sun was so bright, she had thought it was much later.

Sighing, she slumped back against the pillows, not wanting to remember her behaviour of the night before, but incapable of avoiding it as her brain cleared. She had behaved childishly, she knew, running out on Pamela, as if her sister was to blame for her predicament. But she had felt so strange and disorientated, and Pamela's apparent acceptance of the situation had seemed like a betrayal.

Shaking her head, she put up a slightly unsteady hand and began to loosen the woven strands of her hair. Perhaps, after a shower, she would feel less conscious of her own shortcomings, she thought flatly. Right now, she was far too aware of Jason's savage condemnation, and his brutal words were still resounding in her head.

The incisive sound of something—or someone—slicing into the pool below her windows brought her foot tentatively out of bed. There was a distinct difference between the surging roar of the ocean and the crisp lap of water on tiles, and swiftly crossing the floor, she ventured out on to the balcony.

The warmth of the sun was revitalising, the strengthening rays still containing an element of coolness that dispelled the sense of lethargy still gripping her. Breathing deeply, hardly aware that with her hair loose about her shoulders she looked bemused and slightly fey-like, she leaned her arms on the balcony rail, and gazed down at the dark head in the pool.

It was Jason. There was no mistaking the lithe muscularity of his body cleaving through the water, leaving a rippling backwash in its wake. He was covering the pool easily, his vigorous strokes taking him swiftly from one end to the other. At each turn, he performed an underwater somersault to head him back in the opposite direction, and Laura's attention was briefly held by the speed of this manoeuvre.

But her initial instincts were to draw back and leave him to his solitary enjoyment. She had no wish to be observed. Yet, she assured herself, it was much too early for him to expect her to be about, and there was something rather pleasurable about watching him, unseen.

Her innocent voyeurism was rudely arrested when he swam to the side of the pool, and pulled himself out of the water. He was naked, the powerful muscles of his body exposed as he swept the excess moisture out of his hair with a careless hand and bent to pick up the towel lying on a chair nearby. Rubbing himself dry, he was unconsciously sensual in his movements, and in spite of everything that had gone before, Laura could not deny the unwilling stimulation of her senses.

Then, as if sensing her eyes upon him, he looked up, and Laura had no chance to avoid his gaze, even if she had wanted to. Besides, to dart back into the room would have been an admission of guilt, and she had nothing to feel guilty of, she told herself fiercely.

'Did you sleep well?' he inquired, dropping the towel to pick up a dark red towelling robe, and Laura pretended to look at the distant ocean as he tied the cord about his waist.

'I slept very well, thank you,' she replied tensely. It was nothing less than the truth, and she felt infinitely rested this morning. 'Did you?'

'Do you care?' he countered, tipping back his head to look at her, and she acknowledged that his cynicism was not entirely misplaced.

'You're up very early,' she ventured, changing the subject and he shrugged.

'It's almost half-past-seven,' he responded. 'I suppose it depends what you call early. I often get up at this hour.' He paused. 'Particularly if I'm sleeping alone.'

The content of his words overwhelmed her instinctive embarrassment, and she frowned. 'Half-past seven?' she echoed. 'I only make it half-past five!'

'That's because your watch is still set for London time,' essayed Jason flatly. 'You've slept for the best part of fifteen hours. Come down, and we'll have breakfast together.'

Laura hesitated. 'I was going to take a shower.'

'Take it later.' Jason regarded her steadily. 'Come as you are. You can always take a dip in the pool.'

Laura swallowed. 'All right.' She moistened her lips. 'Give me five minutes.'

'You got it,' he responded laconically, with a lazy inclination of his head, and Laura hurried back inside, her heart beating rather quickly.

The dressing room was a shambles. The maid had managed to hang most of her crushable clothes away the night before, but her half-empty suitcases were still lying on the floor, strewn with filmy underwear and shoes still wrapped in tissue paper. She had found the cotton nightdress she was wearing and left everything else, and now she made another invasion, rummaging about for a swim suit.

She rinsed her face at one of the twin hand-basins that lined the opposite wall of the dressing room from the long fitted closets. Above the basins, a bank of mirrors had little compassion for her pale complexion, but her skin was good and she hadn't the time—or the inclination—to use cosmetics. She hesitated longest over her hair, half convinced she should restore it to its usual neatness, but time was pressing, and it did protect her shoulders from the sun. On impulse, she simply ran a brush through it, and snatching up a thigh-length beach wrap and dark glasses, she left the room.

It was not until she was halfway down the stairs that she realised how submissively she had rushed to do Jason's bidding, and deliberately slowing her footsteps, she tried to govern her racing pulses. But it was useless; she had no control over her emotions, and giving up the effort, she allowed a trembling breath to escape her.

By the time she emerged into the sunshine, a glass-topped table had been set beneath a circular umbrella, with a jug of freshly-squeezed orange juice looking infinitely inviting to Laura's thirsty eyes. A coffee pot was giving off the rich aroma of ground beans, and warm rolls filmed the perspex cover of a serving dish.

'I took the liberty of ordering for both of us,' remarked Jason appearing from the direction of the cabanas, and Laura's lips parted at the sight of his lean bronzed body. He had shed the towelling robe in favour

of frayed denim shorts, and his almost animal
magnetism was distinctly pronounced.

'Thank you.'

Glad of the protection of her sun glasses, Laura
slipped into a bamboo-framed chair at the table, and
helped herself to some orange juice.

'Aren't you warm with that thing on?' Jason inquired
drily, nodding at the beach wrap, and Laura had to
admit its folds were a little confining.

'I—I'll just put it over the back of the chair,' she
murmured, slipping her arms out of the sleeves rather
self-consciously. The simple one-piece maillot she was
wearing was quite revealing, and she was still absurdly
sensitive with him.

'So you decided to wear a bathing suit,' Jason
remarked, pouring himself some orange juice, and she
concentrated on the contents of her glass to evade his
sardonic gaze.

'I could hardly come down without one,' she
countered, when she had herself in control again, and
he shrugged.

'Why not? That's one of the advantages about this
place. It's completely private. Apart from Leah and the
others, of course.'

'Apart from Leah and the others,' put in Laura
quickly. 'We're not exactly on our own here, are we?'

His eyes lifted. 'Do you wish we were?'

'I didn't say that. I simply meant—I can hardly go
around in the nude in the circumstances, can I?'

'Point taken.' Jason's smile was sardonic. 'I shall
have to give them the day off.'

'Jason!' Laura breathed a little restrictedly, and
struggling to remember exactly why she was there, she
said, 'Can't we talk seriously? You've never told me
what you said to Pamela before you brought her here.'

'You've never asked me.'

'I haven't had much chance.'

'I wouldn't say that.' Jason regarded her through his
lashes. 'What do you want to know?'

Laura sighed. 'Did ... did you tell her you knew
Mike Kazantis?'

'I may have.'

'And did you tell her he was married?'

'Did you expect me to?'

Laura shook her head. 'I don't know. I don't know how she's taking this ... this change of scene. She seemed ... contented enough last night.'

'And that bothered you?'

'No.' Laura spread her hands. 'I just want to know what will happen if Kazantis comes here.'

'He won't.'

'How can you be so sure?' Laura gazed at him. 'He is your sister's husband!'

'Irene knows how I feel about Kazantis,' responded Jason laconically.

'I don't.'

His eyebrows arched. 'Am I supposed to understand that?'

'You should.' Laura lifted one slim shoulder. 'How do you really feel about—about what's happened?'

'How do you think I feel?'

'Oh, stop talking in riddles!' Laura was unnerved. 'Do you believe Pamela?'

'The letters seem to prove it, don't they?'

Laura's eyes widened. 'She's shown you those?'

'Apparently.' He shrugged. 'I wasn't what she expected.'

'What do you mean?'

'Well ...' Jason hesitated. 'She seemed to have gathered, from your conversation, that I was middle-aged and rather pedantic.' He made a careless gesture. 'Much like your employer in London, I guess.'

'Leave Pierce out of this.'

'Okay.' He studied her indignant face with gentle mockery. 'But, in spite of what was said on the yacht, you can't deny you hadn't elaborated on our relationship to her, had you? I think she had the impression I was doing this because your typing speeds were so good.'

Laura's lips parted. 'You didn't ... you didn't ...'

'... tell her what I really like about you?' inquired Jason lazily. 'That would have been indiscreet, wouldn't it? I bet she has no idea what a sexy ...'

'Jason, please!' Laura interrupted him hotly, her cheeks burning, and his eyes dwelt with infuriating satisfaction on her agitated face. 'After—after what you said last night, you can hardly pretend your motives for bringing me here are in any way . . . emotional!'

'What did I say last night?'

'You know what you said.' She licked a drop of orange juice from her lip and faced him determinedly.

'That you were a hag?' he suggested softly, revealing he knew exactly what he had said, and Laura clenched her fists. 'I was angry. I say a lot of things when I'm angry. It doesn't follow that I mean them.'

Laura pressed her lips together. 'I think you did mean it.'

'You're determined to put words into my mouth, aren't you?' His eyes darkened. 'And you definitely don't look like a hag this morning. In fact, if I were a more fanciful man, I'd say you looked rather bewitching. You should wear your hair loose more often. I always preferred it that way.'

Laura looked down at her hands. 'If I'm going to spend any time out here, I may consider having it cut,' she said. 'It wasn't as long as this when . . . when I first came to the islands.'

'Don't!' Jason sobered, reaching towards her and winding a handful of its silken strands around his fingers. 'If you need to keep it in that braid for coolness, then okay. But don't cut it.'

It was a charged moment, and Laura felt the potent strength of his masculinity embracing her, surrounding her, *suffocating* her. Her breathing suspended, and she had to fight to hold on to her self-possession. The radiance of the morning, the pool and its colourful accoutrements; even the muted clamour of the ocean on the reef, all faded, replaced by the compelling brilliance of his eyes.

'I—that's my decision, Jason,' she got out finally, and the dark fringe of his lashes veiled his expression.

'Don't make me make it a condition, Laura,' he warned her roughly, tugging a little cruelly at her hair before releasing her, and she was still trying to control her agitation when she glimpsed a movement beyond the rigid contours of his face.

In the moment it took her to identify her sister's bikini-clad form, Jason sensed her sudden withdrawal. Glancing over his shoulder, he saw Pamela strolling in their direction, and his expression perceptibly hardened. 'Oh, beautiful,' he muttered, but it wasn't a compliment. More a bitter epithet that was accompanied by an even cruder expletive as he thrust back his chair and got to his feet.

'Oh . . . you're up, Laura.'

Pamela's response to her sister's presence was hardly flattering, but Laura was too relieved the other girl apparently hadn't overheard Jason's harsh profanity to feel indignant. Even so, it did occur to her that Pamela had spoken as if Laura's existence was not crucial to her being there, and it reminded Laura that, in spite of being sisters, it was some years since they had been really close. After all, Pamela had been only a teenager when she joined the staff of St Monica's as a probationary nurse. Now, almost twenty-five, she was very much a young woman, and Laura was being forced to regard her in quite a different light.

'Yes,' she answered now, still very much aware of Jason's impatient stance beside her. 'I feel much better this morning. I'm sorry about last night. I must have seemed very rude.'

'Oh, forget it.' Pamela sank gracefully into the chair Jason had pulled out for her, smiling her thanks up at him. 'You really looked shattered. Thank goodness flying's never affected me in that way.'

'No . . . well . . .' Laura realised Jason was waiting for her response, and shifted a little uneasily. 'It was an extremely long journey.'

'Hmm.' Pamela shrugged. 'Not to worry. Jason and I had a cosy dinner together, didn't we?' This as Jason came round from behind her chair. 'I don't think he was too disappointed.'

Laura felt a twinge of something at this blatant attempt to exclude her, and she looked up at Jason sharply, wondering with a sudden hollowness, exactly what his feelings towards Pamela were. Was his resentment at Pamela's intervention what it seemed, or was he impatient with her for creating a situation he was not yet prepared to deal with? It was a development Laura had never anticipated—that Jason might be attracted to her sister—and she couldn't deny the fierce anger that gripped her at the thought.

'I guess we both made the best of it,' he responded now, meeting Laura's gaze without flinching. His smile was controlled. 'If you'll both excuse me, I have some telephone calls I want to make. Enjoy your breakfast. I'll see you later.'

Laura didn't know if it was her imagination, but the air seemed distinctly cooler after Jason had departed, and she was not entirely surprised when Pamela looked across at her with resentment marring her fair complexion.

'Why didn't you tell me?' she demanded, gazing at her sister with angry eyes. 'You must have known I would find out, sooner or later.'

'Tell you what?' inquired Laura, playing for time, and Pamela tapped her nails against the glass surface of the table in obvious frustration.

'Don't pretend you don't know what I mean!' she retorted. 'Although, if I hadn't heard it myself, I would never have believed it! You were Jason's mistress, weren't you? My God!' She shook her head. 'And I was afraid to tell you about Mike and me!'

Laura poured herself some coffee with more confidence than she had known she possessed. 'Is that an accusation?' she inquired, reaching for a *croissant*. 'I don't see that it affects you, one way or the other.'

'Don't you?' Pamela flung herself back in the chair, her jaw clenched sullenly. 'But that's why Jason agreed to have us here, isn't it? I just wonder how you forced him into this position. He must hate your guts!'

Laura continued to butter her croissant, even though her hands were shaking so much she could hardly hold the knife. It was hard to do anything in the face of such a scathing allegation, and for a few moments she was unable to speak at all. That her sister should believe *she* could force *Jason* to do anything? she thought, half hysterically. Obviously, Pamela had no idea of the character of the man they were dealing with.

'It's not your problem, Pam,' she managed to say at last choosing her words with care. 'You're here, aren't you? And on your own admission, you think this is a heavenly place. That's all that need concern you.'

'No, it's not.' Pamela regarded her sister without liking. 'I don't like the idea that—that I'm being *used* to get back at Jason for the way he treated you in the past! I like him. I *really* like him. And I don't think it's fair to expect him to support both of us!'

Laura was aghast. 'Pam . . .'

'I don't care what you say. I won't change my mind,' retorted Pamela sulkily. 'If I'd known what was going on before you left San Francisco, I'd have told you then. As it is, I see no point in your staying on here until I have the baby. It's not as if I need a chaperon, or anything. You can come and see the bungalow, if you like. It's very self-contained. Once . . . once it's over, we can talk again.'

Laura absorbed what the other girl was saying with a feeling of disbelief. Was this really her younger sister talking? Was this really the girl who, only two weeks ago, was threatening to take her own life? What had happened in the interim to change the situation so drastically? And what about the man who had fathered the child she was carrying? Why had his name not even been mentioned?

Jason!

Without needing to seek any further, Laura guessed exactly why Pamela had lost all interest in Mike Kazantis. Probably without even trying, Jason had driven all thoughts of the other man out of her head, and Laura's stomach contracted as her earlier fears were re-kindled.

'Was—was it Jason who told you about—about our relationship?' she ventured now, feeling her way, but Pamela shook her head.

'Of course not,' she exclaimed scornfully. 'It's not something he'd talk about, is it?' She shrugged. 'No. As

a matter of fact, it was Leah. I don't think she realised I
didn't already know about it.'

'Oh.' Laura breathed a little more easily.

Pamela went on, 'She asked if I'd ever visited the
penthouse apartment in Honolulu, where you and he
used to live?' Her lips twisted. 'Naturally, I said no. My
God, it was all I could do not to ask her what the hell
she was talking about! I'm glad I didn't. It was quite an
education.'

Laura lifted one shoulder. 'I see.'

'Is that all you can say? *I see*?' Pamela stared at her
angrily. 'Well? What are you going to do about it?
Surely, you must see, you can't stay here now. It isn't
fair on Jason, and it isn't fair on me.'

Laura moistened her lips. 'Why isn't it fair on you?'

'Well—well, because it isn't.'

'I gather you're not intending to leave, whatever
happens,' Laura commented quietly, and Pamela had
the grace to colour.

'I can't, can I?' she muttered reluctantly. 'I mean—it
would be stupid!' She hesitated. 'Jason says that after
I've had the baby, he might be able to find me a job
here in Hawaii. It would be crazy to turn a chance like
that down. Even you must see that.'

'And the baby?' Laura arched one brow. 'Have you
decided what you're going to do about that?'

'Keep it, I suppose.' Pamela shrugged. 'There
wouldn't be much point in my being here otherwise.'

'No.' Laura acknowledged this with some reluctance.
But she couldn't help the unwilling suspicion that
Pamela had weighed all the alternatives in the balance,
and come up with the one that suited her best. And
enabled her to stay here, on Jason's estate, added Laura
silently.

'So . . . what are you going to do?'

Pamela had regained much of her self-confidence
now, and she was evidently waiting for some reply. So
Laura gave her one. 'I suggest we leave the situation as
it is for the time being,' she declared with determined
brightness. Until she had spoken to Jason, she didn't
want to get involved in any more argument. Ignoring

Pamela's sulky features, she got up from her chair and
sauntered with forced casualness to the edge of the
patio. Shading her eyes for a moment, she looked at the
ocean. 'I think I'll go for a swim. The water's
deliciously cool at this time of day.' She glanced back at
Pamela. 'You ought to try it.'

'If I want to swim, I'll swim in the pool,' retorted the
other girl shortly. She paused. 'Do you intend to go on
living in this house?'

Oh, really! Laura sighed. This was becoming
ridiculous. 'What alternative do I have?' she demanded,
in a driven tone, and Pamela rose to her feet.

'You could share the bungalow with me,' she replied
at once. 'There are two bedrooms. You'd have plenty of
room.'

'Then why don't you suggest that to Jason?'
exclaimed Laura tersely, weary of trying to find excuses.
'I'm going down to the beach. You can tell Jason that,
too, when you see him!'

CHAPTER NINE

LAURA was soaking in one of the twin tubs when a kind of sixth sense warned her she was no longer alone. Turning her head, she was hardly surprised to find Jason behind her, his shoulder propped indolently against the frame of the bathroom door. He was watching her, his eyes narrowed and intent, and her face suffused with colour at the arrogance of his appraisal.

'What do you want?' she asked, checking to make sure the water was lapping concealingly above her breasts, totally unaware that with her newly-washed hair wound into a careless knot on top of her head and her face flushed and defensive, she presented an infinitely provocative picture.

'What do you think I want?' inquired Jason, countering her question with one of his own. Then, less aggressively, he added: 'I came to find you. Pamela said you'd gone swimming, but evidently she was wrong.'

'I ... did swim for a while,' said Laura quickly. 'But that was over an hour ago. And I wanted to rinse the salt off my skin.'

'Ah.' Jason nodded. 'Did you enjoy it?'

'Mmm.' Laura sighed reminiscently. 'It was beautiful!'

'Good.' He straightened away from the door and strolled across the marbled tiles with bare feet. 'So ... are you ready to tell me what you've been telling your sister? She seems to think you've been blackmailing me.'

Laura bent her head, unknowingly exposing the sensitive curve of her nape, with its vulnerable curls of damp silk, to his gaze. 'Is that what she said?'

'As good as.' Jason squatted down beside her, his feet scarcely inches from the rim of the tub. 'Why didn't you tell her the truth?'

Laura lifted one slim shoulder, supremely conscious

of his nearness. 'I don't think she'd have believed me,' she admitted honestly. She moistened her lips. 'You seem to have made another conquest!'

'Is that my fault, too?' Jason's arms were resting along his thighs, his knees wide apart, his whole attitude disturbingly sensual. And Laura was not unaware of it.

'I—perhaps not,' she murmured, flinching when he dipped one hand into the water and disturbed its protective surface.

'There's no "perhaps" about it,' retorted Jason, straightening abruptly. Wiping his damp fingers on the seat of his denim shorts, he regarded her broodingly. 'Your sister's being here suits *my* purpose: not hers.'

Laura drew a slightly unsteady breath. 'Did you tell her that?'

'I told her you would not be moving into the bungalow,' he responded grimly. 'If you want me to be more explicit, I can be. I just didn't know what crazy tale you'd been concocting for her benefit, and I didn't want to call you a liar!'

Laura swallowed. 'Am I supposed to thank you?'

'No!' Jason spoke aggressively. 'I guess she'll get the picture when I tell her I'm taking you with me to the mainland tomorrow.'

Laura's lips parted in consternation. 'Tomorrow!' she echoed aghast.

'Those calls I made,' Jason reminded her evenly. 'Loath as I am to uproot you again so soon, I do have to be in San Francisco tomorrow night.'

Laura's heart sank. The idea of more travelling, when she had hardly recovered from the journey from England was almost as daunting as what the trip would entail in other ways. Alone with Jason, she would have no chance to avoid him.

'Do ... do I have to go?' she asked tentatively, glancing up into his hard handsome face. 'I mean—if it's a business trip ...'

'I know exactly what you mean,' retorted Jason harshly. 'And yes, you *do* have to go. Now, I suggest you get out of that bath and come downstairs. Lunch will be ready soon, and Leah was asking after you. She was most concerned that you didn't eat dinner last night.'

Laura's lips pursed. 'Yes, *sir*,' she responded tautly, and Jason's jaw tightened as he met her resentful gaze.

'Do you want me, Laura?' he inquired with grim purpose, bending down to lift the burnished gold plug that released the water, and she watched with horrified eyes as the level in the bath began to fall.

'You—you have to be joking,' she exclaimed, presenting him with the downy curve of her back and rounded buttocks as she scrambled to reach a towel. 'Will you get out of here?' she added, grasping the fluffy apricot bathsheet and wrapping it closely about her. 'Am I to have no privacy, as well as no choice?'

'So long as you continue to antagonise me, why should I consider your feelings?' retorted Jason. Grasping one end of the towel, he dragged it savagely out of her grasp. 'You shouldn't arouse me if you're not prepared to take the consequences.'

'I didn't invite you to come in here,' Laura exclaimed, as he stepped down into the rapidly draining tub and lifted her struggling body into his arms. 'Jason, don't do this!'

'Why not?' His eyes dwelt briefly on the parted curve of her mouth and against her will, she felt a tremor of emotion sweep through her. 'Why don't you yell for your sister?' he suggested thickly. 'Right now, I'd be happy to show her exactly what the situation is between us.'

'Let me go!' cried Laura in protest, but Jason wasn't listening to her. Almost without effort, he stepped out of the tub and carried her through to the bedroom, apparently uncaring of the fact that his feet were leaving damp patches on the carpet or that the loosened tendrils of Laura's hair were dripping wetly down his chest.

'Why do I always end up fighting you?' he demanded, dropping her down on to the bed, and Laura gazed up at him warily when he didn't immediately fling himself beside her. 'You know how I feel about you, and yet you persist in treating me like some kind of pervert! Does that give you some satisfaction? Do you like the idea of making me squirm?'

'I don't know what you——'

'Yes, you do,' he contradicted her harshly, sinking down on to the side of the bed. 'Last night you knew exactly what you were doing. It may please you to know I spent the hours you were sleeping catching up on the correspondence that had accumulated while I was away.'

Laura propped herself up on her elbows, more disturbed than she wanted to admit by his bitter confession. 'I . . . my hair's wet,' she murmured, not knowing how to answer him, and with a smothered oath, Jason bore her back against the jade satin.

'So what?' he muttered against her lips, the abrasive hardness of his chest crushing her breasts. 'Your body's wet, too.' His hand slipped sensuously along her inner thigh. 'And God, Laura, don't stop me! Help me——'

His hand moved to the buttoned fastening of his shorts, and with the hungry possession of his mouth sending the blood flowing wildly through her veins, Laura sensed his impatience. No longer in control of her actions, her fingers moved intuitively to the recalcitrant button, loosening it swiftly and pressing down the zip, so that the tumescent strength of his manhood surged hotly into her hands.

'Oh, Jason,' she breathed, unable to deny her instinctive reactions to his powerful body, and with a groan, he thrust into her, filling her completely.

'God,' he said unsteadily, burying his face in the scented warmth of her neck. 'Don't tell me you don't want this, because I won't believe you!'

Laura couldn't answer him, and even had she been able to, she doubted she would have argued with him. As it was, the sensual probe of his tongue was like velvet in her mouth, and the mounting heat of his body was driving her almost to distraction.

With a moan of submission, she wound her arms around his neck. Then, surging towards him, she urged him on with little broken sounds of pleasure, until the sweating rhythm of their bodies reached the summit and beyond . . .

Jason was still sleeping when Laura went downstairs.

She had drowsed, too, but only for a few minutes, and when she eventually roused herself to an awareness of her surroundings, Jason was lying on his stomach beside her. One arm was resting across her breasts, his fingers coiled in the still-damp tangle of her hair, while his leg rested between hers, a possessive weight of bone and muscle.

Laura was curiously reluctant to move at all, despite the proof that once again he had demonstrated his authority over her. In other circumstances, she would have been quite content to remain where she was until the sexual languor left her. Jason was unknowingly vulnerable in his unconscious state, and the consuming passion of his lovemaking had made her relaxed and sleepy.

But the remembrance that Pamela was downstairs, no doubt drawing her own conclusions for their continued absence, drove Laura to an unwilling activity, and releasing herself carefully, she slid off the bed. Jason made some involuntary protest, but he didn't open his eyes, and she guessed his sleepless night was catching up on him. With a groan of exhaustion, he stretched more expansively on the mattress, and without stopping to consider her actions, Laura lifted the folds of the bedspread to cover his naked body. Even in sleep, he possessed a potent magnetism, and she had no wish for one of the young maids to come upon him in this state. She didn't examine her motives for feeling this way too closely however. If it was jealousy, she didn't want to know about it. All she did know was that Jason had been right earlier when he had said she wanted him. She wanted him still, if she was honest, she acknowledged, moistening her lips with a quivering tongue.

She dressed in a simple cotton vest and wrap-around skirt, both in the same shade of hot pink. She chose the vivid colour deliberately, in an effort to shake off the mood of desperation that had gripped her, ever since she had admitted to herself that her feelings for Jason were as ambiguous as ever. She didn't want to think about the implications of that admission, and she certainly didn't want to consider how Jason might react if he should discover her weakness. Somehow, she had to hold on to the reasons that had driven her away from Jason in the first place; not succumb to his practised charm that was as treacherous as it was hollow.

Laura found Pamela waiting for her in a sunlit room overlooking the terrace. Her sister had evidently been back to her bungalow to change her clothes, and now she was coolly elegant in a drop-waisted tunic made of blue and white striped linen. Looking at Pamela with objective eyes, Laura had to admit she was an attractive young woman. Tall, though perhaps not quite as tall as Laura, nevertheless she carried herself with confidence, her slim body showing no signs as yet of the reason she had appealed to her sister for help. Her hair, which had never aspired to the purity of Laura's, she had had tinted to an attractive tawny shade, and curling as it did about her ears, it softened the contours of her pointed features.

A table had been laid for lunch, and before Pamela could ask where Jason was, Leah appeared. 'So you decided to put in an appearance at last,' she remarked, with the familiarity of long service. 'Be thankful it's a cold meal. You have any idea how long it's been waiting?'

Laura felt her colour deepen, but she couldn't help it. 'I'm sorry, Leah,' she said, glancing awkwardly at her sister. 'And would you mind just serving two? Jason's asleep.'

'Is he?' Leah flicked a look from one to the other of them. 'Well, I do know he was up mighty early this morning.'

'That's right, he was.' Laura grasped the excuse with both hands. 'He—he's exhausted. I expect he'll get something later, when he wakes up.'

'Good enough.'

Leah seemed satisfied with this explanation, but after the two girls were seated at the table, Pamela regarded her sister with less conviction. 'Jason told me you wouldn't be moving into the bungalow,' she remarked tersely. 'Do you mind telling me why? Just so I don't make any more gaffes where you're concerned.'

Laura sighed. 'It's a long story, Pam. I'd rather not go into it right now.'

'Why not?'

'Well, is it important?'

'It is to me.' Pamela forked a slice of marinated cucumber into her mouth. 'If you and Jason still have a thing for one another, I'd like to know why you haven't seen one another for the past three years.'

'We don't still have "a thing" for one another,' retorted Laura swiftly, eager to stifle the thought before it could take root. After the anxiety of her own thoughts upstairs, she had no wish for Pamela to put into words something she could not—and would not—acknowledge. 'I can't explain. Just take my word that Jason is only helping us because it suits him to do so.'

Pamela looked thoughtful. 'I see.' She paused. 'But your being here is part of the deal.'

'Yes.' Laura expelled her breath with relief. She had not expected it to be so easy. Pouring herself a glass of orange juice, she raised it to her lips and thirstily drained it. 'I'm glad you understand.'

Pamela frowned. 'Just one thing.'

'Yes?' Laura was wary.

'When you and Jason split up—whose fault was that?'

Laura inwardly groaned. Obviously her relief had been premature. 'Does it matter?' she asked, refilling her glass. 'We had a—a difference of opinion. These things happen. It was no one's—fault.'

'It must have been some difference of opinion for you to give up your life out here,' remarked Pamela impatiently. She hesitated. 'Was someone else involved?'

'I'd really rather not talk about it, Pam.'

'But you must admit it's an odd situation,' exclaimed her sister frustratedly. 'I mean—if it was Jason who was playing around, why should he be willing to help us now? And why should you even think he might? You did approach him, didn't you? It wasn't the other way about.'

'Jason has his own reasons for doing things,' replied Laura wearily. 'He likes—manipulating people. I don't know why I thought he might be willing to help us. I suppose because he was the only person I could think of who could.'

Pamela absorbed this, and then she said shrewdly: 'Why don't you admit it, Laura. You walked out on Jason. I guess you found him with some other woman, or something equally as petty. My God! Imagine giving all this up! You must have been crazy!'

Laura wondered anew at her ignorance of her sister's character. When had the confiding teenager she remembered turned into this cynical adult? 'The reasons I left Jason were not petty!' she retorted, stung into retaliation. 'The advantages of wealth are not a precept for happiness!'

Pamela grimaced. 'Don't be pompous, Laura. We're not all as sanctimonious as you are. However, you have reassured me. I don't like stepping on anyone's toes, and as you don't want Jason, you can't blame me if I don't share your views. It seems to me, you've had it your own way far too long, and if it's happened before, it can happen again. I'm quite prepared to settle for a man, not a saint.'

Laura spent the afternoon with Leah, trying unsuccessfully to escape from the memory of that distasteful scene with her sister. To her relief, Pamela had returned to her own bungalow after lunch, and Laura sought Leah's company in an effort to restore her sense of balance.

To begin with, her conversation with Jason's housekeeper bore the strains of her own tortured nerves, and she would not have blamed Leah if she had made the wrong connection. After all, she was fiercely protective of Jason's interests, and she had every reason to distrust the English girl after what had happened.

But if the Polynesian woman felt any resentment, she did not openly display it, and inevitably Laura's agitation eased in Leah's undemanding presence.

After taking the girl on a conducted tour of the ground floor of the house, Leah invited her into the kitchen. Like the other rooms, this too was light and airy, and after seating her guest on a padded bamboo stool, the housekeeper produced a jug of strawberry daiquiris from the refrigerator.

'Oh, I don't know,' murmured Laura doubtfully, when Leah set a tall glass overflowing with slices of fruit and topped with a pale pink blossom in front of her. 'I don't usually drink in the afternoons. As a matter of fact, I don't usually drink much at all.'

'Lighten up,' advised Leah drily, pouring herself a glass of the same. 'You look as if you need it. Why do I get the feeling that it's you, and not your sister, who needs Jason's help?'

Laura sighed. 'I'm all right.'

'Are you?' Leah regarded her doubtfully. 'You know, when Jason said he was bringing you here, I thought he was a fool! And I said so. When you walked out on him, I thought if I ever saw you again I'd want to black your eye. But, Jason made me promise not to upset you, and when I saw you yesterday afternoon, I knew why he said it.'

'Oh, Leah!'

'I know, I know. You don't want to talk about it. And I'm not going to go back on my word. But, if you've got any sense, you'll hang in there this time. Whatever his faults, and I'm not saying he's without any, Jason's a good man. He wouldn't hurt you like you hurt him.'

'Want to bet?' Laura moved half a strawberry aside and took a sip of the cocktail. 'Mmm, this is delicious!' she murmured obliquely. 'Why do your daiquiris always taste so much better than anyone else's?'

'I guess it's a natural talent,' responded Leah wryly, noticing the change of topic. 'I tell you what, hon—next time I make some, you can watch me.' She paused. 'I know exactly how Jason likes them.'

Laura sighed. 'You've been with him a lot of years, haven't you, Leah? I don't suppose anyone knows him better than you do.'

'I wouldn't say that.' Leah looked at the younger woman out of the corners of her eyes. 'I thought you knew him pretty well, Laura. At least better than any of the other girls he's known.'

'And he's known a lot,' put in Laura bitterly. 'You can't deny that.'

Leah shrugged. 'Some,' she conceded carelessly. 'They didn't mean anything.'

'Oh, come on.' The alcohol in the daiquiri was giving Laura more confidence. 'What about Regina? He married her!'

'Regina!' The way the housekeeper said the other woman's name was scathing. 'You want to know about Regina? Girl, you know he never cared about that Italian bitch!'

Laura licked her lips. 'You don't really know that, Leah. I know you've said it before, but really you're only guessing.'

'Who? Me?' Leah was indignant. 'Jason married Regina to please his family. Believe it! I wouldn't lie to you.'

Laura shook her head. Once, perhaps, she had believed her, but not now. Once, she had had aspirations in that direction herself, and she had believed anyone who told her Jason's reputation was not what it appeared. It had seemed quite reasonable to put his single venture into matrimony down to a family commitment, and even the fact that Regina had divorced him had not really been a cause for concern. Now, however, she had her own painful experiences to guide her, and Leah's well-rehearsed reassurance had little power to convince.

'Leah, Jason wouldn't marry anyone just to please his family,' she declared now, wondering why the juicy piece of fruit from her glass suddenly tasted so sour. 'He's not that kind of man. You know it, and I know it. So, let's stop pretending, shall we?'

Leah regarded the girl with some uncertainty, and

then she said heavily: 'You didn't use to be so bitter, girl. What have you been doing since you made off back to England?'

Laura shrugged. 'This and that. I'm a secretary now, to a famous thriller writer. It's very interesting work. It's quite different from anything else I've ever done.'

Leah frowned. 'This writer—he's a man?'

'Pierce Carver, yes.'

'Are you involved with him?'

'Leah!'

The housekeeper grimaced. 'I'm just trying to find out why you've gotten so hard, Laura,' she declared flatly. 'For someone who walked out on Jason, you're pretty sore towards him, aren't you?'

Laura sighed. 'Leah, I'd really rather not talk about that.'

'I know, I know.' Leah sniffed. 'You just want to go on, believing the worst of him!'

Laura bent her head. 'You could be right.'

'Well, it isn't fair.'

'Fair?' Laura's head jerked up. 'Leah, what are you trying to say? When was Jason ever fair—with anyone? Including Regina.'

Leah hesitated. 'What if I was to tell you the real reason Jason married Regina? The reason why he and his Daddy don't see one another any more?'

Laura gasped. 'Leah, you're priceless . . .'

'No, I mean it.' Leah looked unusually sombre. 'I was told never to talk about it, but . . .'

'Leah, stop it!' Laura's patience was stretched. 'Look, I understand your loyalty towards him, and I know he would never do anything to hurt you, but isn't this carrying things a little too far? I mean, when it comes to inventing stories . . .'

'It's no invention.' Leah was indignant. 'Jason's father wasn't always as successful as he is now. There was a time when he'd have done anything to make a dollar—including marrying his own son to the daughter of one of his most powerful enemies!'

'Oh, really?' Laura was openly incredulous. 'I understood Regina was a model.'

'So she was.' Leah considered her words before continuing: 'But she was also Paulo Enrico's daughter.'

Laura gazed impatiently at her. 'Are you really telling me that Regina's family are as wealthy as the Montefiores?'

'They get along.'

'Do they?'

'Listen ...' Leah glanced about her apprehensively, as if suspecting someone might be eavesdropping on their conversation, and then added huskily, 'Marco—that's Jason's father ...'

'I know.'

'... he had gotten involved in some deal that didn't work out. He was in hock—*debt*—to the tune of some ten million dollars. Not a lot by today's standards, maybe, but sufficient to put his company in danger of collapse. He needed the money. Enrico provided it.'

'Just like that.' Laura was sardonic.

'There were conditions.'

Laura grimaced. 'Jason's marriage to Regina?' She shook her head. 'If the two men were enemies, as you say, why should this man, Enrico, want Jason to marry his daughter?'

'I don't guess he did.' Leah sniffed. 'But Regina wanted Jason. And she got him.'

'How sweet!' Laura didn't believe a word of it. 'And that's why Jason doesn't speak to his father.'

'That's part of it.'

Laura finished her drink and set the glass down again rather heavily. 'So tell me, if Regina's family are so wealthy, why is she constantly coming to Jason for money?'

'If you think that's why she comes to Jason, you're a fool,' retorted Leah shortly. 'And the rest of the story isn't so pretty. But forget it! I've said too much as it is.'

'Oh, you have.' Laura slipped off the stool to face her. 'Leah, I know you mean well, and I do appreciate your—your confidence. But Jason has his own rules. And—and so do I.'

Laura had tea on the patio alone, and then went for a walk along the beach. It was so peaceful there, with only the surf and the wind soughing through the palms to keep her company. She didn't want to go back to the suite while Jason was sleeping, but when she eventually returned to the house, she found him lounging on the low wall that circled the terrace, evidently waiting for her. He was dressed now, in close fitting cream cotton pants and a knitted cashmere sweater, and Laura couldn't help the sharp contraction of her stomach at his unconscious sexuality.

He got to his feet at her approach, and stepped aside when she made to go up to the terrace. But, before she could avoid a confrontation, his fingers closed about her forearm. 'I wanted to tell you,' he said. 'Before your sister gets here, and before we get bogged down in the kind of small talk women seem to think is so important. I've changed my mind about tomorrow.'

For a moment, Laura's mind went blank. After the conversation she had had with Leah, her head had been filled with other things, and she could only stare at him. 'Tomorrow?'

'Our proposed trip to San Francisco,' said Jason flatly. 'Remember?'

Laura stiffened. 'It's not something I'd forget,' she lied. 'What is there to say?'

Jason released her arm and pushed his hands into the waistband of his pants. 'I've decided not to take you with me,' he declared without emotion. His eyes probed hers. 'Much as I shall miss the stimulation of your company, the violent nature of our—relationship, shall we say—could prove something of a distraction. And it is a business trip, after all.'

Laura couldn't speak. It should have been what she wanted; it should have been a source of some relief that she was not to be expected to play a role that was abhorrent to her. But it wasn't. What she truly felt was a sense of bereavement, and when she did find words to answer him, they mirrored her pained frustration.

'So who is going with you?' she inquired tightly. 'Or is that a leading question? Why don't you take Pamela? I believe she wouldn't object.'

Jason stared at her with cold assessing eyes. 'I believe

you could be right,' he responded harshly. 'Though why it should give you so much pleasure to say so, I can't imagine. However, loath as I am to refute that damning opinion you have of me, I am going without female companionship!'

Laura quivered. 'You surprise me.'

'Yes.' Jason's jaw clenched. 'I surprise myself sometimes. Not least, when I continue to want you, even when I know you really hate my guts!'

CHAPTER TEN

LAURA did not speak to Jason again before he left. Contrary to her expectation, he made no attempt to invade her rooms after she had retired for the night, and she learned the next morning that the plane she had heard taking off soon after midnight, had in fact had Jason as its passenger. He had apparently decided to take advantage of an overnight flight, and she assumed his early departure would precipitate his eventual homecoming.

In the days that followed whenever she heard the sound of an aircraft overhead, she expected it to be Jason. But the days stretched into a week, and then into two, and still he did not return. If Leah had heard from him, she did not say, and Laura was too proud to ask the housekeeper for information. Instead, she endeavoured to create a pattern for her days, and did her best to maintain a relationship with her sister, although that wasn't always easy.

For her part, Pamela seemed to have adapted very well to her new surroundings. Lazing in the sun; splashing about in the pool; occasionally joining Laura on one of her frequent walking expeditions—she seemed happiest doing nothing at all, and Laura found it simpler to avoid talking about the future. Now and then, Jason's name would be mentioned, usually by Pamela and usually concerning his prolonged absence. But generally their conversations encompassed impersonal things, and Laura suspected Pamela was as unwilling as herself to discuss Jason's possible intentions.

Even so, as each succeeding day went by, Laura found her own emotions less easy to control. In spite of assuring herself that she was glad of his absence, it simply wasn't possible to sustain that belief after she got to bed at night; and sleeping in his house, and his rooms, and his *bed*, made a difficult situation unbearable. Wherever she looked, she was reminded of him; his shaving equipment was in one of the glass cabinets in the bathroom; his hair brushes resided on a tray in the dressing room; his clothes hung in the closet opposite hers. Even the fragrant aroma of the sheets reminded her of him, and more than one night she had awakened to find herself clutching his pillow to her chest. The fact that the pillow, too, had been damp with tears was another cause for self-condemnation.

In consequence when, fifteen days after his departure, the Learjet flew in low over the island, she could hardly wait for one of the servants to go the airport to meet him. Had it not been for Pamela's curious eyes upon her, Laura knew she would have offered to go and meet Jason herself, but instead she was forced to wait, tense and nervous, until the familiar sound of the automobile was heard from the front of the house. She didn't know what she was going to say to him; she didn't even know how she would react when she saw him; she only knew she had missed him more than she would have thought possible, and her blood raced hotly at the realisation that the aching need she had hardly suppressed was soon to be assuaged.

It was late afternoon when Laura heard the sound she had been waiting for, and abandoning any attempt at hiding her relief, she got hurriedly to her feet. Because Pamela was with her, she had not had an opportunity to change her clothes, but the loose-fitting sleeveless smock, worn over baggy Bermudas, was not unattractive. Although the two shades of rose-pink did not exactly match, they blended well together, and accentuated the pale tan that covered her bare arms and legs. Her hair was in its usual thick braid, but she could loosen that later. When she and Jason were alone, she thought unsteadily, as she walked along the terrace and turned the corner of the house.

The cream convertible was where she expected it to be, but as she started eagerly towards it, her steps faltered. It was not Jason who was getting out of the passenger seat, and she fell back into the shadows as a young woman wearing tightly-fitting white jeans and a black blouson appeared. Her hair was dark and curly, and its expertly-cut style framed her narrow face with provocative tendrils, She was quite tall, and slim, and from the familiar way she was speaking to Jonah, it was not her first visit to the island. Who was she? Laura wondered faintly, a hollow emptiness replacing her earlier anticipation. Another of Jason's women, come to view the opposition? Or the reason for his prolonged absence—his next move in his plans to humiliate her?

'Who is she?'

Unaware, Pamela had followed her, and now Laura had to steel her features before turning to face her sister. 'How should I know?' she responded tensely, eager now to get out of sight. 'Why don't you ask her?'

'*Laura!*'

Their brief exchange had apparently attracted the girl's attention, and Laura knew a hopeless sense of frustration as the newcomer turned from directing Jonah's efforts with her luggage to come towards them. Just for that moment, the fact that the girl knew her name hardly registered. All Laura could think of was that once again she had been a fool—that Jason cared no more for her now than he had ever done.

'Laura!' the girl said again, less confidently now, and although there was still at least fifty feet between them, suddenly Laura knew who it was.

'Lucy?' she ventured disbelievingly, and then more strongly, 'Lucy, is it really you?' She shook her head. 'Dear God! I wouldn't have recognised you!'

Ignoring Pamela's terse: 'Who is Lucy?' Laura abandoned her reserve and rushed down the steps to meet Jason's daughter halfway. 'Oh, Lucy!' she exclaimed, feeling the girl's arms close around her and the dampness of uncontrollable tears on her own cheeks. 'I'm sorry. I thought you were someone else!'

'Who?' demanded Lucy at last, pulling back to look at the girl she had come to regard with affection. Before Laura walked out on her father, they had become the best of friends, but like the other people who knew him,

Jason's daughter was now looking at her with some suspicion. 'Who were you expecting?'

'Oh—no one—I mean—well, Jason, I suppose,' murmured Laura unhappily. Then, surveying the young woman facing her with some amazement, she added, 'When did you grow up?'

'You have been gone three years, Laura,' Lucy pointed out drily. 'I'm nearly eighteen. Not a child any more.'

'I can see that.' Laura held her at arm's length and smiled. 'You're quite—beautiful! I'm sure your father would agree.'

'Do you think so?' Lucy's instinctive plea for reassurance was very childlike suddenly, but then her dark eyes narrowed. 'Oh—was that what you thought? That I was one of Daddy's girlfriends? Yes. Yes, I can see that you did. Shame on you, Laura. He's really not like that. I thought you knew.'

Laura's hands dropped. 'Oh . . . I . . . don't be silly, Lucy. Why should it matter to me if your father brings a woman here? Didn't he tell you? I'm only here because of my sister. Where is he, by the way? Did you leave him at the airport?'

'Daddy?' Lucy shook her head. 'He's not here.'

'He's not!' Laura managed to control the incipient catch in her voice. 'Wh . . . where is he?'

'In Honolulu, I think,' replied Lucy carelessly. He told me to tell you his business is taking longer than he thought.' She looked beyond Laura and frowned. 'Is that your sister—over there?'

'Oh yes.' Laura gathered herself with an effort, and turned. 'Come and meet her.' She moistened her lips. 'Pam—this is Jason's daughter, Lucia. Lucy—this is Pam.'

'Jason's daughter?' Pamela gazed at the girl disbelievingly. 'I didn't even know he was married!'

'He's not.' Lucy answered her. 'He and my mother were divorced almost fifteen years ago. But—Laura and I are old friends.'

'Really?' Pamela arched her dark brows. 'How nice.'

'Yes, isn't it?' Despite her youth, Lucy had already sensed the other girl's hostility. Tucking her arm through Laura's, she led her up the steps. 'Come and talk to me while I change. I can't wait to get into my bikini.'

While Lucy spoke with the maid over where she wanted her suitcases unpacking, Laura leaned on the balcony rail, trying to come to terms with the fact that Jason would not be returning in the foreseeable future. Was that why he had sent his daughter here? she wondered. So that Lucy could keep an eye on her? However uncharitable this notion might be, she could not dismiss it, and she turned to look down at the patio, biting her lips in raw frustration.

Pamela had returned to her seat by the pool, she noticed, her sister's slim form visible beyond the sheltering canopy of a striped umbrella. Obviously she was not going to allow Lucy's arrival to upset her, and Laura half envied Pamela's ability to think only of herself.

'She's not at all like you, is she?' remarked Lucy, in her ear, and Laura turned to find the younger girl had shed her jeans and blouson and was standing unashamedly in only a lace-trimmed pair of panties. 'Is she really in love with Uncle Mike? She doesn't look very heart-broken to me.'

Laura walked back into the bedroom, as much to prevent Pamela from overhearing their conversation as a need to remind Lucy that she might be observed by one of the servants. 'Your father told you about that, hmm?' she murmured, taking hold of one of the carved posts that were set at each of the four corners of the bed.

'No. It was Nonna, actually.' Lucy slipped the narrow bra of a white bikini over her small breasts. Then her fingers moved to the buttoned fastening of her panties. 'She asked me if I had seen you since you came back. She wanted to know what my father plans to do.'

'I see.' Laura's palms felt moist against the polished wood. 'And what else did your grandmother say? Does she intend to tell Irene when she gets back from Italy?'

Lucy stepped into white bikini pants. 'Since when did Aunt Irene go to Italy?' she asked, surveying her reflection in a long antique mirror. 'She's at home right now. Daddy had dinner with her the other evening.'

'He did?' Laura looked blank. 'But I thought . . .'

Lucy frowned. 'Did Daddy tell you Aunt Irene was in Italy?'

Laura bent her head. 'I thought he did.'

'Oh, well——' Lucy shrugged. 'It's no big deal, is it? I guess he forgot—or was mistaken, or something.'

'Yes.' Laura appeared to accept the girl's explanation but inside she was a mass of conflicting thoughts and emotions. Why would Jason lie about a thing like that? Unless . . . unless, he had intended to prevent her from contacting Mike Kazantis. Would he go so far to protect his sister? She thought he would.

'Anyway, Nonna was surprised when Daddy told her you were back.' Lucy grimaced. 'I was, too, but probably not for the same reasons.'

'What do you mean?' Laura was intrigued in spite of herself.

'Oh . . .' Lucy shrugged, and turned away from her reflection without conceit. 'I always knew Daddy wanted you back. Heavens,' she grimaced, 'you couldn't live with him after you went away!'

Laura bent her head. 'I think you're exaggerating.'

'No, I'm not.' Lucy was indignant. 'You knew how he felt about you. I almost hated you for what you did to him!'

Laura drew an uneven breath. 'You don't understand . . .'

'No, I don't.' Lucy squared her shoulders. 'Like I said, I was pretty mad when you walked out on him.' She shrugged. 'But then—I figured, it must be something pretty important for you to fade out of that kind of a relationship. I mean—I thought you were crazy about him, I really did. But when you left . . .' She shook her head. 'I never expected you'd come back.'

'Nor did I,' said Laura painfully, wishing she had never started this. 'So . . . what was so different about you and your grandmother?'

'Nonna didn't know the way it was.'

Laura's brows drew together. 'The way it was?'

'Yes. Sure.' Lucy lifted her shoulders defensively. 'She . . . well, she thought my father made the break. She didn't discuss it with him. She never would. And I . . . well, I guess I let her go on thinking it.'

'Ah!' Laura nodded. 'That's why she was so surprised.'

'Yes.' Lucy inclined her head. 'I'm sorry.'

'Don't be.' Laura was quick to reassure her. 'It's not important.' She hesitated. 'But you didn't tell me what your grandmother said. Does—Aunt Irene know about . . . about what happened?'

'You mean you and Daddy?'

'No. I mean your Uncle Mike and Pamela,' responded Laura patiently. 'Did your father discuss it with her?'

'Oh, I don't know.' Lucy looked confused. 'Uncle Mike is always in trouble of some kind or another. He and Aunt Irene don't live together any more. They separated six months ago.'

'*Separated!*'

'They're still married, of course. But that's more because of the children than anything else. They live with Aunt Irene. Did you ever meet my cousins?'

Laura blinked. 'I . . . I may have done . . .'

'There are four of them, you know. Dino and Tina—they're the twins—they're sixteen. And Marco; he's twelve; and the youngest Sophia, she's seven.'

Laura shook her head. 'And your father knew this?'

'What?'

'That Mike Kazantis and his sister were separated.'

'I guess.' Lucy pulled a face. 'It's not a secret.'

'No.' Laura managed to put on a brave face. 'I've obviously misunderstood.'

'Hmm.' Lucy was unaware of the bombshell she had dropped. She turned back to her reflection. 'Do you think I look all right? You don't think this suit is just a bit—well, out-of-date?'

'Out of date?' echoed Laura blankly. 'I—not to me, Lucy. Could you wear anything less?'

Lucy giggled. 'You wouldn't believe it!' Then, she

sobered again. 'Say—are you all right, Laura? I mean—
you look kind of . . . stunned. What did I say?'

'Nothing. Nothing at all.' Laura managed to
convince the girl that she was mistaken. 'So, when is
your father coming back? Or is that a closely-guarded
secret, too?'

'Too?' Lucy picked up on the word, but then she
shrugged. 'I'm not sure. In a few days, I guess. Why
don't you ring him? I can give you the number of his
suite at the Ilikai.'

Laura was tempted. Her sense of frustration at the
realisation that Jason had been lying to her all along
was such that she longed to confront him with his
duplicity. But the telephone was such an unsatisfactory
way to conduct any kind of argument, and she wanted
to see his face when she told him she knew what he had
done.

'It's all right, Lucy,' she responded now, realising
she could not involve Jason's daughter in this affair.
'I can wait. Now, why don't we go down and have
some tea? Or perhaps you would prefer something
cooler?'

In the days that followed, Laura became the unwilling
recipient of many more confidences. Lucy seemed to
think that Laura's return was permanent, and Laura
could hardly disillusion her without involving herself in
explanations she had no wish to share. In consequence,
Lucy began to treat her like a member of the family,
and Laura was forced to listen, particularly when the
girl spoke of her mother.

'She got married again, you know,' she remarked a
couple of mornings later, as they sunbathed on the
beach. It was early, too early for Pamela to join them,
even had she wanted to, and Laura had noticed that
Lucy seemed to enjoy these times best. 'My stepfather's
an oil man; Ellis Hammond, have you heard of him?
No? Well, you've probably heard of his company:
Hamco.'

Laura frowned. 'When did she get married?'

'About two years ago.' Lucy grimaced. 'I guess, when

she finally accepted that Daddy wasn't about to renew her contract.'

Laura stared at her. 'What do you mean?'

'Oh, you know!' Lucy sighed. 'She's been angling for him to remarry her for years. Surely you knew that.'

Laura wondered exactly how much she had known of the man she had lived with for more than two years. She shook her head. 'I didn't think of it.' She hesitated, and then added reluctantly: 'After all, your mother did divorce your father, didn't she? Not the other way around.'

'Oh, that!' Lucy was scathing. 'That was just so there was no hassle over my custody. Daddy could have divorced my mother half a dozen times over. It wasn't exactly a love-match—on his side, at least.'

Laura expelled her breath carefully. 'You're very cynical.'

'Wouldn't you be? For years my mother used me to get back at Daddy. If it hadn't been for you and Nonna, I'd have thought all wives acted that way.'

'Oh, Lucy . . .'

'No, it's true.' Lucy ran restless fingers through her damp curls. 'I used to dread going to the office. I used to dread being unloaded like a sack of potatoes.'

'Oh, Lucy, your father always cared about you, you know that.'

'Well, yes. I guess he did. But until you went to live at the apartment, I never felt at home there.'

Laura bent her head. 'Thank you.'

'I mean it. Those other women . . .' She flushed as she realised what she had said; but Laura urged her to go on: 'Well—there were other women—but they meant nothing to him. They were just—there. You were different.'

'Was I?' Laura's tone was ironic, and Lucy frowned.

'You know you were,' she exclaimed fiercely. 'You're here, aren't you?'

Laura shrugged. 'For the present.'

'What do you mean?'

Lucy looked anxious, and Laura found herself

reassuring her. 'Who knows?' she said, making light of her words. 'Who can foretell the future?'

Lucy still looked doubtful. 'You know—Daddy never talks about why you and he split up.' She paused, and then added softly: 'Why did you?'

'It's a long story.' Laura had suspected this was coming and now she reached purposefully for her towel. 'I'll tell you some day.'

'Why not now?'

'Because, like I said, it's a long story.'

'We've got time.'

'Oh, Lucy ...'

'I know it had something to do with the Ridgeways, didn't it?' Lucy burst out, before the other girl could get to her feet, and Laura gazed at her, dry-mouthed.

'You know?'

'My mother told me,' admitted Lucy unhappily. Then, realising she had to say more, she went on: 'It was something to do with Ellen Ridgeway, wasn't it? Mom said that Daddy threw you over for her, but I didn't believe it!'

Laura's shoulders sagged. 'What else did your mother tell you?' she demanded heavily.

'Not much.' Lucy coloured. 'Was that it? Was that why you walked out? Because you thought Daddy was having an affair?'

Laura expelled her breath wearily. 'I suppose that sounds pretty stupid to you, hmm?' she inquired flatly.

'Stupid?' Lucy looked troubled.

'Yes.' Laura shrugged. 'You said yourself your father always had women around.'

'Not when he was with you?' exclaimed Lucy defensively. 'I told you ...'

'But your mother seems to have thought he was involved with Ellen Ridgeway, doesn't she?'

'She would.' Lucy was impatient. 'Did she tell you that? Was that why you left?'

Laura shook her head. 'I wouldn't have believed anything your mother told me.' She grimaced. 'Perhaps I was wrong.'

'No, you weren't wrong.' Lucy was fierce in her

father's defence. 'And if he was involved with Ellen Ridgeway, why didn't he go on seeing her, after you went back to England?'

'How do you know he didn't?'

Lucy gasped. 'Because I do. I was with him for most of that year. There were no other women.'

Laura plucked at the hem of the towel pressed against her chest. 'I imagine even your father has some sense of decency,' she declared tensely. 'I'd really rather not talk about it.'

'But you have to talk about it,' protested Lucy. 'If Daddy knew how you felt, he would want you to.'

'Would he?' Laura doubted it. Her feelings concerning Ellen and Jeff Ridgeway had never concerned him. 'Well—shall we go back? It's almost time for breakfast, and I'm ready for some coffee.'

Lucy followed her example and got to her feet, but her expression was still anxious. 'You won't ... you won't tell Daddy I've said anything, will you?' she ventured awkwardly. 'He ... he wouldn't like to think that Mom had—had discussed it with me.'

'Don't worry,' said Laura gently. 'It's unlikely to come up. So far as the Ridgeway deal is concerned, it's a closed book.'

Lucy had not said how long she planned to stay, and Laura did not like to ask her, in case the girl thought she wanted her to leave. In fact, Laura was glad of her company to ease the situation between herself and Pamela, which had not improved in the weeks since Jason had gone away. Laura sometimes wondered if her sister thought of Mike Kazantis at all, as she lay sunning herself beside Jason's pool. She had evidently resigned herself to his disappearance, but had she forgotten it was his child she carried?

Lucy, she knew, regarded the other girl with some resentment, but she knew better than to anger her father by getting involved. Nevertheless, she found it hard to understand why Laura hadn't just told Pamela who Mike Kazantis was.

'I mean,' she said one afternoon, as they drove into

the village so that she could post a letter to her mother, 'it's not as if it's your fault that Uncle Mike is married to Daddy's sister. And as you did come to Daddy for help . . .'

Laura sighed. 'Pamela was . . . unstable at that time, Lucy,' she said unwillingly. 'Didn't your grandmother tell you that?'

'About her O.D.-ing?' Lucy grimaced. 'Oh, yes, she told me. But she doesn't really seem the type, does she?'

Laura shrugged. 'She was desperate. We all do things when we're desperate that aren't exactly typical.'

'Like you walking out on Daddy, hmm?' suggested Lucy slyly, as Laura parked the car in front of the little post office. 'I'm so glad you came back. I can forgive Pamela for almost anything for bringing that about.'

CHAPTER ELEVEN

LAURA rolled over in the bed and stretched tiredly. It was morning at last, she saw, grateful for the sun's rays slatting through the blind. She was not sleeping at all well, and the evening before she had swallowed several large daiquiris to ensure herself of a good night. But she had not had a good night. She had been hot and restless, and there had been times when she had imagined she was not alone in the big bed. She had felt the warmth of someone's body close to hers, and once she could have sworn warm lips had caressed the corner of her mouth. But she knew she had only been fantasizing, and her cheeks were still smudged with the tears she had shed in that unconscious state. It was frightening to realise how, even in her sleep, thoughts of Jason dominated her. Particularly, after what he had done—not just now, but three years ago . . .

She had not been lying when she told Lucy she had not believed anything her mother had said. Regina had always been jealous of her. She had known that. Although she had not really understood why until Lucy explained about her parents' divorce. Nevertheless, what she had not said was that Regina's malicious gossip had confirmed something Laura already knew to be true, and it was partly because of Regina's influence that she had run away from the situation.

But, Ellen Ridgeway had not lied to her. With her husband's body lying dead in his coffin, she had been too distraught to think of prevarication. Her white face, her tears; the haunting fear of guilt in her eyes, had all told their own story, and nothing could alter the fact that Jeff Ridgeway had killed himself because of his wife's involvement with Jason Montefiore. He had been a successful businessman, with companies not just here, in the islands but on the mainland, too. He had had no other reason to take his life, except that his wife was more than thirty years his junior and had evidently been cheating on him with a younger man.

All the pieces had fit. During that last month, Jason had paid unusually frequent visits to the mainland, leaving Laura alone in the apartment, even though she had been willing to go with him.

'It's business,' he had said. 'You'd be bored.' And Laura had believed him, because to her knowledge he had never lied to her before.

Even now, she could still remember the shock she had had when she had discovered Jason was not in San Francisco at all, but right there, in Honolulu. It was quite by chance she had seen him and Ellen Ridgeway together. She seldom left the apartment for meals, when she was on her own, but one fateful afternoon she had been invited, by one of the girls she used to work with at the agency, to a wedding shower they were giving for a girl who was leaving. It was to be held in the Colony Room of one of the larger Waikiki hotels, and when Laura walked into the discreetly-lit restaurant, the first person she saw was Jason, seated intimately in a booth with Ellen Ridgeway.

She shivered, remembering the chilling feeling of enlightenment that had swept over her at that moment. It was so unexpected; yet so predictable; and she had turned and walked out of the hotel again, without even hearing the puzzled reaction of her friends. She should have known it would happen sooner or later, she had told herself, as she walked blindly down the marble steps and out of the foyer. The miracle was it had taken so long. Jason's women seldom lasted longer than a couple of months, whereas she had lived with him for almost two years.

Jason had caught up with her in Kalakaua Avenue. She didn't know what excuse he had offered Ellen Ridgeway, and she didn't care, but the anger in his dark face prevented her from saying what she felt. 'It's not what you think,' he had declared roughly. 'I can't explain right now but you've got to trust me!'

And she had, even then, albeit with some misgivings. She had been so much in love with him, she would have believed anything at that moment, anything that would restore the relationship she had thought they shared. Even when, two days later, Jeff Ridgeway had leapt from the twenty-first floor of his hotel complex, she had sought for reasons that did not implicate Jason, striving desperately not to believe what was staring her in the face.

She didn't know why she had attended the funeral. Jason had not asked her to go. On the contrary, since Jeff Ridgeway's suicide, he had been curiously remote, and Laura had had no chance to question him, even had she felt able to. But the Ridgeways were well-known in Honolulu, and she had felt obliged to go, if only to scotch any rumours which might be circulating about Jason and Ellen Ridgeway.

And, it was Ellen Ridgeway herself who confirmed her worst suspicions. In a tearful voice, she had confessed that Jeff must have found out about her and Jason, and that she would never forgive herself for what she had made him do.

Jason had come upon them then, and Laura had known he was furious at her intervention. In spite of the fact that she had arrived in the powerful little sports car he had bought her to go shopping, he insisted on her driving home with him, and it was in the back of one of his luxurious limousines that they had had their last confrontation.

In trembling tones, Laura had told him exactly what Ellen Ridgeway had said, and far from denying it, Jason had turned on her instead. 'You don't trust me, do you?' he had demanded. 'You never have, and I guess you never will.'

'That's not true . . .'

'What is true then? That you didn't believe I was in San Francisco? That you came to the Colony Room spying on me?'

'No . . .' Laura caught her breath. 'I was invited to a party! I didn't know you might be there. And—and you weren't in San Francisco, were you?'

'I told you I couldn't explain right then.'

'But you never have. have you? You . . . you've

changed. You don't talk to me any more. And ... and since Jeff Ridgeway ... since he ...'

'Killed himself?' put in Jason callously. 'Why don't you say it? Yes? Since Ridgeway took his own life—what? I've been spending time with his widow?'

Laura moistened her lips. 'Have you?'

'Why should I tell you? If I was to suggest that Ellen lied to you, you wouldn't believe me, so why should I give myself the hassle? So far as Ridgeway's death is concerned—I admit it, I was involved. But I don't regret it!'

Laura eventually left that night, while Jason was downstairs in the club, a guest at a dinner party she had refused to attend. He had left after another painful exchange, and Laura had been pacing about the apartment, undecided what she should do, when Regina called.

Jason's ex-wife had asked to speak to her husband first, and Laura had had to explain that he was not available. It hadn't been easy admitting that they were spending the evening apart, and Regina was quick to make the connection.

'I did wonder if you might still be there,' she remarked maliciously. 'If what I hear is right, my dear ex-husband is running true to form.'

'I don't know what you mean.'

Laura had tried to feign innocence, but Regina had heard the catch in her voice, and she was unforgiving. 'The new woman in Jason's life,' she declared mockingly. 'Do not pretend you do not know about her. It is common knowledge that he has been spending a great deal of time in company with the Ridgeways, and even you cannot believe that it was Jeffrey who sustained his interest for so long.'

There was more of the same -dates and places when they had been seen together, which Laura could not refute. And although she had known from the beginning Regina would do anything she could to split them up, she was hurting too much to analyse how much of what the woman said was true. She needed to get away, as far away from Jason as possible, she thought, to get things into perspective. And if Regina's call had precipitated her flight it was no less necessary in the circumstances.

It had been a comparatively simple matter to leave the island. Taking only one suitcase, she had slipped out of the side entrance of the building and hailed a cab, without anyone seeing her. The overnight flight to Los Angeles had connected with a morning flight to London, and she hadn't really stopped to think until she had stopped running.

Now, she pushed these thoughts aside with an aching heart. In spite of everything, she still couldn't think of Jason without feeling that insistent need inside her. Physically, he disturbed her as much now as he had ever done, and it was useless to deny it. She wanted him. She yearned for the hard strength of his body possessing hers, and no matter how rationally she catalogued his faults when she was awake, at night her emotions governed her brain ...

A sudden cessation of sound brought her up on her elbows. Unaware, she had been listening to the sound of running water for some time, but now it had stopped, and her brow furrowed as she looked about the room. She didn't remember the maid coming in and asking her if she wanted a bath, and her pulses quickened instinctively at the automatic connotation. Without hesitating, she thrust her feet out of bed, pausing only a moment when a wave of dizziness swept over her. Too many daiquiris, she thought impatiently, snatching up the satin négligé that matched her nightgown and wrapping it around her. Then, her feet slowing as she reached the dressing room, she approached the bathroom door, turning the handle tentatively and holding her breath as she propelled it inward.

'Did I wake you?' inquired a wry voice at her shoulder, and Laura almost jumped out of her skin. Just as her eyes were registering that—although one of the tubs was three-quarters filled with water—the bathroom was unoccupied, her ears were assaulted by that deep familiar tone. Swinging round, she found

Jason right behind her, naked save for the towel wrapped loosely about his hips, and for a moment she was unable to control her emotional reaction.

'I—why—oh, *God*! It was you!' she breathed, remembering her dreams of hallucinating, her hands stretching out to touch the fine hair that filmed his chest, and Jason's lips twisted.

'Yes, it was me,' he conceded roughly, before his hands reached for her, and as he jerked her close against his lean taut body, he added, 'If I'd known my absence would have this kind of effect, I'd have taken a chance and come back sooner.'

The harshness of his words was more than compensated by the hungry pressure of his mouth. Besides, for the moment, Laura was too absorbed with allaying her own tortured senses, and even the thickness of the towel about his hips was too great a barrier between them. With her arms about his waist it was a simple matter to slide her fingers down the hollow of his spine, invading the cream towelling and loosening its knot. When it fell to the floor, she moved sensuously against him, and the powerful thrust of his manhood surged eagerly against her.

'You want me,' he muttered, threading his hands through the silken curtain of her hair. 'Say it! Say it! I want you to admit it.'

'I want you,' she acknowledged breathlessly, hardly aware of what she was saying, and with a sound of satisfaction, Jason swung her into his arms and carried her back into the bedroom . . .

Some time later, Laura opened her eyes to find Jason propped on one elbow looking down at her, and immediately the realisation of what she had done swept over her. Once again, she had allowed her senses to rule her reason, and this time Jason could be in no doubt that she had initiated their passionate lovemaking.

'Do you know—I believe you've put on a little weight since you came here,' he remarked, running a possessive hand along the curve of her hip and down over her belly.

'Dare I say it suits you?'

'Don't!' With a jack-knifing movement, Laura thrust his hand away and jerked upright, feeling the sweat break out on her forehead when the room revolved as before. 'I ... I ... have to talk to you. But not now. Lucy will be wondering where I am.'

'I should think Lucy has a pretty good idea,' retorted Jason softly, coming up beside her and allowing his teeth to skim lightly over her shoulder. 'Surely she's told you how delighted she is that we're back together again.'

'We ... we're not back together,' said Laura desperately, wiping the back of her hand across her forehead. 'This was a mistake. You frightened me, and ... and I lost control.'

'You did, didn't you?' murmured Jason teasingly, taking the lobe of her ear between his teeth and biting it. 'But it was no mistake. So stop trying to pretend it was.'

Laura breathed unsteadily. 'I must get dressed ...'

'Why must you?'

'Pam—Pam usually comes over in the mornings,' she stammered huskily, finding it difficult to separate thoughts of her sister from the unwelcome memories she had been nurturing earlier. 'She ... she ...'

'To hell with Pam!' Jason's hands slid beneath her arms to cup the swollen fullness of her breasts. 'See ...' he said thickly, his thumbs probing the thrusting nipples. 'You like this just as much as I do.'

'Jason *don't*!' With a supreme effort, Laura forced herself away from him, scrambling on to her knees and groping for her satin wrapper. 'You ... you don't understand. We have to talk about Mike Kazantis. Why didn't you tell me he and Irene were separated? Why did you tell me he was in Italy, when you knew exactly where he was living? Why did you lie to me? Why did you lie to Pam?'

Jason's lean face took on a look of resignation. 'Lucy told you,' he said flatly. 'It figures.'

'Did you think she wouldn't?'

'No.' He lounged back against the pillows and folded

his arms beneath his head. 'You had to know sooner or later. I guess she did me a favour.'

Laura gazed at him. 'You mean—you don't deny it?'

'Deny what? That Mike and Irene are separated? That would be pretty stupid, wouldn't it?'

Laura dragged her robe about her. 'I don't believe this. You deliberately misled me. Why? Why?'

'I didn't want you going and seeing Kazantis,' replied Jason evenly. 'You don't know what kind of man he is. I do.'

Laura gasped. 'And you feel yourself fit to judge him!'

'I do.' Jason regarded her steadily. 'What does your sister say?'

'Pam?' Laura looked blank. 'I haven't discussed this with her!'

'Why not?'

'Why not?' Laura shook her head. 'I—I suppose because I wanted to speak to you first. I couldn't believe you'd do this to us.'

'Do what?' Jason's patience was thinning. 'Grow up, Laura. He's still not free, is he? And Pamela was quite willing to make alternative arrangements.'

Laura's lips parted. 'Pam? But she doesn't even know he's married.'

'Doesn't she?'

'You said you hadn't told her.'

'No.' Jason's hands fell to his sides. 'As I recall it, we never did get to finish our conversation about your sister, did we?'

'But . . . what are you saying?'

'Nothing too obscure.' Jason shrugged. 'Simply that your sister knew the score right from day one.'

'You mean with Mike?' Laura was appalled.

'No. I mean with me,' corrected Jason shortly. 'I guess she suspected I didn't buy that story about her trying to take her own life.'

'You would know about that,' put in Laura bitterly, and Jason's eyes hardened.

'You really are naïve, aren't you?' he said scornfully. 'Didn't you ever wonder how you could fly five thousand miles and yet still get there in time to save her life?'

Laura moistened her lips. 'I . . . I assumed she had waited.'

'Oh, she waited all right. A good ten hours in my estimation.'

Laura wouldn't believe it. 'I—I could have missed the flight. The plane could have crashed!'

'But it didn't, did it? I guess she thought it was worth the risk.'

Laura trembled. 'But if you knew this, why did you help her?'

'You know why.'

'To—to force me to come back to you?'

'Means and ends,' said Jason harshly. 'We all live by them.'

'I don't believe this!'

'Why not?' Jason pushed himself into a sitting position, crossing his legs. 'Haven't you always known I've not been exactly sane where you're concerned?'

Laura shook her head. 'Are you telling me there was never any cause for concern where Pam was concerned?'

'No, I'm not saying that.' Jason spoke tolerantly. 'Obviously, when she took the overdose, she was pretty desperate. As I suspected, Kazantis took off as soon as he discovered she was pregnant, and your sister knew she was in trouble. Apparently she didn't have the money for an abortion, even if she'd wanted one, and telephoning you was her last resort. She had some idea that if you came and spoke with Mike you might be able to persuade him to accept his responsibilities.' He grimaced. 'Some chance!'

Laura stared at him with a growing sense of disorientation. 'So . . . so you decided to use the situation to your own advantage.'

'It wasn't quite like that.' Jason expelled his breath heavily. 'Remember, when you took off for London, I had only your story to go on. It wasn't until I'd spoken to your sister that I got the whole picture.'

'You lied to me!'

'I . . . embroidered the truth.'

'What do you mean? Mike was never in Italy.'

'He could have been. He does have relatives there, you know.'

Laura hunched her shoulders. 'What a fool I've been!'

'Oh, Christ!' With an oath, Jason vaulted over the bed to her side. 'You haven't been a fool. You've acted in what you thought were your sister's best interests, and in so doing given yourself time to realise that what we had is still as powerful as it ever was.' His hand tipped her resisting face towards him. 'Dear God, haven't we wasted enough time? Don't make me wait another three years to tell me you still care!'

His voice was persuasive, his hand gentle against her soft skin, the taut strength of his body shameless in its beauty . . . but Laura knew she could not believe him. Nothing had changed. He was still the man who thought he could do no wrong, and even if she could forgive him his infidelity, she could not forgive him for causing another man to take his own life.

With a moan of anguish, she tore herself away from him, scrambling off the bed and backing up until her shoulders touched the wall behind her. 'Don't!' she said. 'Don't ever touch me again! Just call your pilot. Have him fly me back to Oahu. I'm going back to London, and if you try to stop me, I may just follow Pamela's example!'

CHAPTER TWELVE

LAURA had been back in London three weeks when she had an unexpected visitor.

She was staying in Pierce's house. He had insisted she do nothing about finding a place of her own until she had had time to think about what she wanted to do, and Laura had accepted his dictates simply because she didn't have the strength to argue. Besides, she knew he had not given up hope of persuading her to make her home with him permanently; and with a trip to the Far East coming up, it did not seem practical to take on the expense of a flat until her return.

Pierce had asked remarkably few questions about her sudden change of plans, although he had been surprised to learn that Pamela was staying on in Hawaii. 'I'd have thought she'd want to be with her sister at a time like this,' he commented, when Laura let it be known that she was not returning to England. 'Oh, well ... I suppose she's old enough to look after herself. You never know, she may persuade your erstwhile employer to marry her.'

This was something Laura could not discuss, but as luck would have it, the 'phone rang at that moment and the painful moment passed. Eventually, she would be able to view that possibility with equanimity, Laura told herself, but for the present it was too raw and vulnerable to expose.

Leaving Kaulanai had been the most difficult thing she had ever done in her life. When she had run from Jason before, it had been with the memory of his anger ringing in her ears, and the knowledge that he had already replaced her with Ellen Ridgeway. This time, it was different. This time, he had asked her to stay and when she had refused, he had shut himself away in his study, so that she had not seen him again before Jonah drove her to the airport.

Of course, Lucy had begged her not to go. She had been quite tearful when she said her goodbyes, and Laura's suggestion that she might visit her in London had not met with any enthusiasm. 'Daddy cares about you,' she exclaimed tremulously, cupping her neck with nervous fingers. 'Please, Laura, give him another chance!'

Pamela was surprised, but not disappointed. 'I said it was unnecessary for you to stay here,' she commented, when Laura told her she was leaving. 'What's happened? Have you and Jason fallen out? I had the feeling something was wrong, when he stayed away so long.'

'It's a personal matter,' Laura had responded tensely, not prepared to bare her feelings to anyone. 'It might have been easier if you had been honest with me. Jason tells me you knew Mike was married all along.'

'He was a louse!' said Pamela succinctly, showing no particular malice. 'But you've no idea how I felt—thousands of miles from anyone who cared about me, and Mrs Goldstein threatening to fire me if I was late again.' She shook her head. 'I felt so sick in the mornings—so dizzy! Sometimes I really wanted to die!'

Laura had had cause to remember that particular statement since she came back to England. Several mornings lately she had developed a feeling of nausea when she got out of bed, and the bitter irony of her condition did not make accepting it any easier. She was pregnant. She was sure of it. But unlike Pamela, she had nowhere to turn for help.

She did think about telling Pierce, but she was half afraid of his reaction. Knowing him as she did, she was almost sure he would insist on her either informing Jason of his responsibilities, or marrying himself without delay. Neither alternative had any merit so far as Laura was concerned. To tell Jason he was to be a father for a second time might have certain selfish advantages, but she would not blackmail him into marrying her, even if she could. And as for marrying Pierce—well, she simply couldn't see herself marrying

nyone other than her child's father for, whatever his
ns, he was the only man she would ever love. She
might not respect him; she might not even *like* him; but
eeling as she did, she could not share her life with
nother man.

May had given way to June, and the days were
etting longer. Since Laura's return, the weather had
een unseasonably chilly, but one morning she
wakened to find blue skies and rising temperatures.
ummer had at last arrived, and she got out of bed with
determined sense of optimism. She couldn't go on living
n a vacuum, she told herself firmly. Today, she would
ell Pierce about the baby, and explain to him her
easons for keeping it to herself.

Her recovering spirits received something of a
etback, when nausea sent her hurrying into the
bathroom. Resting her damp forehead against the cool
glaze of the mirror, she acknowledged it would take
more than a sunny day to solve her problems, but
whatever happened, she was going to keep Jason's
child.

At breakfast, Pierce was absorbed with opening his
mail, and sipping her unsweetened tea—she could no
onger face coffee in the mornings—Laura had no
opportunity to broach the subject closest to her heart.
However, when the meal was over, Pierce suggested
attending to the letters he had to write straight away,
and Laura followed him into his study with a sense of
anticipation.

'It's such a lovely day, I thought we might go out
after lunch,' Pierce remarked, seating himself behind his
desk. 'How does a trip to Bournemouth appeal to you?
A breath of sea air, and a walk along the promenade.
Exactly the kind of outing to put some colour into your
cheeks. You're looking pale, Laura. I've noticed it for
some time. Even your tan is fading, and we can't have
that, now can we?'

Laura pressed the palms of her hands together, and
taking her chance, she said carefully, 'As a matter of
fact, Pierce, I did want to talk to you about that.'

'About what?' Pierce was re-reading a letter that

had arrived that morning, and was only half listening to her.

'About—about my not feeling well,' murmured Laura awkwardly, and he lifted his head to fix her with a concerned stare.

'You're not ill, are you?' he exclaimed. His expression deepened to one of anxiety. 'That's not why you came back to England, is it?'

'No. No.' Laura moistened her upper lip. 'I'm not ill ...' and as she sought for words to break it to him gently, they heard the doorbell chime.

Pierce's head lifted. 'Visitors?' he said impatiently. 'At this hour?' He pulled out his pocket watch, flipped open the lid and looked at it. 'How inconvenient!'

Until Mrs Barnes, Pierce's housekeeper, had informed them who it was, Laura could say no more, and she stifled her impatience as the minutes stretched.

The knock on the door, when it came, was almost an anti-climax, and Pierce viewed the buxom figure of his housekeeper with some frustration. 'Not now, Mrs Barnes,' he said. 'Whoever it is, tell them I'm tied up at the moment. Nine forty-five in the morning is far too early for interviews.'

'It's not someone for you, Mr Carver,' Mrs Barnes informed him stiffly. 'It's a lady to see Miss Huyton. I told her you were working, and that you didn't like to be disturbed, but the lady was most insistent. She says she's come all the way from America, and it's a matter of some urgency.'

'Pamela!' exclaimed Laura immediately, springing to her feet. 'Oh, Pierce, I'm sorry about this, but if Pam's come all this way to see me, it must be something important.'

'The lady said her name was Mrs ... Kazandis, miss,' put in the housekeeper uncertainly. 'Would that be your sister?'

'Kazantis?' corrected Laura automatically, stopping in her tracks. 'Mrs Kazantis? But—that must be ...'

'Me!' said a tentative voice from behind Mrs Barnes, and Laura's eyes widened at the astonishing appearance of Jason's sister.

'Irene!' she said faintly. And then, with increasing urgency: 'Is something wrong? Has something happened to Jason? Oh, God!' Her head swam. 'It is Jason, isn't it? You wouldn't have come here otherwise. What's happened to him? Is he ill? Has there been an accident? Tell me! Tell me!'

'Laura, calm down!' Irene came instantly into the study, brushing past the stunned figure of the housekeeper and giving Pierce an appealing look. 'I came to talk to you, that's all.' She put an arm about Laura's trembling shoulders. 'I came straight from the airport. Now ... stop getting yourself in a state, and I'll explain.'

Laura gazed at her with anxious eyes. 'Jason's all right? You swear?'

'Of course.' Irene looked helplessly at Pierce. 'I'm sorry about this. I didn't mean to upset anyone.'

'But you evidently have,' remarked Pierce drily, recovering from his own shock at Laura's reaction. He turned to the housekeeper. 'That will do, Mrs Barnes. We'll call you if we need you.'

'Yes, sir.'

The housekeeper departed with some reluctance, and after she had gone, Pierce came towards the two women, holding out his hand. 'Pierce Carver, Mrs Kazantis,' he introduced himself politely. 'I assume you must be another member of the family.'

'I'm Jason's sister,' said Irene ruefully, returning his greeting. 'I got to know Laura about four years ago. When she and Jason were together.'

'Together?'

Pierce arched one narrow eyebrow, and Laura expelled her breath on a sigh. 'Jason and I lived together for almost two years,' she admitted quietly. 'I was only his secretary for a few months. After that, ...'

'... shared more than his confidence,' finished Pierce ironically. 'Yes.' He shrugged. 'That doesn't exactly come as a surprise to me.'

Laura lifted her head. 'It doesn't?'

'I am not completely unworldly, my dear,' he

responded. 'And I would have had to be totally
insensitive not to comprehend the tension between
you and Montefiore that night at my club. I
suspected you had had a relationship. I hoped that it
was over.'

'It was!' Laura gave Irene a doubtful look. 'It is!'

'Could I talk to Laura alone, do you think, Mr
Carver?' inquired Irene smoothly. 'I do want to talk to
her about Jason, and I'd prefer it if we could speak
privately.'

'Why not?' Pierce's nostrils flared. 'I shall be in the
library, if you want me, Laura. Mrs Kazantis.' He
bowed his head, and moving with his loose-limbed
stride, he left the room.

Alone with Jason's sister, Laura was at a loss for
words. She couldn't imagine why Irene had come here,
and she was still suffering from the shock her
appearance had given her. If Jason had had something
to say to her, why couldn't he have come himself? she
wondered unsteadily. Now that Irene had reassured her
that he was not ill or injured, her indignation at his
continued interference in her life flowered anew. Why
couldn't he just leave her alone? It was hard enough,
carrying his child inside her, and knowing she could
never share it with him.

'Your Mr Carver evidently thinks a lot about you,'
said Irene suddenly, breaking the silence that had fallen
since the door had closed behind him, and Laura bent
her head.

'He's a good friend.'

'He'd like to be a lot more than that, in my opinion,'
remarked Irene drily. 'Are you in love with him?'

'In love with Pierce?' Laura gazed at her blankly. 'Of
course I'm not in love with Pierce. We don't have that
kind of a relationship.'

'So why did you leave Jason?'

Laura's face suffused with colour. 'I beg your
pardon?'

'Laura, please . . .' Irene propped herself on the edge
of Pierce's desk and regarded the younger girl with
troubled eyes. She was like Jason, Laura thought, her

…rt twisting at the realisation. Slim and dark and …ractive, but without his height or muscular build. …e have to be honest with one another. I didn't fly all …s way just to say hello.'

…aura's tongue circled her lips. 'Why did you fly all …s way then? Did Jason send you?'

Jason!' Irene rolled her eyes expressively. 'If my …ther knew I was here, he'd be furious. But—well— …mother begged me to come, and I have to say, I'm …cerned about him myself.'

About who?' Laura swallowed. 'About Jason?' Her …se quickened. 'But . . . you said he was all right. You …d . . .'

I know what I said.' Irene interrupted her, before she …ld work herself into a state again. 'And he's not—ill, …ctly . . .'

What does that mean?'

It means what it says.' Irene gestured to a chair. …hy don't you sit down, Laura. You look as if you …d to. Really, I'll tell you everything, but you must …p jumping to conclusions.

…aura shook her head and remained standing, and …h a grimace, Irene continued. 'Look,' she said, 'I get … feeling that in spite of everything that's happened, … do care what happens to that stubborn brother of …e. So why are you here in London, while he's trying …kill himself out in Hawaii?'

…aura blanched. 'Trying to kill himself?'

A figure of speech.' Irene sighed. 'But that's what …s going to do if he doesn't pull himself together.'

I don't understand.'

Sure, you do. You walked out on him, didn't you? … the second time!'

…aura twisted her hands together. 'You obviously …'t know the whole story . . .'

Oh, I know the story all right.' Irene gazed at her …atiently. 'And in spite of what Jason promised my …er, I'm going to tell you the truth.'

…aura shook her head. 'Irene . . .'

Listen to me.' Irene would not be silenced. 'I know … left Jason because he told you he was implicated in

Jeff Ridgeway's death, but he never told you what Ridgeway had done to our father!'

Laura blinked. 'Your father?'

'Yes.' Irene raked impatient fingers through her cap of dark hair. 'It's a complicated story, but I'll try and make it brief.' She paused, and then went on: 'A lot of years ago, my father got in trouble with the law. I hate to tell you this, but it had to do with drugs, and he was arrested. Well, he was not without influence, and he succeeded, with the help of Regina's father, to shake the charge.'

Laura gazed at her. 'When was this?'

'I've told you. A lot of years ago.'

'How many years?'

'Eighteen, maybe. Nineteen, what does it matter?'

Laura took a breath. 'About the time Jason married Regina?'

'About that time, I guess.' Irene frowned. 'Oh, yes. I see Jason's told you about that. I didn't realise.'

'Jason didn't,' said Laura heavily. 'Someone else did. Please—go on.'

'Okay.' Irene tugged at her ear lobe. 'Where was I?'

'You'd just told me your father wasn't convicted.'

'That's right.' Irene nodded. 'Okay. So we come to Jeff Ridgeway. I guess you would call him a—speculator.'

'He was in business, wasn't he?'

'In a manner of speaking.' Irene bit her lip. 'Somehow—don't ask me how—he'd found out about my father. Unknown to any of us, he'd been blackmailing my father for years, using the money to buy up small businesses that were in financial difficulties, taking over people's lives with as much compassion as he had shown my father. Oh ...' she made a dismissive gesture, 'I'm not saying my father didn't deserve to be punished for what he'd done. He was guilty, and he should have gone to prison. Jason had no sympathy for him, believe me, and if it hadn't been for my mother, he'd never have allowed himself to be used like that. But ... he did, and I guess he thought it was over. We all did. Until Jason became involved.'

Laura's throat felt dry. 'Are you saying that when Jason found out, he chose to punish Ridgeway by seducing his wife?'

'That little ...' Irene bit off an epithet. 'Hell. no. Jason wasn't interested in Ellen Ridgeway.'

'Then why ...'

'Let me finish.' Irene walked round Pierce's desk and flopped down into his deep leather armchair. 'Perhaps I should tell you: when Ridgeway decided to shift his operations to the islands, he assumed he could use Jason in much the same way as he had used my father.'

'You mean ... he tried to blackmail Jason?' Laura was horrified.

'He tried,' said Irene flatly. 'But Jason is not like my father.'

Laura's brow furrowed. 'But what could he do?'

Irene hesitated. 'I suppose you could say, he took the law into his own hands.'

Laura pressed her hands to her stomach. 'He didn't ... he didn't *push* Ridgeway off the balcony?'

'No.' Irene's lips twisted. 'I guess the man took his own life, although there was speculation afterwards that it might have been accidental. These things do happen, though not usually so conveniently.'

Laura nodded. 'Go on.'

'Well ...' Irene considered her words, 'when Jason was approached, he decided to make some inquiries of his own. There's a firm of inquiry agents he sometimes employs——'

'I know.' Laura quivered.

'—and he put them on the job. It took some time—almost eighteen months, I believe—but eventually they came up with something that gave Jason the weapon he needed. Somewhere along the line, Ridgeway had discovered the quick profits that could be made from drugs himself, and although Jason had no actual proof, he knew enough to take a chance and go for it.'

'How?' Laura was confused. 'Surely if Jason got involved with drugs, he was playing into the man's hands.'

'He would have, if that's what he'd done.' Irene

nodded. 'He also knew he hadn't a cat in hell's chance
of getting the man convicted. Ridgeway took no
chances—but that's where Ellen came in.'

Laura stiffened. 'Jason did get involved with her
then?'

'He *used* her. He let her think he was interested in
her, until she was willing to go to any lengths to have
him.'

'Oh, Irene . . .'

'Don't you believe me?' Irene shook her head.
'Laura, I know my brother. I know he's no angel. But if
he says he had nothing to do with Ellen Ridgeway, then
you'd better believe him.'

'He didn't say that,' said Laura tensely. 'All he said
was that I didn't trust him.'

'Well, you didn't, did you?' said Irene practically.
'You don't even believe me.'

'I don't know what to believe any more.' Laura put a
hand to her head. 'I thought Jeff Ridgeway killed
himself because of Jason's affair with his wife.'

'Yes. Well . . . I somehow think it would take more
than his wife's infidelity to shake our victim,' remarked
Irene flatly. 'She was hardly irreplaceable. She was his
third wife.'

'She was?'

'Didn't you know?'

'How could I?'

'Hmm.' Irene shrugged. 'Still, I digress. Where was I?
Oh, yes, you're still wondering how Jason got to him.'
She uttered a short mirthless laugh. 'My brother has
friends in strange places. Using his influence, he
managed to find out when a consignment of heroin was
coming in, and arrange for it to be stolen.'

'Stolen?'

'Don't look so shocked. It was only stolen so that
Ridgeway would be forced to tell the men who paid
him, it was gone. Then, later, after Jason had learned of
Ridgeway's whereabouts from Ellen, it was hidden in
the Ridgeway complex.'

'But why?' Laura was bewildered. 'What good was
that?'

'Can you imagine what Ridgeway's paymasters would think when they found the stuff hidden on his premises?'

'But how would they know?'

'Think about it.'

'Jason . . . told them.'

'Someone did.'

Laura sank down weakly into her chair. 'I can't take this in.'

'No. It's not a pleasant story, is it?'

'Then why didn't he tell me?' Laura shook her head. 'If he'd only told me . . .'

'How could he?' Irene looked at her steadily. 'You were not his wife. You were free to walk out at any time—as you did. How could he put his father's life in your hands?'

Laura swallowed. 'But . . . you've told me.'

'Because someone had to. Laura, Jason loves you. Can't you believe that? My God, do you think either my mother or I would put our whole family at risk, if we didn't believe he cared.'

'And . . . and what about me?'

'You?' Irene lay back wearily in the chair. 'Your feelings, I think, are not in doubt. I guess I knew that the minute I walked in here, and you almost had hysterics because you thought Jason had been hurt.'

CHAPTER THIRTEEN

LAURA spent the night with Jason's parents in San Francisco, and flew on to Oahu the following day. The afternoon flight from the Bay City was delayed, however, and it was early evening before the big jet landed in Honolulu. Once again, Laura had to run the gamut of the holidaymakers who were flocking to the islands, and she was grateful for the chauffeur-driven hire car Jason's father had arranged to pick her up at the airport.

She asked the driver to take her first to the Ilikai, the famous hotel by the yacht harbour where Jason kept a suite of rooms at his disposal. Irene had told her that Jason had left Kaulanai the same day she did, and since then he had been virtually inaccessible. The only person who had had any conversation with him was Lucas Kamala, and it was he who had informed Jason's mother of her son's declining mental state.

'Luke says he's been drinking more than is good for him, and he's hardly eating a thing,' Irene explained, on the flight from London to San Francisco. 'I tried to speak to him on the 'phone, and my father actually went to the club to try and reach him, but he wasn't available—or said he wasn't! Whatever you do, Laura, don't let him turn you away. He needs you. He wants you. But he's just stubborn enough to imagine you've come to him out of pity.'

'Pity!' Laura had gazed unseeingly out of the window of the plane, wishing she had had the faith to ignore what Ellen Ridgeway had said and believe him. 'He may never forgive me,' she murmured, speaking barely audibly, but Irene heard her and squeezed her hand.

'You've got to make him. For all our sakes,' she said fiercely. 'Remember—my father blames himself for everything that's happened.'

In the car, driving to the Ilikai, Laura wondered, a little cynically, whether Marco Montefiore might not be more concerned with saving his own soul, rather than that of his son. Jason's mother seemed genuinely concerned, but his father had used him once, and was perhaps not above using Laura, too. For the first time, she understood why Jason had so little respect for the man who had sired him, and it made her all the more determined to convince him that she cared.

It was odd, she thought, how Pamela's reckless actions had given her this second chance. Without her sister's involvement with Mike Kazantis, she might never have seen Jason again. She might even have married Pierce one day, never knowing that the man she had cared for so deeply was still there in her life, a silent witness to his own betrayal.

The spacious lobby of the Ilikai was full of tourists, checking in and checking out. Porters hove back and forth with trolleys loaded with suitcases and plastic bags, and there was a bustling air of organised chaos. The desk was busy, but Laura managed to attract the attention of a young receptionist, and asked if Mr Montefiore was in the hotel. If the man was surprised that a rather travel-weary young woman was asking for one of his most wealthy clients, he hid it very well, though Laura had to admit to herself that the short-sleeved blue shirt and peg-waisted cotton pants had suffered in the prolonged wait at the airport and the five-hour flight from the mainland.

'Mr Montefiore is not in his suite,' he responded politely, probably relieved that he could be honest, Laura suspected. 'I'm sorry. I don't know when he'll be back. I should try again tomorrow.'

'Thank you.'

Laura accepted her dismissal with good grace, acknowledging that it had been unlikely that Jason would be in his room at nine o'clock at night. She could only pray now that he might be at the Blue Orchid Club. The idea that he could, conceivably, be finding solace elsewhere, did not bear thinking about.

It was a short distance from the Ilikai to the Blue Orchid, and after getting out of the car, Laura dismissed the driver. If Jason wasn't here, she would have to wait until the morning to reach him, and she could not keep the man hanging about indefinitely, when she could just as easily hail a cab.

Entering the club, in such casual attire and with her suitcase in her hand, Laura felt horribly conspicuous. It was three years since she had last been here, and although she knew Jason had said Lucas Kamala was in charge, she saw no one she recognised as she crossed the veined marble lobby.

'Can I help you?'

She had known there was no chance of her reaching the lift without being apprehended, and now she turned to face the man who had spoken with determined brightness. 'I ... er ... I'm looking for Mr Kamala,' she began, deciding she might have more success if she spoke to Jason's assistant, and then her lips parted in surprise as she recognised the man who had addressed her. 'Phil' she exclaimed. 'Phil Logan!' She admired his white dinner jacket and neatly-creased trousers. 'I didn't realise it was you.'

The man, who had worked in the club bar when Laura had last seen him, gazed at her in disbelief. 'As I live and breathe!' he exclaimed. 'What are you doing here? I thought Jason said you had gone back to England.'

'I had. I did.' Laura glanced nervously towards the lifts. 'I ... I'm looking for Luke. Is he upstairs?'

'Yes.' Phil regarded her doubtfully. 'But he's not alone. Jason's here, you know.'

Laura's breath escaped in a fluttery sigh. 'He is?'

'Sure.' Phil hesitated. 'If you like, I can ask Luke to come down here. I guess you don't want to see Jason. As I hear it, you and he are all washed up.'

Laura's eyes darted to his. 'Who told you that?'

'I don't know. Luke, I guess.' He paused. 'You want me to ring him?'

'*No!* That is . . .' Laura swallowed to ease her parched throat. 'Could I just go up, do you think? I . . . would like to see Jason, too.'

Phil frowned. 'Look . . . it's none of my business, I know, and Jason bawled me out the last time when you rang the club, and I wouldn't give you his number. But—well, I don't think it's a good idea for you to go up there right now. Let me ring Luke. He'll put you in the picture.'

'Jason's sister's already put me in the picture,' said Laura quietly. 'Phil, let me go up. I have to see Jason, so it might as well be now, hmm?'

He let her go with some misgivings, offering to take charge of her suitcase until she came back. But, as the metal cylinder made its speedy ascent to the penthouse floor, Laura guessed he would not be able to contain his uncertainty, and she was not really surprised when Lucas Kamala was waiting for the lift doors to open.

'Long time, no see, Laura,' he said gently, his drawling island tones almost reducing her to tears. 'Phil had to let me know you were coming. Don't be too mad with him. He's only doing his job.'

'Oh, Lucas!' Laura stepped back from his embrace and scraped the back of her hand across her cheeks. 'I have to see Jason. Irene told me he won't talk to anyone, but he's got to talk to me.'

Lucas regarded her compassionately, but his words were less sympathetic. 'I'm not sure that would solve anything, Laura,' he said frankly. 'Seeing you again is not going to change the situation. I think perhaps you should have stayed away.'

Laura gasped. 'But why?'

'You know why.' Lucas spread his hands. 'When you walked out on him three years ago, he took it badly. For months, he lived the life of a recluse. Why do you think he got out of this apartment? Because it held too many memories of when you were together!'

Laura stared at him. 'I didn't know . . .'

'How could you?' Lucas shook his head. 'Then—a couple of months ago, Jason told us you were coming back. I didn't hear the details until later, but it seems you had asked him for his help with your sister, and we all thought you were back for good. When you left again, I tell you, Jason really went to pieces.'

Laura trembled. 'But he's here, isn't he?'

'Yes.' Lucas acknowledged the fact with some reluctance.

'So let me see him.'

'You can't. At least . . . not right away.'

'Why not?' Laura was defensive. 'Lucas, I can't tell you the whole story right now, but I'm not about to walk out on Jason again.'

Lucas expelled his breath heavily. 'How can I believe that?'

'You just have to.' Laura held up her head. 'Lucas, I haven't flown all this way, just to be turned away by . . . by someone else. If Jason doesn't want me, let him tell me so himself.'

'He can't. Not now.' Lucas glanced uneasily along the carpeted corridor which led to the penthouse suite. 'Laura, let me talk to him first. Let me tell him you're here. If you haven't already checked in to a hotel, do so. I'll 'phone you as soon as I've spoken to him, I promise.'

'No.' Laura stood her ground. She was very much afraid that if she left here—if she allowed Lucas to speak to Jason first—she would get no further than his father had. She had to stand firm. It was her only chance.

'Laura, please . . .'

Lucas put his hand on her arm, but when she realised he was trying to urge her back into the lift, she pulled away from him. 'No,' she said unsteadily. 'No, I won't let you do this!' and before he could prevent her, she ran off along the corridor.

She heard him following her, but Lucas was not as young as he used to be, and too many business lunches and the wine he had consumed with them, slowed him down. Besides, she knew the layout of the penthouse floor as well as he did, and the door to

what had been Jason's apartment was standing ajar.
Rushing through it, she half expected to find Jason in
the living room, but although the lamps were lit, the
room was empty.

She halted uncertainly, and the few seconds she took
to survey her surroundings gave Lucas a chance to
catch up. 'Laura, this isn't very sensible,' he panted,
stomping into the apartment behind her, and when his
eyes swung warily across the room, Laura guessed
where Jason must be.

Without giving him a chance to catch his breath, she
strode swiftly through the door which she knew from
past experience led to the bedrooms. Unhesitatingly,
she paused before the room she and Jason used to
share, and then, with trembling fingers, pushed the door
open.

As she had suspected, Jason was lying on the bed. In
the light from the hall behind her, she perceived he was
still dressed, however, though he had shed his jacket and
his shirt was unbuttoned. His eyes were closed when the
door was opened, but the intruding light caused him to
shift restlessly in its illumination, and he muttered
indistinctly, 'For Christ's sake, Luke—you're blinding
me!'

But Luke was not there. When Laura automatically
glanced behind her, she saw that Jason's assistant had
not followed her. She was on her own—alone with a
man who hadn't yet identified her, and who was
evidently somewhat the worse for alcohol. There was a
half empty bottle of Scotch on the table beside the bed,
and the sweet-sour smell of strong liquor pervading the
atmosphere.

There was a lamp by the door, and before shutting
out the light and losing all knowledge of her
whereabouts, Laura bent down and turned it on,
flooding the room with a warm amber radiance.
Then, as Jason groaned and rolled away from the
glow, she closed the door and advanced towards the
bed.

'Jason,' she ventured tentatively. 'Jason, it's not
Luke, it's me—Laura.'

Jason moved then, a sudden twisting movement that brought him up against the pillows, to gaze at her with wary eyes. 'Laura?' he echoed harshly. 'My God! Am I hallucinating?'

'You're not hallucinating. It's really me,' said Laura huskily, trying to hide her dismay at his appearance. At least two days' growth of beard was bristling on his chin, and his pale eyes were red-rimmed and bloodshot. He looked ill—ill and gaunt; and her heart twisted painfully at the knowledge that she had played some part in his condition. 'I—just arrived a little over an hour ago. I went to the Ilikai, but of course you weren't there . . .'

'How did you get in?' Jason was recovering from the shock of seeing her, and his voice had perceptibly hardened. 'I told Luke. He knew . . .'

'He tried to stop me,' Laura put in hurriedly, 'but I wouldn't let him. I have to talk to you, Jason. Please, can I——'

'We've got nothing to talk about,' he retorted bleakly. Then, raking back the tumbled hair from his forehead, he reached for the bottle beside the bed. 'I want you to go—now; this minute. We've got nothing to say to one another, and you're just wasting my time.'

'Your drinking time, you mean?' demanded Laura unsteadily. 'I wouldn't have thought it of you, Jason. I thought you had more—*guts* than that!'

'What would you know about it?' he inquired grimly, raising the bottle to his lips. 'What would you know about me? You never knew me; you only thought you did.'

'Obviously.' Laura took a deep breath. 'But for someone who reputedly despises other people's weaknesses, you're not exactly a prime example of self-control, are you?'

'Go away, Laura.' Jason's mouth compressed. 'I don't have to listen to a lecture from you. I'll go to the devil my own way. Keep your moralising for those who need it!'

'Oh, Jason . . .'

'Oh, Jason—what? Why have you come here, Laura. It's not because you care what happens to me. You made your feelings very clear the last time we spoke together. You want out of our relationship; well, okay—I want it, too!'

'No, you don't!' Laura gave a hopeless little groan, and sank down on to the bed beside him. 'Jason, why didn't you tell me how you really felt? Why did you let me go on thinking you were only using me?'

'I don't know what you're talking about,' said Jason broodingly, gazing down at the bottle in his hand. 'Okay, so when you came back, I thought you wanted to make up. I was soon disabused of that notion, wasn't I? All we seem to do is hurt one another, Laura, and quite frankly I don't care any more what the hell you do!'

'That's not true!'

'It is true.' This close his eyes had a brittle penetration that frightened her by its opacity. 'I don't need you any more, Laura. You were like a fever in my brain, but now I'm exorcising you.' He lifted the bottle. 'That's what this is. The natives used to call it fire water. The heat of this—fire water—is burning you out of my blood!'

'I don't believe you!'

With an impulsive gesture, Laura snatched the bottle out of his hand and flung it away across the room. It shattered against the far wall, and the gurgling sound of leaking alcohol was magnified in the silence that followed.

Then, with uncontrolled fury, Jason swore at her. 'You crazy bitch!' he burst out savagely. 'What are you trying to do to me? Why have you come here? What do you want? Oh, don't tell me—my father sent you. He's scared to death I'm going to follow Ridgeway's example. Well, don't worry. I won't involve you. I won't involve any of you. Just let me live my own life, will you?'

Laura's shoulders sagged. 'Jason . . .' She had to tell the truth. 'Jason—Irene came to see me . . .'

'Really?'

'Yes, really.' Laura moistened her lips. 'She . . . she and your parents are worried about you.'

'I'll bet!'

'They are. And . . . and so was I.' She twisted her hands together. 'Particularly when Irene told me that—that I'd been wrong about you and—and the Ridgeways.'

Jason's lips twisted. 'They must be desperate!'

'They are.' Laura put out her hands towards him, but he shifted so that she could not reach him. 'Jason I'm sorry. I know that's hardly adequate, but I am sorry. If I could undo the past, I would. I was a fool. I should have believed you. But . . . I . . . I could see no other reason why a man like Jeff Ridgeway would take his own life. It was naïve perhaps, but not so unlikely, surely. And—and it wasn't as if we were married, was it?'

'Married?' Jason's tone was bitter. 'No. No, I didn't make that mistake a second time. That's one thing in my favour.'

Laura winced. 'Jason, please . . .'

'Look. Why don't you get out of here, hmm? Okay . . . it was good of you to come, and I'm sure my family appreciates it, but like you said, you can't undo the past. We had our chance, and we blew it. That's all there is to say.'

Laura got up from the bed. 'So you don't want me,' she said, through stiff lips. 'Irene was wrong.'

Jason's smile was sardonic. 'She surely was,' he drawled mockingly, and the derisive twist to his lips broke Laura's resolve. His anger she could take; his bitterness she deserved; but his deliberate cruelty was more than she could bear.

Backing away from the bed, she made it to the door, fumbling behind her for the handle and wrenching it open. The air in the corridor was infinitely cooler, and less charged, and with a supreme effort she turned and walked back into the living room.

Lucas was there, as she had expected, his face mirroring the anxiety he was feeling. 'That sound,' he said. 'Like breaking glass. What happened? What did you do to him?'

'What did *I* do to *him*?' choked Laura, struggling desperately to hold back her tears. 'Lucas, I . . . I . . .'

'She smashed the bottle of Scotch,' said Jason's voice from behind her, and Laura's knees would hardly support her as she turned disbelievingly to face him. 'Sorry about the mess, Luke,' he added coolly, propping his shoulder against the door frame. 'I'll get someone to clean it up. Just get out of here, would you? Laura and I have some things to clear up.'

It was difficult to decide which of them was the most shocked, and Laura saw Luke's mouth sag as the order—for it was nothing less—was issued. 'You want *me* to leave?' he echoed blankly, and Jason massaged his neck muscles as he moved into the room.

'Briefly,' he agreed, and meeting his gaze Laura could glean nothing from it. 'We'll get out of here in fifteen minutes. Just give me time to shave and take a shower.'

'Okay.' Lucas looked at Laura's pale face. 'Are you all right?'

'She's fine,' said Jason, with an edge to his voice, and Lucas shrugged.

'Right. Right, I'm going,' he muttered, shaking his head. 'I guess I'll see you later.' He grimaced. 'Take your time.'

The minute the door closed, Jason turned back towards the inner hall that led to the bedrooms and bathrooms. 'Take a seat,' he said, for all the world as though Laura was some stranger he was entertaining, and she looked after him weakly, not knowing what to think.

Five minutes of pacing about the living room brought her no nearer a solution, and abandoning her constraint, she went after him. Why was he keeping her here if what he had said was true? Was it only for appearances that he was being civil to her? Was this elaborate façade just a means to deceive his employees?

The shower in the bathroom adjoining the main bedroom was running, and although she knew the most sensible thing to do would be to wait until he was

finished, Laura wasn't feeling very sensible right then.
Her mind was catapulting from one thought to another,
and her body was reacting to the stress she was putting
on it. She had to see him; she had to talk to him; she
had to know if this was an end, or a beginning.

'Jason ...' she said tentatively, stepping into the
bathroom and stopping short at the sight of his lean
body, twisting and turning beneath the cooling spray.
He had left the cubicle door open, and she saw, with a
pang, how much weight he had lost since her departure.
He was losing it, and she was gaining it, she thought
tremulously, running nervous hands over her still-flat
stomach, and it was as she was doing this that he
became aware of her.

He had shaved, she saw at once, the streaks of blood
on his chin evidence of the unsteadiness of his hand,
and it was this that made her take one more chance.
'Oh, Jason,' she said distractedly, 'Jason I never
stopped loving you!' and he jerked off the tap and
came unsteadily towards her.

'You know,' he said, resting his wet arms on her
shoulders and looking down into her eyes, 'fire water
takes a hell of a time to work its way through your
system. I don't think it's had much success so far. I've
still got the fever. I guess it's incurable.'

Although Laura protested that Luke might object to
their using his bed, Jason wasn't really listening to
her. From the moment his arms had closed about her,
hauling her slender body close against his muscled
frame, he had been barely coherent, and Laura's
opposition melted beneath the possession of his
hands.

'I'm wet ... I know I'm wet,' he muttered, his fingers
finding the buttons of her shirt with little consideration
for the fact that he was making her wet, too. 'We'll dry
one another,' he added, disposing of the remainder of
her clothes with the same urgency. 'Oh, God, Laura—I
need you!' His mouth sought the parted contours of
hers, letting her feel the intimacy of his tongue. 'Why
did you leave me?' he grated, the weight of his body an

intoxicating stimulant. 'You know that without you, I'm only half alive!'

His lovemaking was intense and passionate, a ravishing assault on her senses, that Laura was more than eager to facilitate. They were hungry for each other, and not until the blissful aftermath of sexual satiation enveloped them, did Jason display a trace of the hostility he had exhibited earlier.

'So now you know,' he said harshly, pushing back the damp tendrils of hair from her forehead with half angry, half tender, fingers. 'I haven't been exactly sane since you left. Are you back to stay, or is this just another flying visit?'

'Do I have to answer that?' Laura cupped his face in her hands, brushing away the lingering smears of blood from his chin with her thumb, and sucking the pad deliberately. 'Jason—I love you. I always have and I always will. And that's something you've never said to me.'

Jason was lying between her legs and now he supported himself on his elbows to look down at her. But when he would have moved, she wound her arms round his neck, and he subsided again with a not uncontented sigh. 'I thought I'd proved how I felt about you,' he said huskily, burying his face between her breasts. 'Over and over and over again. Dear God, there never was another woman, all the time we were together. Do we really need words to make a commitment?'

Laura lifted his head. 'If—if—I hadn't gone away, would you have asked me to marry you?'

Jason's eyes darkened with emotion. 'Would you have accepted?'

'You know I would.'

Jason bent to bestow a lingering kiss on her mouth. 'Will you marry me now?' he asked softly. 'If you are going to stay, I'd like to get it in writing.'

'Oh, Jason . . .'

'Well . . .' He grimaced. 'You've no idea of the hell I've been through since I let you go that first time. I kept telling myself that if we had been married, the situation might never have arisen. And you might have been more prepared to trust me, if I hadn't let you keep your freedom.' He sighed, nuzzling her shoulder. 'What did Irene tell you? Did she reveal the fact that I *was* indirectly responsible for Ridgeway's death, albeit for different reasons.'

'Yes.' Laura spoke honestly. 'She told me everything—all about your father, and his arrest, and how he managed to escape imprisonment.' She paused. 'You could have told me, you know. I would never have done anything to hurt you.'

'But you did.' Jason's smile was ironic. 'Again, for the wrong reasons.' He shook his head. 'I wanted to tell you, and I would have done when it was all over, but you took off before I had recovered from the unpleasant after effects of knowing I'd destroyed a man's life!'

'Was that why you . . . you seemed so withdrawn?'

'I was bitter, I guess. I know I still blamed my father for the mess he had made of my life. But I blamed myself, too. Even you couldn't change that.'

Laura shook her head. 'If only I'd not jumped to conclusions . . .' She gazed up at him. 'But you had been away so much, and when I walked into the Colony Room and saw you with Ellen Ridgeway, I just wanted to die!'

'It wasn't my best moment,' admitted Jason wryly. 'I hated lying to you, and there were times when I wanted to drop the whole thing and give Ridgeway his pound of flesh! But, blackmailers never give up. They just go on, getting more and more greedy, and I couldn't live with that.'

'You know what Ellen said to me, don't you?' murmured Laura huskily, delighting in their intimacy. 'I couldn't believe a woman who had just lost her husband would lie to me.'

'Ellen was trying to insure her future,' replied Jason carelessly. 'I guess she realised that Ridgeway's death would make a lot of changes in her life. Not least, financial ones. I had seen her on several occasions, and if you don't think it's too conceited, I'll admit she did make certain . . . suggestions to me.'

Laura's tongue circled her lips. 'I can imagine.'

'I didn't follow them up,' he declared flatly. 'But while we're having this conversation, I'll explain that that was why I bought the Ridgeway complex.'

Laura's lips quivered. 'As compensation?'

'If you want to put it like that.'

Laura's nails scraped his shoulder. 'What other way is there?'

'Okay.' His expression darkened. 'So now we know why you walked out on me—both times, I guess.' His mouth twisted. 'We hurt one another. I don't want that to happen again.'

'When did you hire a private investigator to watch me?' asked Laura suddenly, and Jason pulled a wry face.

'Would you believe three years ago?' He moved a little restively, and she felt the hard male strength of his body against her thighs. 'Don't ask me why. I guess I had some crazy notion that you might find out and come and see me. I just had to know that you were all right. I even came to London once to see you—to try and convince you I wasn't the bastard you thought I was. But the agent told me you'd found someone else— a man called Carver, with whom you spent more than just office hours. I didn't stay.'

'Oh, darling!' Laura wrapped her arms around him, and pulled him down to her, and for several minutes there was silence in the apartment.

When he finally spoke again, Jason's voice was thick with emotion, his hands possessive as they moved upon her body. 'If you want us to be out of here before tomorrow morning, don't do that again,' he told her unevenly, forcing himself up from her. 'Let me explain how I felt when you came to see me about your sister. I don't want to talk right now but we've got to.' He grunted. 'I never thought I'd have reason to be grateful to Mike Kazantis, but I did.'

'Where is he?' asked Laura frowningly, and Jason sighed.

'I believe he's serving time for fraudulent conversion,'

he admitted heavily. 'Now, do you understand why I
didn't want you mixed up with that?'

Laura's lips parted. 'He's in prison?'

'For the present,' agreed Jason drily. 'Don't worry. I
told Pam the whole story. Like I told you a few weeks
ago, your sister is not as fragile as you think.'

'Oh, I know that.' Laura bit her lip. 'She told me if
... if I didn't want you, she did.'

Jason groaned. 'That is not my fault.'

'I didn't say it was.' Laura sniffed. 'But I do want
you, so I'm afraid she's out of luck.'

'She'll be okay,' said Jason, rolling on to his side and
taking her with him. 'When she's had the baby, I'll see
she gets a job. And sufficient funds to pay a
babyminder, if that's what she wants.'

Laura swallowed. Jason's words about Pamela's
baby reminded her of her own disturbing condition,
and trailing the tips of her fingers across his chest,
she murmured softly, 'Do you really want to marry
me?'

'I really do,' he said huskily. 'As soon as it can be
arranged.' He frowned. 'You're not changing your
mind, are you?'

'Oh, no.' Laura spoke fervently. 'I ... I just
wondered why you ... why you took so long to ask
me.'

Jason grimaced. 'The truth?'

'Of course.'

'Well, okay. Living with Regina hadn't exactly
endeared the institution to me, and I guess I thought I
had plenty of time. Then there was Lucy. I thought you
didn't think I was such a great father to her, letting her
stay with her mother when it was obvious Regina was
using her against me. I did think that if we did get
married, Lucy could live with us for at least half the
time, but it didn't seem fair, loading you with a
stepdaughter only eight or nine years younger than
you were.'

'Oh, Jason!' Laura gazed at him. 'I love Lucy. You
know that. And ... and when we are married, I shall
want babies.'

'As many as you like,' promised Jason humorously, and Laura sighed.

'Do you mean that?'

'Of course, I mean it.' Jason grimaced. 'Why?'

Laura struggled up into a sitting position and looked down at him with anxious eyes. 'It might be sooner than you think,' she admitted ruefully. 'I was going to call him Jason Huyton, but I suppose Jason Montefiore sounds better.'

Jason jerked her down to him. 'Are you saying— you're pregnant?' He looked stunned. 'Why didn't you tell me?'

'I thought I was doing,' said Laura huskily. 'Do you mind?'

'Mind?' Jason closed his eyes for a moment. Then, opening them again, he fixed her with a penetrating stare. 'You weren't going to tell me, were you? I mean, before Irene came to find you.'

'How could I?' Laura pressed her face into the hollow of his neck. 'I didn't want you to think that all I wanted was a father for my child. Afterwards—afterwards, I might have written to you . . .'

'Written to me?' Jason groaned. 'Oh, love—and I almost sent you away again!'

'But you didn't,' she pointed out softly, and he pressed her closer.

'I couldn't,' he admitted honestly. 'Even though I kept telling myself that all I needed was time, it didn't work before, and I couldn't take the risk. When you walked out of the bedroom, I had to practically drag myself after you. You've no idea how grim I felt when I made it to the door.'

'And now?' she whispered, and he gave her a rueful smile.

'Better—much better,' he conceded roughly. 'How about you?' He drew back to look at her. 'And how do you feel about this baby?'

'*Our* baby?' she murmured, rubbing her chin back and forth against the fine hair on his chest. 'Well—I've had a little longer than you to get used to the idea, and my feelings have never been in doubt.'

'Nor have mine,' declared Jason fiercely, bringing her mouth to his, and Laura knew that this time she had come home.

BETRAYALS, DECISIONS AND CHOICES...

BUY OUT by David Wind   £2.95

The money-making trend of redeveloping Manhattan tenement blocks sets the scene for this explosive novel. In the face of shady deals and corrupt landlords, tenants of the Crestfield begin a fight for their rights – and end up in a fight for their lives.

BEGINNINGS by Judith Duncan   £2.50

Judith Duncan, bestselling author of "Into the Light", blends sensitivity and insight in this novel of a woman determined to make a new beginning for herself and her children. But an unforeseen problem arises with the arrival of Grady O'Neil.

ROOM FOR ONE MORE by Virginia Nielsen   £2.75

At 38, Charlotte Emlyn was about to marry Brock Morley – 5 years her junior. Then her teenage son announced that his girlfriend was pregnant. Could Brock face being husband, stepfather *and* grandfather at 33? Suddenly 5 years seemed like a lifetime – but could the dilemma be overcome?.

These three new titles will be out in bookshops from MAY 1989

W●RLDWIDE

Available from Boots, Martins, John Menzies, W.H. Smith, Woolworths and other paperback stockists.

THREE UNBEATABLE NOVELS FROM
W●RLDWIDE

STOLEN MOMENTS by Janice Kaiser   £2.75

To escape her tragic marriage Lacey Parlett kidnaps her daughter and is forced into hiding. Now, with the FBI closing in, she is desperate to stay anonymous – but one man is dangerously near to discovering her secret.

SARAH by Maura Seger   £2.95

The first of three novels in top author Maura Seger's captivating saga on the Calvert family introduces Sarah – a formidable woman torn between the man she loves and a society she hates during the American Civil War.

STRONGER BY FAR by Sandra James   £2.50

Kate McAllister's ex-husband has been kidnapped. With less than 48 hours to meet the ransom demands, she has only one option left. . . one she had sworn never to take!.

These three new titles will be out in bookshops from April 1989.

Available from Boots, Martins, John Menzies, W.H. Smith, Woolworths and other paperback stockists.

How would you like a years supply of Mills & Boon Romances ABSOLUTELY FREE? Well, you can win them! All you have to do is complete the word puzzle below and send it in to us by October 31st. 1989. The first 5 correct entries picked out of the bag after that date will win **a years supply of Mills & Boon Romances** (*ten books every month - **worth around £150***) What could be easier?

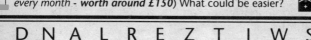

```
R D N A L R E Z T I W S
E O N M C H I N A A C C
G M U I G L E B N N U O
Y E C E G W H I Z C B T
P D R H S E R I A Z A L
T N S M P E R U N D D A
N A W I A T P I I E N N
Y L A T I N A N A N A D
N G S T N H Y D E M L Q
W N O J A M A I C A L A
R E L A D A N A C R O R
T H A I L A N D D K H I
```

ALY	THAILAND	SCOTLAND	SWITZERLAND
ERMANY	IRAQ	JAMAICA	
OLLAND	ZAIRE	TANZANIA	
ELGIUM	TAIWAN	PERU	
GYPT	CANADA	SPAIN	
HINA	INDIA	DENMARK	
IGERIA	ENGLAND	CUBA	

PLEASE TURN OVER FOR DETAILS ON HOW TO ENTER

HOW TO ENTER

All the words listed overleaf, below the word puzzle, are hidden in the grid. You can find them by reading the letters forward, backwards, up or down, or diagonally. When you find a word, circle it or put a line through it, the remaining letters (which you can read from left to right, from the top of the puzzle through to the bottom) will spell a secret message.

After you have filled in all the words, don't forget to fill in your name and address in the space provided and pop this page in an envelope (you don't need a stamp) and post it today. Hurry - competition ends October 31st. 1989.

Mills & Boon Competition,
FREEPOST,
P.O. Box 236,
Croydon,
Surrey. CR9 9EL

Only one entry per household

Secret Message _____

_____

Name _____

Address _____

_____

_____

_____ Postcode _____

You may be mailed as a result of entering this competition

COMP 6